THE FOREMAN'S HANDBOOK

BOOKS BY CARL HEYEL

The Foreman's Handbook
  Third Edition

How to Create Job Enthusiasm

How to Think about Management Problems

Human Relations Manual for Executives

114 Check Points on How to Prevent Grievances
  With Bleick von Bleicken

Practical Management Research
  With Alexis R. Wiren

Reading Course in Executive Technique
  General Editor

Standard Business-conference Technique

Standard Management Practice Series
  Editor

Cybernetics and Society
  Editor

Modern Management for the City of New York
  Editor

THE FOREMAN'S HANDBOOK

Edited by

CARL HEYEL, P.E.

Management Engineer
President, New York Chapter, Society
for the Advancement of Manage-
ment, 1949–1950, 1950–1951
Executive Assistant to the Mayor's
Committee on Management Survey
of the City of New York, 1950–1953

THIRD EDITION

Completely revised, with additions to text covering *Developments in Statistical Quality Control, Predetermined Time Standards, and the "Standard Minute System,"* and with Chapter XII, *Job Evaluation* completely rewritten, plus an entirely new section
SELF-QUIZ FOR EXECUTIVE DEVELOPMENT

New York · Toronto · London

McGRAW-HILL BOOK COMPANY, INC.

1955

THE FOREMAN'S HANDBOOK

Library of Congress Catalog Card Number: 55-8899

THE MAPLE PRESS COMPANY, YORK, PA.

PREFACE

This edition of "The Foreman's Handbook" is the second completely revised version of the original work which appeared in 1943. Needless to say, it is a source of gratification to the authors and editor that continued demand through the 12 years since its first appearance has called for successive issues.

All chapters have been examined critically. In addition to the necessary updating of statistical material and topical references, certain other changes have been made in accordance with the needs of the field as indicated by the editor's experience in professional practice. Thus, the chapter on job evaluation has been completely recast to depart from the pure "factor-comparison" system given in previous editions. It is the editor's conviction that the combination of point system and factor comparison as here presented in some detail will be of much more practical use in the average industrial situation—and that even where the simpler straight "N.E.M.A.-type" point system is introduced into or is in use in a plant, the principles discussed in Chapter XII will provide the underlying rationale. A rather complete treatment is provided, and the chapter is now, in effect, a usable manual on job evaluation that does not require supplementary references to other publications for point values, factor definitions, and the like.

In the chapter on quality and waste control, a second part has been added to provide the foreman with an understanding of at least the principles underlying modern statistical quality control, now in more and more widespread application. Here, however, it was felt that no more than an appreciation of the concepts and technique, rather than comprehensive operating-type information, was called for, since a functional department will in all likelihood have technical responsibility.

Because of recent strides in predetermined time standards, a second part has been added to the former chapter on time and motion study to cover that subject. Here again the treatment is fairly complete, and advantage was taken of the MTM Association's kind permission to reproduce *in toto* its four-page card containing its ten copyrighted tables of methods-time measurement application data. As a third part of this same chapter, further new material has been added in the form of an explanation of the widely applied "Standard Minute" system of wage incentive payment. Here the editor has exercised his prerogative of choice—feeling that the advantages of expressing output in the common denominator of time, and the latter in terms of standard minutes rather than percentages of an hour, merit the express treatment given to a specific system.

Finally, an important addition to the handbook as a whole is the entire seventh section, "Self-quiz for Executive Development." The idea behind this section is the well-known learning principle that material absorbed by reading "sticks with" the reader if he attempts to write out the important concepts in his own words. Thus the handbook now goes beyond merely providing authoritative reference material for the foreman, and presents a pattern by which he can reflect constructively on what he has read and test his retention of it. Since a company's production team is no better than its foremen, the advantages of such review material are obvious.

However, despite all changes and additions, the basic objective as stated in our 1943 preface remains as it was: "This handbook for foremen was designed to be more than the usual book on foremanship. It is presented as an authoritative reference text that the foreman will want to keep on hand for frequent consultation. . . . *The book does not confine itself to the immediate things the foreman or supervisor must know and do in connection with his day-by-day duties. It discusses the background information he must acquire and the attitude or 'mental attack' he must develop to prepare himself for larger responsibilities.* Its major purpose is to help the foreman develop his job beyond the point at which he assumed it—to help him grow."

Aside from the very important addition of the work-simplification section in the 1949 edition and the review section in this one, the general organization and sequence of the material have been preserved as given in the first edition, with the chapters now grouped into seven sections. The intervening years have proved, in terms of popular response, that the then novel approach was sound: Although the book is comprehensive, it is so arranged as to emphasize the kind of *practical information* a foreman needs in his work; it has not been made to read like a collection of professional engineering papers. At the same time, this handbook is not oversimplified, and it does not insult the intelligence of an alert, aggressive foreman by "talking down." The breezy journalistic style of so many books purporting to be especially written for foremen has been avoided, as well as the academic style of many writers on professional subjects. The editor worked with the contributors to eliminate specialized terms where possible or to define them carefully where they had to be used.

One departure in presentation followed in all editions is that the type of general information which usually takes up the early chapters in foremanship texts is offered here for what it really is—background information. This is not meant to deprecate its importance. It is treated with thoroughness but reserved for the closing instead of the opening chapters. Moreover, each chapter stands on its own feet—it can be read as a separate article, independent of preceding or succeeding chapters. This arrangement should satisfy two kinds of readers: The foreman who wants to read the book consecutively will find that he gets into practical, "meaty" chapters immediately, and that all chapters follow in logical order. The foreman who wants to refer to the book on specific subjects can expect comprehensive coverage, conveniently segregated. It was deemed logical to put the section on Work Simplification at the end of the text since it was conceived as a special "philosophy" to be presented to foremen thoroughly grounded in the fundamentals of their job as presented in the preceding sections.

In organizing the material and in working over it with the contributors, the editor strove to preserve the distinction among matters of direct forman responsibility, matters on which the foreman must co-operate with functional departments which themselves assume primary responsibility, and information of a more general, educational nature.

The list of contributors bespeaks, by their standing in their fields, the authority with which the subjects in this handbook are treated. All these authors have written extensively in other management media, but it was the editor's privilege in the first edition to introduce many of them to the foreman audience.

The editor was gratified to note, in working over material in the original edition, how basic that presentation was. As he was bold enough to hope in a preface 12 years ago, the handbook has stood the test of time. And the additional material presented in this edition should make it of even more practical, everyday usefulness.

CARL HEYEL

CONTENTS

xi

Section Three—The Foreman's Direct Personnel Responsibilities

Section Four—The Foreman's Co-operative Personnel Responsibilities

Section Five—Background Information for the Foreman

Section Six—Work Simplification and the Foreman

Section Seven—Self-quiz for Executive Development

CONTRIBUTORS

T. O. Armstrong, Assistant to the President, Dumas Steel Corp. & Subsidiaries, Pittsburgh, Pa.; Vice-President, Pittsburgh Plastic Corp., Pittsburgh, Pa.; formerly Director, Plant Labor Relations, Westinghouse Electric Corporation, Pittsburgh, Pa.; Chap. III, Part One.

James J. Bambrick, Jr., B.S., M.B.A., Labor Relations Specialist, National Industrial Conference Board, New York; formerly Executive Director, The Labor Bureau, New York; Chap. XVII.

Lawrence L. Bethel, Ph.D., President, Fashion Institute of Technology, New York; formerly Director, Y.M.C.A. Junior College, New Haven, Conn.; co-author (with G. H. E. Smith, F. S. Atwater, and H. A. Stackman), "Industrial Organization and Management"; editor and co-author (with W. L. Tann, F. S. Atwater, and E. E. Rung), "Production Control"; editor and co-author (with G. H. E. Smith, F. S. Atwater, and H. A. Stackman), "Essentials of Industrial Management"; Chap. IV.

Bleick von Bleicken, Director of Institute of Modern Management, Louisville, Ky.; formerly Vice-President, Labor Relations Institute, New York; author, "Practical Guide to Collective Bargaining," "Employee Training Handbook," "Your Wage-Hour Liabilities and Exemptions"; co-author (with T. J. Newton), "The Foreman's Place in Management," and (with Carl Heyel), "114 Check Points on How to Prevent Grievances"; Chap. XVIII.

Samuel L. H. Burke, Director, Personnel Administration, General Foods Corporation, White Plains, N.Y.; formerly Director of Industrial Relations, Pittsburgh Plate Glass Company, Pittsburgh, Pa.; co-author (with E. J. Benge and

E. N. Hay), "Manual of Job Evaluation"; co-author of Chap. XII.

Phil Carroll, Professional Engineer, Maplewood, N.J.; author, "Timestudy for Cost Controls," "Timestudy Fundamentals for Foremen," "How to Chart Timestudy Data," "How to Control Production Costs," "How Foremen Can Control Costs"; Chap. V, Part One.

Charles A. Drake, Ph.D., Dr. Com. Sc.; formerly Head, Methods Department, United Merchants and Manufacturers Management Corporation, New York; author, "Personnel Selection by Standard Job Tests"; Chap. XIV.

R. S. Driver, Manager of Personnel Administration, The Atlantic Refining Company, Philadelphia, Pa.; Chap. XIII.

H. P. Dutton, Consultant in Management; formerly Professor of Business Management, Illinois Institute of Technology, Chicago, Ill., and Member, Board of Directors, The Hess Company, Chicago, Ill.; Chap. XI.

George H. Elliott, President, George H. Elliott & Company, Inc., New York; Chap. V, Part Three.

Glenn Gardiner, Director, Forstmann Woolen Company, Passaic, N.J.; author, "Better Foremanship," "Vitalizing the Foreman's Role in Management"; Chap. VII.

Lydia G. Giberson, M.D., C.M., Personal Advisor, Metropolitan Life Insurance Company, New York; Chap. X.

Howard W. Haggard, M.D., Director, Laboratory of Applied Physiology, Yale University, New Haven, Conn.; Chap. IX.

Carl Heyel, P. E., Management Engineer; Director of Planning, Mergenthaler Linotype Company, Brooklyn, New York; Staff Associate, National Foremen's Institute, New London, Conn.; foremerly Executive Assistant to the Mayor's Committee on Management Survey of the City of New York; Chap. I; co-author of Chap. XII; General Editor.

A. L. Kress, Management Consultant, Princeton, N.J.; author, "Foremanship Fundamentals"; Chap. II.

Andrews M. Lang, Secretary and Director of Research, George H. Elliott & Company, Inc., New York; formerly Secretary, MTM Association for Standards & Research; Chap. V, Part Two.

J. K. Louden, Vice-President and General Manager, Commercial Division, York Corporation, York, Pa.; author, "Wage Incentives"; co-author (with T. J. Newton), "Job Analysis"; contributor to Chap. XII.

T. J. Newton, Director of Training, Armstrong Cork Company, Lancaster, Pa.; co-author (with Bleick von Bleicken), "The Foreman's Place in Management," (with J. K. Louden), "Job Analysis"; contributor to Chap. XII.

E. H. Mac Niece, Special Representative in Europe, Johnson & Johnson, New Brunswick, N.J.; author, "Organizing for Quality and Waste Control," "Production Forecasting, Planning, and Control," "Industrial Specifications"; Chap. III, Part Two.

Robert Wray Porter, Robert Wray Porter Organization, New York; author "Design for Industrial Co-ordination"; Chap. XVI.

Charles Reitell, Management Consultant, Elmira, N.Y.; formerly of Stevenson, Jordan & Harrison, Inc., New York, and School of Business, Columbia University, New York; Chap. VI.

Lewis K. Urquhart, Managing Editor, *Factory Management & Maintenance*, New York; Chap. XV.

Roger Williams, B.A., Late Director of Safety Service, New York State Insurance Fund, New York; Chap. VIII.

Clem Zinck, Training in Work Simplification, Allentown, Pa.; author, "Controls for Co-ordinating Factory Operations," "The National Foremen's Institute's Ten-session Course on Work Simplification"; Chap. XIX.

Section One

THE SCOPE OF THE FOREMAN'S JOB

CHAPTER I

A BREAKDOWN OF THE FOREMAN'S JOB

BY CARL HEYEL

Some men just naturally seem to acquire new duties and responsibilities—they constantly grow—while others never develop a job beyond the point at which they assumed it. And some men, of course, do not take hold at all when additional responsibilities are assigned to them. They soon find themselves eliminated or back in the ranks.

A job can be made to expand or contract, depending upon the initiative and capabilities of the man holding it. That is why company organization charts must always be checked against actual operating conditions, to guard against their becoming mere historical blueprints with no relation to facts.

Accordingly, it is not an easy matter to give a general definition of a foreman's job, beyond, perhaps, saying that his job is what he makes it. However, it is possible to discuss what any foreman must know and do in order to make his job grow. This chapter will consider such a breakdown. Later chapters will discuss in detail the important points touched upon here.

Obviously, if we consider the foreman's job as something that should be growing at all times, a breakdown of that job will include more than the immediate things he must know and do in connection with his day-by-day duties. It will have to include the kind of background information he must acquire and the kind of attitude, or "mental attack," he must develop to prepare himself for larger responsibilities.

THE FOREMAN AS A PART OF MANAGEMENT

First of all, the foreman is definitely part of management. It may be somewhat difficult for a new foreman advanced from the ranks to accustom himself to this idea. And it must be confessed that in some companies top management does not go out of its way to impress it upon him. However, nothing is more important to the foreman's success than to keep this fact constantly in mind. Every problem, every decision, every act must be considered with a "management slant."

The word "management" as used here has two meanings, and the foreman must keep both of them in mind in connection with the preceding remarks. First, it means the group of people actually "running" the company, as distinguished from the rank-and-file employees. As part of this group, the foreman definitely shares responsibility for a company's profit and loss and for the livelihood and well-being of hundreds —perhaps thousands—of employees. Obviously, he should make it his business to know and understand company policy as it affects his department.

Second, "management" means a way of getting things done, as stated in the following definition developed by the American Society of Mechanical Engineers: "Management is the art and science of preparing, organizing, and directing human effort applied to control the forces and utilize the materials of nature for the benefit of man." Thus, when a man, by becoming a foreman, has entered the ranks of management, his efforts from then on will be directed not toward doing things himself, but toward getting *others* to do them, that is, toward "preparing, organizing, and directing human effort." He will no longer be working directly with materials, machines, and tools, but with people. That is why in any discussion of a foreman's job the matter of "human relations" always receives so much attention. A man who is made a foreman is usually given his chance because he knows the technical aspects of the work of his department. But he will stand or fall as a foreman on the strength of how well he is able to handle the people under him.

THE FOREMAN AS A LEADER

This emphasis on working with people brings out the second important point in our breakdown of the foreman's job—the foreman must be a leader. He must know thoroughly all about the work of his department and have fully acquired the "management slant" in thinking about it; but unless he can win the confidence and co-operation of the employees who report to him, he will never make a success of his job. He must not only be able to tell his people how to do their jobs in the right way, but must also be able to tell and instruct in such a way that they will *want* to do the job right. He must be able to handle people so that they will be "for" him at all times, especially in an emergency, when a department can come through only if everyone does more than has ever been expected or even considered possible.

This leadership part of the foreman's job is doubly important: Not only must the foreman do all his work through people; he must also remember at all times that he and his fellow foremen are usually the *only* men in the operating organization who have direct executive authority over the rank-and-file employees.

Therefore, in the daily operation of the business every policy, instruction, or request of higher management must sooner or later channel through the foreman. And at the same time, the foreman is the first contact management has through which to sense the attitudes and reactions of the employees. That is why management must always fall back upon the foreman in controlling problems that involve the human element—such problems as too many accidents, excessive labor turnover, too much scrap, poor worker attitude, and the like.

To be a better leader, the foreman must make it his business to learn about people—why they act the way they do, what things they will respond to, how to put them at ease, how to "get a man told" without antagonizing him, how best to make a new man a "paying member" of his working group, and the like. Points such as these are developed in Chap. II.

THE FOREMAN'S KNOW-HOW

But emphasizing human relations does not mean that the ability to get along with people is the chief stock in trade of the successful foreman. Many persons who have that knack would nevertheless make poor foremen. In any organization that has passed beyond the stage of a small shop run by the owner and employing a few men, definite systems of organization and control have been developed. Under such systems "scores" are kept which show up a foreman's efficiency or inefficiency: unit costs, scrap records, time standards, and the like. These call for a third item in our breakdown of the foreman's job, the "know-how," or definite, specialized knowledge that enables the foreman to turn out work in the right amounts, on time, and up to quality standards.

Of course, the required know-how will vary widely, depending upon the type of operations and the organization setup. In our breakdown, however, this item should probably be subdivided somewhat in the following manner, no matter what the foreman's company or industry may be.

The Technical Job

First, the foreman's job calls for a fairly high degree of familiarity with the mechanical or technical phases of the work of the department. Of course, this does not mean that the foreman need be expert on all, or even any, of the jobs under his jurisdiction. Indeed, experience has amply proved that the best mechanic does not necessarily make the best foreman. But the foreman who thinks he can limit himself entirely to "paper work," with only a superficial knowledge of detailed operations, runs the risk of missing many important little things that add up to inefficiency, and, worse still, he runs the risk of losing the respect of his men.

No handbook or other source outside his own company can do more than generalize about this phase of the foreman's job. It is up to him to make this subdivision of his job breakdown and to see where improvement is called for.

Quality and Waste Control

A second part of the know-how is quality control and waste reduction. Excessive scrap will stand out on a foreman's record like a sore thumb; no management will tolerate continuation of it. The foreman must know the best way to do each job and see to it that his employees do it that way.

Although *machines* and *materials* have a direct bearing on scrap, every foreman soon discovers that a third *m, manpower,* is the principal key to the solution. Therefore, as pointed out in Chap. III, the most successful attack is on the human-relations aspect of the problem—stimulating employees to do good work.

The foreman who approaches quality in that way soon finds his over-all problem of supervision greatly simplified. He does not constantly have to be a troubleshooter, with all his time taken up by one departmental crisis after another. If his employees not only know how to do their jobs, but really *want* to do them with *A*-quality ratings, the department exercises a sort of automatic control over quality, with the foreman having to take a personal hand only in special situations.

Because of the growing application of statistical techniques in quality control, it is well that the foreman be aware of developments in that field. Accordingly, in this edition of this handbook, Part Two has been added to Chap. III to cover this subject.

Planning and Scheduling

A third know-how subdivision is planning and scheduling so that the work will flow through the foreman's department smoothly and on time. Even where a separate department exercises functional control over scheduling, the foreman has a definite responsibility in making the control system work, and it will pay him to familiarize himself with modern planning and scheduling, as outlined in Chap. IV.

Methods Improvement

Fourth, know-how must certainly include methods improvement, a constant endeavor on the part of the foreman to eliminate waste of time, effort, and materials. Actual time study and rate setting are, of course, the functions of a separate specialist or department. However, this work is so closely tied up with the foreman's own responsibilities that he should learn all he can about it. Study of Chap. V should give him a good working knowledge of the subject. As pointed out there, a foreman's attack on methods improvement will profitably start with a study of just how time is used in his department and where it is lost.

Basing compensation on engineered performance standards has become so important that two additional parts have been added to Chap. V in this edition of this handbook—Part Two on predetermined time standards, in connection with which techniques have recently been greatly improved, and Part Three on the Standard Minute system of wage payment. In addition, an entire section, Section Six, "Work Simplification and the Foreman," gives the foreman an understanding of one of the most effective techniques available to management for improving methods and increasing the productivity of employees.

Cost Control

All the foreman's activities are ultimately, of course, directed toward lowered unit costs. The cost-control item of the know-how refers here to the formalized system set up by management to control and keep track of costs. As a rule, the foreman has little voice in the formulation of this control system, but he does play an important part when the system is so set up as to furnish him with usable information on costs coming within his control.

If the foreman considers the "growing" part of his job as well as his current responsibilities, he will be especially interested in cost-control methods since they will inevitably be an important part of the next production job to which he is advanced. He should also, of course, try to understand thoroughly his company's costing and cost-reporting system in order that he can discuss his operations intelligently if he is asked to attend a factory meeting called to interpret and discuss a cost report.

THE FOREMAN'S DIRECT PERSONNEL RESPONSIBILITIES

Since people are the tools with which the foreman does his work, he will be successful only if he assumes certain definite, direct personnel responsibilities. These are grouped here as the fourth major element in our breakdown of the foreman's job.

Although most companies have personnel departments, some of which assume a wide range of duties in addition to employment, personnel administration will function properly only if every foreman becomes, in effect, a personnel manager for his own department. As a personnel manager, his most direct responsibilities are training, safety, and working conditions.

Training

Training has, of course, always been a part of the foreman's job, but the tremendous industrial expansion during the Second World War greatly dramatized its importance. The need to double or treble production almost overnight often made it necessary for a foreman to take on men or women who knew nothing at all about the work of the department and who, indeed, may never have been inside an industrial plant.

Even in postwar years, emphasis is on *quick* training rather than on long apprenticeship systems with formalized courses under specialized instructors. The burden of quick training is usually placed upon the foreman. Good foremanship, therefore, demands that the foreman not only know how operations in his department should be performed but also know how to teach these operations to green workers—or at least be sure they are being taught correctly by lead men and others. Chapter VII analyzes these training responsibilities and presents fundamental teaching techniques that will work for any type of industry.

Safety

The second direct personnel responsibility of the foreman is safety. Like the problem of training, that of accident prevention was greatly dramatized by forced-draft production during the Second World War. Although company management can do much in the way of special safety books and other literature, posters, safety meetings, and the like, the day-in, day-out job of seeing that workers, especially new workers, do not get hurt falls squarely on the foreman's shoulders. He must, therefore, ground himself thoroughly on fundamental safety principles, be "tough" about enforcing plant safety rules, and keep even more alert than before against hazards in his department. These and related points are elaborated upon in Chap. VIII.

Working Conditions

It is so obvious that employees cannot be expected to turn out their best work unless physical conditions are satisfactory, that this phase of the foreman's job need not be discussed in detail here. Most American manufacturing companies provide working conditions of a high standard, and the foreman's responsibility in this connection need usually extend only to a strict enforcement of "good housekeeping."

However, there is one physical problem of special importance when circumstances call for stepping up production—employee fatigue. Many investigations have shown that, unless definite steps are taken to guard against excessive fatigue, stepping up the tempo of production or lengthening the hours of work will not result in proportionate increases in output. It will, therefore, pay the foreman to study Chap. IX to familiarize himself with facts and qualified opinions on this matter.

As important as physical working conditions are the emotional conditions under which people work. It is part of the foreman's leadership responsibilities to see that his people get along with each other and to try to render sympathetic help when personal troubles afflict someone in his department.

Special Problems in Supervising Women

Women entered industry in great numbers during the Second World War, and many who had a chance to do so stayed on after the emergency. Any breakdown of the foreman's job today should, therefore, include problems arising in the supervision of women as an important part of the foreman's direct personnel responsibilities. Of course, the foreman's basic objectives do not change when his employees are women. However, as pointed out in Chap. X, some of the factors in his problem differ vitally. That chapter takes them up in detail.

THE FOREMAN'S CO-OPERATIVE PERSONNEL RESPONSIBILITIES

In the past 35 years, management has made tremendous strides in personnel administration. Old methods have been improved and new ones developed in a wide range of activities affecting the management of men and women on the job. Many of these have led to specialization, so that they are often administered by separate departments or by outside consultants. This, of course, is true with respect to the foreman's direct personnel responsibilities just mentioned, and so in many companies he is able to obtain help from, say, a Training or Safety Department. However, the point to be emphasized with respect to direct personnel responsibilities is that they will always be primary foremanship functions, no matter how much help he can get from staff departments.

In addition to direct personnel responsibilities, it seems logical, therefore, to consider co-operative personnel responsibilities as the fifth major element in our breakdown. These include those personnel activities which are more definitely the function of special departments and in which the foreman's part can usually be merely one of intelligent co-operation. He will co-operate best, and stand to benefit most, if he acquires a working knowledge of the basic principles involved. Following are four important phases of management in which the foreman may be expected to work with staff specialists or consultants.

Methods of Wage Payment

Intelligent paying of labor is one of the most important functions of good industrial management. Over the years, many types of wage-payment plans have been developed, plans calculated to furnish the best possible incentive for maximum output by employees. For a while there was quite a fad for complicated incentive systems, many of which later proved unwieldy or otherwise unsatisfactory. More recently, the tendency has been toward simpler schemes.

Although wage-payment plans differ widely and seem almost limitless in number, they do fall into certain recognized patterns. It will give a foreman a better understanding of the plan in use in his own company if he has some idea of the development of these plans and of the types of plans in more or less common use today. Chapter XI will give him such an over-all picture. With a knowledge of general principles as a foundation, he should then, of course, be sure that he thoroughly understands the plan in use in his own company; for it is up to him to interpret it to his employees. (As stated, because of its tie-in with time study, a detailed description of the Standard Minute system has been included in Chap. V.)

Job Evaluation

An important part of any wage-administration plan is the method set up to ensure that rates for all jobs within the organization bear a fair relationship to each other. Dissatisfaction and poor morale in general result when men find out that jobs requiring much less skill or calling for much less effort than their own are, nevertheless, paying higher rates.

To guard against such a condition and to put all their wage payments on a common-sense footing, more and more companies are resorting to "job evaluation." This is nothing more than a careful weighing of all the factors that make up a given job— the duties performed, skill required, responsibilities called for, working conditions, etc.—in order to arrive at a fair rate.

When this concept is applied in a company, a special department or an outside consultant makes the investigations needed and submits rating recommendations. However, most of the information about the jobs must be obtained from the foreman or through him from the actual operator, and so this part of wage administration is definitely one of the foreman's co-operative personnel responsibilities. Moreover, foremen are often asked to be members of special job-evaluation committees, and they are always the key men in "selling" a program of job evaluation to the rank-and-file employees.

Even if his company is not now actually engaging in job-evaluation work, it will pay the alert foreman to acquaint himself with the fundamentals of the subject, so that he will be ready when his management gets around to using this technique. Details are given in Chap. XII.

Merit Rating

Modern wage administration makes careful distinction between rating *jobs*—determining, on the basis of the requirements of the job, the rate or range of rates to be paid for it—and rating *people*—setting up a system whereby the performance and abilities of a given person can be watched and rated, to determine when he is really ready to advance either to a higher rate on his present job or to a better paying job. The latter activity has come to be known as "merit rating." Where it is in force, the foreman's job of assigning and advancing his employees is made immensely easier.

As with job evaluation, merit rating is usually made the direct responsibility of a specialized person or department. However, the most important part of the whole system, the actual rating of the men and women on the jobs, is always up to the foreman or first-line supervisor, with suitable discussions and checkings by department heads and others. To do his part intelligently, the foreman should understand the principles behind the system. These are discussed in Chap. XIII.

Even where no formal merit-rating system is in force, the foreman should make it his business to understand the principles involved, for he can apply many of them "on his own hook" in his department. Everyone with executive responsibilities is constantly rating his subordinates, either by intuition (hunches based on experience), or in accordance with some plan. A plan, even if it is only a simple one, will usually make the treatment of employees more fair and will enable the foreman to utilize his manpower more efficiently.

Use of Psychological Tools

Ever since the First World War, when the Army used psychological tests on a broad scale, industry has been making more and more use of applied psychology. Psychologists have made great strides in developing tests to aid in the selection of employees and have brought their specialized knowledge to bear on problems of "induction" (getting a new employee properly started on his job), training, the attitudes and general morale of employees, and dealing with people most effectively. All these problems, of course, are directly related to the foreman's work, and any scientific help he can get on them will make his problem of supervision that much easier.

Where management is properly careful in the selection and use of psychological tests and in other applications of psychological principles, it leans heavily on professional help—in the form either of consultants or of staff specialists. The foreman, therefore, is not expected to become an industrial psychologist. However, it will help him on his job to keep abreast of the field, so that he will not dismiss as "impractical theory" principles that have been thoroughly proved in practical application elsewhere. Chapter XIV will give him such a working knowledge.

BACKGROUND INFORMATION

In the beginning of this job breakdown, the importance of looking upon the foreman's job as *growing* was stressed. A man can make his job grow only if he keeps looking beyond his immediate bench or desk, if he keeps broadening his perspective. This implies a kind of "mental stretching," which must go on continuously. As soon as it stops, the man and his job stop growing.

A man stretches himself mentally when he views his operations broadly and makes it his business to find out about things that have a bearing on the whole picture even though they do not affect his immediate work. He acquires a long-term as well as a short-term view. In a word, he begins to develop a *background* on his subject that strengthens his judgment.

The Background of Scientific Management

To broaden his perspective, a foreman should know something about the history of the movement that has come to be known as "scientific management." A knowledge of its beginnings—of the work of Frederick W. Taylor and others who followed him—will help to fix fundamental principles in his mind and so make possible the kind of mental attack required to solve present-day problems. Chapter XV briefly presents such background information. The foreman whose interest is aroused by this chapter will find it profitable to continue his reading on the subject.

Of special interest should be Frederick W. Taylor's own book, "The Principles of Scientific Management." As a pioneer in this field (he is known as "the father of scientific management"), Taylor had to write in terms that everyone could understand. The movement had not grown to the point where a special vocabulary had sprung up, intelligible only to the experts. Hence his book is unusually clear and offers easy reading.

Forms of Industrial Organization

The foreman should also have a working knowledge of the various forms of industrial organization, so that he may better see how he and his department fit into the organization structure of his own company. If he knows the basic reasons behind various industrial setups, he can more readily understand the logic behind his company's grouping of departments and responsibilities; he will better appreciate the differences between staff and line functions and so will be able to co-operate more effectively. Forms of industrial organization are discussed in Chap. XVI.

Economics

Tied up with the problem of internal industrial organization is the broader one of how a company fits into an industry and how the company itself and the industry as a whole are subject to economic forces beyond the control of one person or group. Therefore, further to broaden his perspective, the foreman should acquire some knowledge of economics, an understanding of broad principles that govern all types of business and industrial operations, so that he may see how wages, hours, working conditions, profits, investments, and the like are all tied together in an economic system and that no one of them can be tampered with without all the others being affected. Without such background information, the foreman carries out orders more or less blindly, without really understanding basic company policies.

Moreover, because he is considered a leader by his subordinates, the foreman should be able to take an intelligent part in discussions among his men of national issues. In every large working group there is bound to be a number of radicals and troublemakers, whose "isms" can be countered only by sound information. Chapter XVII will give the foreman useful, basic information about economics.

Labor Legislation

In recent years, legislation and rulings affecting labor made by governmental bodies have been multiplying almost beyond count. Many of these affect foremen, because they vitally change the "rules of the game." Foremen today must be cautioned about a great variety of matters which they should not irresponsibly discuss with their subordinates.

Of course, laws and rulings are being made almost every day, and no foreman can hope to keep up with them. However, the confusion is more apparent than real, and Chap. XVIII should serve to clarify his thinking. Despite rulings and amendments, the basic principles underlying existing laws will not change greatly in the immediate future, and the chapter as revised describes their purpose and content.

* * *

So much, then, for a breakdown of the foreman's job, considering the job as a growing, not a static, thing. The chapters that follow "put meat on the skeleton." In the meantime, the next page presents the breakdown in chart form, to provide a quick, bird's-eye view of the major points discussed so far.

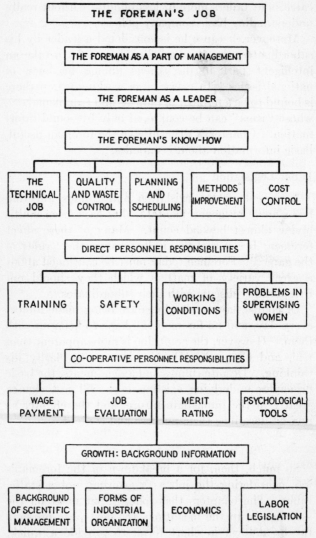

FIG. 1.—Schematic diagram of the breakdown of the foreman's job.

CHAPTER II

THE FOREMAN AS A LEADER

By A. L. Kress

Shakespeare said that "some are born great, some achieve greatness, and some have greatness thrust upon them." So it is with leadership. Some men are born with a capacity for leadership. Some acquire the art by watching and studying the actions of those around them. Other persons find themselves thrown into unusual situations which require them to draw on resources they never realized they had, and events bring out marked leadership. Most of us are never put to such tests. Most of us are not born leaders. We belong to the group of those who, if they want to lead, must *develop* the art of leadership.

We often hear people say, "He's a great guy to work for." We see men go out of their way to do things for certain supervisors. We see them carry out instructions cheerfully and well or add something to the doing of the job which was unexpected or not what may be termed "in the line of duty." In other words, they put themselves into the job and give it that "plus effort" which one gives only when he feels that he is part of the team, that he is making a contribution to its success, that his contribution is understood and appreciated.

Now this is not something which just happens. It is built on a man-to-man relationship. It is a reflec-

21

tion of the man's attitude toward his job, his supervisor, and his company. Where it exists, it has been developed over a period, as a result of three simple elements: confidence, co-operation, and understanding. In such a situation, we say morale is high. That is only a short simple way of saying that men are interested in their jobs, that they feel the company is a good one to work for, and that their foreman understands them, appreciates their efforts, and tries to give them all a square deal. Here is what one man in one plant said about his job:

"I enjoy my work and the association of those with whom I work. A spirit of helpfulness and co-operation exists between our employer and all employees, which creates a homelike atmosphere. This treatment brings out a desire to do our best all the time."

This man's morale must have been high, or else he would not have made this unsolicited statement. If we could get everyone to feel that way toward his job, many of our problems of supervision and personnel would be simplified.

WHAT IS LEADERSHIP?

Leadership is the ability to get other people to work willingly through the leader's influence or example. Leadership has to do with the art of dealing with persons, of knowing how to reach the traits which move people to put forth their best efforts.

There are certain characteristics which mark a leader of men. He likes people; he likes to rub shoulders with them. He enjoys seeing others develop and grow under his guidance and direction, but he never makes his pleasure obvious. He has a directness, a forthrightness in all his acts. He possesses a sense of fairness, moral courage, "humanness," and a sense of humor. Along with these go a devotion to duty and a realism which lets him always see things as they are. He never indulges in wishful thinking. He understands human nature, its frailties and peculiarities, and so he is never disillusioned by the acts of others. He takes people as they are and enlists their interest, co-operation, and effort in a common cause.

THE FOREMAN AND HIS JOB

The major immediate duties and responsibilities which call for leadership will here be considered under five broad headings:

1. Maintaining quality standards
2. Getting out the day's work on time
3. Improving methods
4. Keeping down costs
5. Dealing with personnel problems

Everything that the foreman is called on to do in the course of his day's work comes under one of these headings. Almost every situation he must deal with calls for leadership if he is to get results. If he is interested in getting the kind of results which comes because he has the interest, enthusiasm, and co-operation of the working force, one of the first ways to begin to build these attitudes is through an analysis of his own duties and responsibilities. For, clearly, one of the first requirements for effective leadership is to know one's own job.

Next, the foreman should ask himself whether he is clear as to company policies which affect his operations. Unless such policies are clearly understood, situations may arise which will react unfavorably on his reputation for leadership.

WHAT AN EMPLOYEE EXPECTS OF HIS FOREMAN

Periodically, every foreman should ask himself what an employee expects of him. Unless he takes a look at that phase of his job, he will not develop an adequate picture of what effective leadership means. Fortunately, he does not have to look into a crystal ball to get the answer. An employee expects from his foreman exactly the same kind of treatment that the foreman expects from his own superior. The reactions of the man on the job are largely the same as the reactions of the foreman himself. He reads the same papers, he looks at the same TV programs, he has his own ideas about current events. And because he lives in a democracy and because he believes in free speech, he knows he has a right to his own opinions.

Let us go back several generations to another world. Most of our population still lived on farms or in small towns. There were few large factories. The word "neighbor" meant something. If someone was in trouble, he turned to his neighbors.

Today, all that is passing. We are a nation "on the move." Many people have few roots and little to tie to. But man, being a social animal, has to have some contacts with others. Where does he spend the larger part of his waking hours? Why, on his job. For many men and women those hours make up most of their lives. They have to talk with other people, tell them their troubles, their hopes, their ambitions. For them the factory offers the only opportunity for contacts with others, for group relations, for social life.

People, therefore, are going to look for more personal satisfaction from their jobs. One of the factors in this satisfaction is their relations with the person over them. The impression that every employee forms of the company—whether he thinks it is a good place to work, whether he is interested in his job—is based largely on the way he is handled by his immediate supervisor.

To learn what an employee expects of him, all the foreman has to do is put himself in the other fellow's place. Approaching the subject from that angle, the foreman will agree that the following are some of the things expected of him by the men and women in his department:

1. That the foreman know his job
2. Courteous and consistent treatment
3. Necessary tools, material, and instructions to do a good job
4. Fair play—no favoritism
5. Fair wages
6. Opportunity to talk things over freely
7. Understanding of the employee's problems
8. Prompt handling of any grievances
9. That the foreman let the employee "know where he stands"
10. Adequate representation of the employee's point of view to top management
11. Recognition for a job well done
12. That the employee be looked on as an individual making his own contribution to the successful operation of the business

Knowing the Job

We all respect the man who knows his job, even when we do not like him. We all like to work for someone we can look up to, someone from whom we think we can learn. The foreman who does not know his job thoroughly cannot gain the respect and confidence of his men.

There is still another angle to this. The foreman who does know his job plans his work, sees that tools and materials are available, sees that his equipment is kept in good repair, and anticipates trouble. He is not an opportunist waiting for things to happen before he does anything himself. He has no use for the squeaky-wheel-gets-the-grease policy. He is concerned with *preventing* bad situations from developing. He is constantly on the alert, watching for changes that may affect his output, costs, quality, and, most important of all, the mental attitude of his men.

Courteous and Consistent Treatment

The importance of the part courtesy plays in our lives is demonstrated in a large crowd at a baseball game, an excursion, or a convention. Almost everybody in such a gathering is good-natured and shows some consideration for the rights of others. Courtesy saves time; it saves wear and tear on the nerves. Most important of all, it eliminates initial opposition to a superior on the part of an employee.

In the operation of a department, courtesy can be a lubricant of good will. It is just one more step in looking on each employee as an individual, in putting oneself in his place. It does not make any difference how the foreman may feel from day to day; whether the going is rough or smooth, there is only one course for him. Unless he is always courteous and consistent, his effectiveness as a leader will be lessened.

Unfortunately, it is common to run across the supervisor who seldom talks to his men unless he wants to bawl them out, who somehow cannot bring himself to say good morning or to inquire about some personal problem. If one of his men tries to greet him, all he gets in return is a grunt. Such a supervisor is not effective. Even more important, he is missing the most interesting and constructive part of his job—the opportunity to know and understand his men.

Sometimes one hears it said, "He is a funny guy; you never know how to take him." What is meant is that one can never be sure how to approach the man or what his reaction will be. In other words, he is not consistent in his treatment of others. Such an attitude slows down the process of getting results. People avoid consulting such a person simply because they do not like to do business with him. We all have our "off days," but the man who can keep his head in a trying situation will gain the respect of those around him.

Tools and Materials

Most persons want to do a good job. Many times the reasons why they do not, lie outside their control. Management—and that includes supervision—has a definite responsibility for seeing that the work is properly planned, that tools and material are available at the right place at the right time, and that the man on the job is given the necessary instructions. In short, it is a prime responsibility of leadership to see that all the conditions necessary for efficient production are set up and maintained. Even though we must recognize the importance of building employee good will, efficient production must always be the goal.

Fair Play

A frequent source of dissatisfaction is the feeling that someone else got a better deal. One of the surest ways to create ill will is to show favoritism. Thus, the foreman's concern must be to treat everyone alike in a like situation. That is not always an easy thing to do. He must remember that he operates "in a goldfish bowl." Every one of his actions and statements soon becomes common knowledge around the department. They will be picked up, taken apart, and talked about.

Of course, it is natural to do things for those persons whom one likes best. But it is essential to avoid even the appearance of favoritism in day-to-day relations. Some of the areas where the foreman should be especially alert are:

1. Making differences in wages which are not warranted by the relative skills of the jobs or abilities of the men.

2. Assigning work on any basis other than the man's ability to do the job well.

3. Letting some people get away with something contrary to shop rules and then disciplining someone else for a similar act.

4. Letting personal feelings rather than ability and service determine transfers and promotions.

Fair Wages

The term "fair wages," as we shall use it here, has to do with questions of rate comparisons within the department or plant. How a company's general level of wages compares with other plants is a problem beyond a foreman's direct control. Every foreman does, however, share a definite responsibility for seeing that the rates of pay in his department are in line, and he should consider it one of his most important responsibilities. Three simple principles can help him make effective recommendations to management:

1. Rates of pay between jobs should reflect differences in the skill, experience, responsibility, working conditions, and hazards involved.

2. Differences in rates of pay between men on the same job should reflect differences in quality, output, or service.

3. Everyone in a like situation should be treated alike.

One of the most effective ways in which the foreman can assure fairness in the rates on the jobs in his department is to set up a job classification. He can do this even though his company does not have a formal job evaluation program, as outlined in Chap. XII. He should list the jobs and then select the most highly skilled and compare each job with it in terms of skill, effort, responsibility, and job conditions. His next step is to group jobs which he thinks are about equal and then to determine what seems to be a fair differential between groups. Such analysis will enable him to base recommendations for future adjustments on supportable data.

The foreman should remember that every employee knows substantially what every other employee receives. Employees are always comparing their rates with other persons and wondering why somebody else gets more. Clearly, there should be some reasons, and anyone should be entitled to know them if he chooses to ask. In too many plants there is little rhyme or reason to the rate structure. Here is a very concrete opportunity for the foreman to do a constructive job which will go far toward convincing others of his desire to be fair.

Opportunity to Talk Things Over

There are persons to whom others seem to turn naturally when they want to talk things over. Usually the main reasons for this are:

1. The person possesses the confidence of others.

2. Others value his advice and judgment.

3. He is a good listener and has a capacity for understanding.

In this fast-moving age, many problems come up, both on and off the job, which affect a man's attitude and output.   Most employees welcome an opportunity to talk these things over with the person they work for. The real leader does not try to give them pat answers. Rather, by discussion he helps the man to analyze his own problem and to develop the right answer after the man has weighed all the facts.

A leader of men will give those under him ample opportunity to talk things over with him.   He will encourage them by being approachable, by listening, by drawing out the story, by suggesting various alternates, by always making the man think through his own situations until the answer is clear.

Prompt Handling of Grievances

A grievance is anything which adversely affects the man's attitude toward his job, his foreman, or the company.   Its cause may be real or imaginary; it may arise from conditions within the plant or entirely outside.   Whatever the true cause, the fact remains that output and quality may suffer unless something is done about the grievance.   The handling of complaints or grievances is an essential part of every foreman's job.   Nobody can or should do that for him. The way in which the foreman handles such cases either builds confidence and good will, or it lessens them.   Here is a definite field for leadership.

There are two basic steps in handling a grievance— getting at the facts and doing something about the complaint.   In getting at the facts, the foreman should keep these points in mind:

1. He should remember that the man had to screw up his courage to come to him in the first place. Whatever he has on his mind, he thinks it is important.

2. He should put the man at ease, draw him out, listen to him patiently, let him do all the talking, not hurry him.

3. He should avoid arguing with him. The foreman's job is to keep calm and cool no matter what the man says.

4. He should be careful not to do or say anything which might make the man wish he had never brought up the matter.

5. He should get *all* the facts and avoid snap judgment.

6. He should restate the man's main points and ask him whether those are the real issues as he sees them. This will make sure that both are talking about the same thing.

While the man is talking, the foreman should ask himself whether he can settle the issue himself or should pass it up the line. It would be unwise for him to decide a matter of basic company policy, where his action might establish a precedent more or less binding upon the company in future similar cases.

It is also well to remember that the unions usually claim that the individual workman cannot get a satisfactory adjustment of a grievance from the foreman, because the foreman talks the man down. To lean over backward in this respect, the foreman should consider these additional points:

1. He should be fair in appraising the man's complaint and should try to understand his point of view.

2. He should give the man the benefit of the doubt on any minor points.

3. If the foreman has made a mistake, he should admit it. The man who is afraid to admit he was wrong is not big enough to be a leader of men.

4. If he feels that he can decide the matter, he should give the man a definite answer or tell him he would like to think it over. In the latter case he should promise an answer at a stated time.

5. He should not "kid a man along." If he thinks the man has no basis for complaint, he should tell him so and tell him why.

6. He should know how to say no when the facts warrant, but he should stand up for the man when the complaint is just.

7. He should keep his superiors informed on all important grievances and not be afraid to ask for advice and counsel.

8. The foreman should try not to hold it against a man if he goes over his head, either in the first instance or in an appeal from his decision.

9. After the foreman has discussed a grievance with a man, he should tell the man that he is glad he had a chance to talk it over and to understand his point of view.

"Know Where He Stands"

Most of us like to know how we are doing from time to time. This does not necessarily imply that we are looking for praise, but we like to be told if we are not doing the job as well as expected. Everybody has a right to expect helpful criticism from his supervisor if he is not doing the job he should do.

A leader is interested in developing those under him. He keeps close to his men, he sizes up their shortcomings, and he tries to build them up. Under such a policy it is the simple and obvious thing to talk over the performance of each individual and to encourage him to strengthen any weak points. In this way, the man always knows where he stands.

Representation to Top Management

Occasionally there are situations where the men expect their supervisor to "go up the line" for them, to get action on a major problem. They like to feel that he has the courage to stand on his own feet and present a factual picture of their case all the way up the line if necessary. They like to feel that if their cause is just their immediate supervisor will plead their case earnestly and well. It is hardly necessary to add that a good leader always looks out for his men.

Recognition

A plant blacksmith once told about the various "bosses" he had had. One in particular, he said, was hard to understand because he never gave a man the slightest recognition for a job well done. He told about making a grappling hook for use in 30 ft. of water without any sketch or drawing. It worked the first time in raising some equipment from the bottom of the race; yet the blacksmith had to ask a yard helper whom he saw two days later to learn whether his device (which he had worked on all night) had done the job.

Here was an unusual opportunity to build morale and good will. It would have taken so little to thank the man personally and to tell him how the job could not have been done without his ingenuity and help. That would have been leadership. That would have been recognizing a job well done, looking on the man as an individual who had made a real contribution to the success of that project. That would have appealed to his job pride and his responsibility.

SUMMARY

Every supervisor has a choice as to the approach, methods, and devices he will use to get results. On the one side is top management, and on the other side the men. Times change. What was good enough 25 years ago no longer meets today's needs. The successful foreman is the one who possesses the ability to adapt and adjust himself to new conditions.

The essentials of leadership do not change, because they deal with the motives which underlie human conduct.

If the foreman wants to get the results which come from the interest and co-operation of his employees, he may well follow the fundamentals of effective supervision outlined below:

1. Always be courteous.
2. See yourself in the other fellow's place.
3. Maintain consistent standards of conduct, performance, and quality.
4. Take a personal interest in your men.
5. Play no favorites.
6. Do not promise things you can't deliver.
7. Get all the facts before you act. Never jump at conclusions.
8. Give full credit to others when it is deserved.
9. Never discipline a man in front of others.
10. Never lose your temper.

In relations with top management:

1. Understand and carry out all company policies and procedures.
2. Always back-check with your own superior if in doubt.

3. Keep your superior informed.

4. Know how the work in your section stands all the time.

5. Make sure your instructions are always clear, simple, and understood by the person to whom they are given.

6. Follow up your instructions to make sure they are being carried out as you intended.

7. Be constantly alert to see that quality standards are maintained.

8. Don't pass the buck.

9. Keep an open mind.

10. Discard the policy of "greasing the squeaky wheel" and seek to prevent bad situations from developing.

Some unknown author wrote these lines:

> Here lies the tragedy of our race,
> Not that men are poor,
> All men know something of poverty;
> Not that men are wicked,
> Who can claim to be good?
> Not that men are ignorant,
> Who can boast that he is wise?
> But that men are strangers.

In the midst of problems which involve materials, tools, costs, equipment, production schedules, and quality standards, the foreman should remember that there is always an individual or group of individuals involved. It is some *person's* quality which is not up to standard; it is some *person* who fell down in getting out a job on time. It is some *person* who misunderstood or failed to follow through. It is in this human area that problems arise to test the foreman's leadership. The way for him to begin his success is to know his men—to see that they are not strangers.

The foreman can make his own job easier and improve the over-all results of his department if he chooses to develop teamwork, interest, and co-operation by treating everyone as he would like to be treated.

Section Two

THE FOREMAN'S KNOW-HOW

CHAPTER III

QUALITY CONTROL AND WASTE REDUCTION

Part One—A Case Study

By T. O. ARMSTRONG

(This material is based on the experiences of more than 1,000 foremen, group leaders, and gang bosses—responsible for assemblers, fitters, toolmakers, heat-treaters, warehousemen, etc.—who met with the writer in conferences on Production and the Supervisor.)

Every foreman knows that production can be counted only at the end of the line in the number of pieces passed as "O.K." and ready for the customer. To attain such *A* quality consistently, the foreman has three tools with which to work:

Machinery. The machines, tools, gauges, and fixtures necessary to machine, measure, test, and hold the materials.

Materials. The varying materials, brass, copper, wire, steel, subassembly parts, cloth, etc., essential to produce the finished product.

Manpower. People—workers essential within an organization, those who work with the machines, materials, tools, and gauges; those who work with system, scheduling, engineering, etc.; and those who direct an activity or supervise others.

THE PROBLEM

In general, the problem of quality control has been intensified by various characteristics of mass-produc-

39

tion techniques, all of which tend to place further emphasis upon the management function of the supervisor. These characteristics include:

1. *Subdivision of labor*, which has taken the form of reducing each job to a single operation, or at least to a single part.

2. *Decrease of skills* in the use of machinery and tools. The operator tends to depend too much upon the machine to get the work out.

3. *By-product changes of mass production*. Large operations tend to minimize personal interest. In large conveyors and assembly lines man is merely a small unit of a large group.

4. *Incentive payment plans*, which emphasize more production, stressing quantity rather than quality.

5. *Inspection organizations*, which often imply lack of responsibility on the workman's part. In other words, where control of quality is emphasized by the addition of more and more inspectors, the workman tends to develop a feeling that the responsibility for quality rests alone with the inspector. ("Let him worry about it. That's his job.")

Compare the attitude of the old artisan with that of the present-day mass-production worker. The artisan felt the direct effect of quality. He had a part in the final product. Too often the present-day worker is far removed from the finished product. Often he has no realization of what the final product is or the part that he plays in making that product. He does not "get a kick" out of being a part of it.

It is therefore a primary responsibility of present-day supervision to recreate some of the old-time pride in quality work.

As far as the physical tools of production are concerned, the foreman has no quality problem until one or any of the parts break down. It is, therefore, a second supervisory responsibility to prevent breakdown through proper maintenance by the foreman or supervisor himself, by those responsible for maintenance under his charge, or by the operator or worker himself.

It will be helpful for the foreman to draw up a check list of his maintenance responsibilities. Following is an example of such a list, drawn up by the group of foremen, group leaders, and gang bosses mentioned in the beginning of this chapter.

MACHINE MAINTENANCE

Regular cleaning, with sufficient time allowed for it
Frequent checks of motors, bearings, etc.
Running machine one or two cycles before placing the work in it
Proper feed and speed for the job to be done
Keeping dirt and chips out of the way and bedding points
Clamping the work into the fixtures properly
Bedding the work into the machine properly

TOOL AND GAUGE MAINTENANCE

Grinding tools properly and often enough
Having spare tools on the job if possible
Careful handling of tools
Providing proper place for tools when not in use
Checking tools and gauges periodically for accuracy, sharpness, etc.
Proper "coolant" for the tools
Cleaning gauges, cleaning or wiping before use each time
Cleaning fixtures, cleaning before use
Changing the gauges when tools are changed

Making sure that tools and gauges are matched to the drawings for the particular job

Making sure that proper tools and gauges are on the job when engineering changes are made

MATERIAL MAINTENANCE

Shot in the forgings

Mixed forgings—not running regular

Scant stock—not enough to finish properly

Seamy, hard stock, hard to handle or cut

Periodic checks on size, hardness, and condition

Proper storage of materials

Proper trays for holding the finished part

Proper trays and skids for transporting the part from one point to another

More frequent check on close-tolerance parts

WORKING CONDITIONS

The regard that a company holds for quality workmanship is usually reflected in the working conditions it provides for the workmen. Here the foreman plays a leading part, since the best intentions of management are ineffective without his full co-operation. A workman's attitude is often determined by the example of orderly housekeeping set by the foreman.

One company, whose principal product was dependent wholly upon keeping dirt and dust from the bearings of its unit, provided white coats for its workers and an enclosed glass room, air-conditioned the room to keep out dirt, and painted all the walls, machinery, and benches white. Cleanliness was the byword in that department, and a pride in keeping self as well as the product clean was the result.

Important factors to be considered under working conditions are:

Proper lighting and heating

Elimination of drafts

Elimination of dust and dirt

Elimination of crowding that comes from poor planning. (As one workman expressed it: "You can't move around this place to do any work. The truckers pile the stuff on top of your feet. How can I keep my mind on my work?")

Emphasis on employee orderliness

TRAINING AND FOLLOW-UP

Many of the things mentioned thus far point directly to the workman. We cannot, however, expect a workman to know about them unless he has been properly trained. This manpower factor in quality control, therefore, calls for two important foremanship functions:

1. Getting the *new employee* started right

2. Maintaining the *old employee* in the proper habits and attitudes toward quality with which he started out

The New Employee

The supervisor has no problem if a good job of training has been done. This implies:

1. That the supervisor knows all the details of the job on which the worker is to be trained.

2. That the supervisor knows the fundamentals of training and presenting new or different ideas to others.

3. That the supervisor is assured that others who may be doing the training for him (training center or other under his own supervision) know the details of the job on which the worker is to be trained, and the fundamentals of training.

The fundamentals of training are expressed in the following principles emphasized during the Second World War by the Training Within Industry Division of the War Manpower Commission, in its Job Instructor Training program.

1. *Have a plan.*   Be able to determine how much skill the learner is expected to have and how soon.

2. *Analyze the job.*   Know the principal steps in the operation and be able to pick out the key points, knacks, hazards, etc., in the job.

3. *Have everything ready.*   The right tools, equipment, and materials should be on hand.

4. *Have the workplace properly arranged.*   Prepare the shop exactly as the worker will be expected to keep it.

The supervisor or the man responsible to him for the job instruction should familiarize himself with the training techniques discussed in Chap. VII, learning how to instruct clearly and completely, taking up one point at a time and never more than the new employee can master at one time.

The Old Employee

How to maintain the standards set in the original training is the second major interest of the supervisor. What are some of the things employees do that cause poor-quality workmanship?   Here are some important check points developed by the supervisory group mentioned before:

Skipped operations

Careless setups

Disinterest among workmen

Running the drills too long

Not checking the gauges

Changing the tools without gauges
Improper burring
Passing the work without checking
Passing work outside gauge limits

A Review of Reasons for Poor Workmanship

It will pay to keep the following in mind:

1. *Conditions of the Workplace*

Improper working conditions have already been mentioned with respect to cleanliness and good housekeeping. Cold, heat, drafts, hard floors are conditions which have a bearing upon quality of work because of fatigue factors affecting the workman. The older worker especially is affected. Good lighting is particularly important in work requiring the employees' attention to close tolerances.

2. *Changing Men Around Too Often*

Often, particularly in times of increased production and lack of experienced help, an apt worker is frequently moved around from one job to another, so that he does not have the opportunity to acquire the skills of any one job well. Of course, many situations of this sort are beyond the individual foreman's control, but he should do all he can to prevent unnecessary confusion.

3. *Employees Improperly Placed on a Job*

The square peg in the round hole is an old story to most foremen. Nevertheless, it is worth repeating that lack of interest often comes from the fact that the employee himself knows that he is not suited to the job but feels that he cannot do much about it. This feeling results in lack of interest, fatigue, defective workmanship. In most companies the foreman has a voice in the final selection of a man or woman for his department. He should take this selection responsibility seriously.

4. *"Work off Standard Was Passed Before, Why Not Now?"*

The old story of the shepherd boy crying "Wolf! Wolf!" is applicable here. One of the best methods of training is that of example and demonstration. The foreman cannot expect a workman to believe that he wants "top-standard" material if he has been willing to let it go at less than top standard when he was rushed for production. The employee may begin to question the importance of the standard.

5. *No Encouragement from the Supervisor for Work Done*

"I never see my boss," said a workman one day. "Do you know how I stand with that fellow?" To this his listener replied that only the day before he had heard his boss mention the fact that he would hate to lose the man, because he was one of the best grinders on the job.

"Well, I had just about made up my mind to quit. I've been working up there for a year and a half, and no one yet has told me whether I was doing well or doing poorly. I don't know whether I'm worth anything to this outfit or not. I'd just about decided I wasn't. I'd made up my mind that I would slip backward if I stayed here much longer."

When this situation was called to the foreman's attention, his comment was, "Gee, what's the matter with these fellows anyway? Are they soft? Do you have to nurse them all the time? He is supposed to do good work, isn't he? And, if he does, he gets paid for it, doesn't he?"

How practical was this foreman? If commended, the man would certainly continue to produce a good-quality job, knowing that what he did was appreciated by the boss. On the other hand, there was a chance that the man was about to leave, indicating that credit for a job well done, to which he was entitled now and then, was the difference between interest and lack of interest in the job.

6. *"Tight Standards—Can't Make Time"*

We cannot expect the worker to believe that we are interested in quality workmanship if we are not willing to provide proper incentive for his interest in his work. Often a review of the time study with the workman will reveal that he is not doing all the operations in the proper sequence or that he is not doing the job in the way it should be done or that he is doing more than he should to get out the quality desired. It is the foreman's responsibility to see that all circumstances surrounding the job are such as to make possible the desired quality with relative ease. If the circumstances are not good, the worker tends to produce poor work in an effort to "make his time."

7. *Poor Wage Scale for Type of Work Being Done*

Quality suffers if the employee thinks the company does not feel that his job is very important in relation to other jobs he sees around the department. Often this problem is not one of his wage scale but of the wage scales of another operator on a job which he feels requires a lesser skill. One cannot expect a sense of pride in quality of work from a man who feels that he is discriminated against.

8. *Employees Cannot Work to Close Tolerances*

This is often a matter of improper selection. Some people do not like to work where the responsibility for close tolerances is essential. Their capacity for attention to detail is not great. They tire easily, become discouraged, lose interest in the work, and want to be moved. Or the condition may be physical —men or women will complain of headaches and will blame the close-tolerance work they have to do. A visit to the optometrist may uncover an eye defect which can be corrected.

9. *Lack of Interest*

Often a workman, particularly on a routine job (drilling, subassembly, ordinary benchwork), lacks interest in his work. He must be reminded of the importance of his function in the whole operation. This can be done by developing a group or departmental spirit, perhaps by such bulletin-board notices as "Assembly Group No. 19 Ahead of Schedule for the Week of May 19" or by notices picturing or calling attention to the use, in the finished product, made of the part on which the group is working.

Often, of course, lack of interest may be due to outside causes—worries, sickness, financial troubles, or other interests greater than the job. These call for qualities of leadership on the part of the foreman, as stressed in other sections of this book.

Often the operator sees no reason for what he feels are extreme tolerances—a whim of the Engineering or Inspection Departments. In one case, this was corrected by arranging a meeting between the employees of the Machining Department and those of the Assembly Department.

The assemblers tore down and built up a complete fan, pointing out to the machine workmen the parts they made and the necessity for the tolerances called for. The result was appreciation of the need for the tolerances; appreciation by the machinemen for the part they played in building complete fans; fewer complaints from the assembly-department employees who were critical of the machining section for not delivering standard materials; more production because the assemblers could assemble the mechanism without having to sort the shafts before assembly.

An excuse frequently heard by the foreman is, "I didn't know the tolerances." One way to overcome this is to post in plain view in front of the operator, on the bench or machine, the tolerances for the parts he is making.

10. *Maintenance of Discipline*

The relation of this factor to the problem of quality can be illustrated by the experience in one plant. Much scrap had been traced to workmen throwing waste or rags at an operator in the act of bedding, or clamping, a piece of work in a fixture, drawing the attention of the workman away from his job and thereby causing improper bedding, or clamping, of the work.

The foreman must always be severe about such "tomfoolery." To allow actions of this kind to continue would certainly break down morale and cause employees to be indifferent to quality.

11. *"Too Many Men to Supervise"*

This condition may, of course, actually exist. However, the foreman should make sure that the trouble is not his own lack of supervisory ability. If he has not learned how to instruct, train, or inspire his people to produce a quality product, he has a job of endless supervision.

12. *Supervisor Pays No Attention to Suggestions*

There is probably nothing more important to a man than his own ideas. If a workman feels that an idea of his will improve a condition or product, the foreman should listen and take a sympathetic attitude. If the idea cannot be put across, he should take the time to explain why.

Requests for help come under this same head. For example, from a man who was continually making defective parts, a complaint came that no one seemed to be paying any attention to his trouble. He claimed that the fixture was wrong and that the supervisor had said he would help but that he always seemed too busy. A meeting was called. The employee had a chance to iron out his difficulty, and the committee was able to help the supervisor overcome the difficulty.

13. *"Pushed for Production by the Schedule Man"*

This is a popular complaint in rush times. The foreman must see to it that employees do not develop the attitude that production is more important than quality. "Others get away with it" is a common expression, but it points directly at supervision.

14. *Undeserved Blame*

Undeserved blame will always react against good workmanship if the workman does not have a chance to explain. In one plant a committee made up of the foreman, the inspector, and the union representative meets once each day, or as often as is necessary, with a workman and discusses with him the reasons for the scrap that he made the previous day. This provides a chance for all the facts to be "laid on the table." These men meet to discuss *what* was right instead of *who* was right. Often it turns out that scrap is being made by a new man who had not been properly instructed. Everyone, then, agrees to "pitch in" to help this worker.

15. *Not Enough Gauges*

"I'm working on a new job," complained an operator. "There are three shifts. There are not enough gauges for all three shifts. I wasted a lot of time looking for a particular gauge, only to find that the operator on a preceding shift had locked it up. After considerable red tape, we opened the locker and got the gauge."

The solution to this problem was a meeting of all the men on the three shifts, with the following result:

"We got together, and everything was straightened out. The rest of the fellows had the same complaint. Then and there we agreed to leave the gauges in a certain location, and ever since, everything has been o.k. In fact, it works out so well that we decided to do the same thing with all tools and fixtures used on the job. Result—we are making more parts, making better parts, and making more money."

16. *Operator Does Not Gauge Work Properly, and Not Often Enough*

Frequently the trainer will instruct a workman in the details of the job to be done and will merely say, "Use this gauge to measure your work once in a while."

Often more training is needed in the use of the gauges to measure the work than in the details of the job to be done. It is also essential to point out the reason for the frequency in gauging the work, opportunity being thereby provided for pointing out the importance of the work and correcting the gauging.

17. *Favoritism*

We tend to favor those we like, and too often it is not because of performance or ability. Favoritism breeds contempt among the more skilled operators. It usually involves many employees, and the results are hard to overcome. It works two ways, both tending to produce defective work: (1) employees favored become lax in their work; (2) employees disfavored become dissatisfied, angry, resentful, or indifferent.

18. *Too Much Criticism*

If a foreman makes a worker say to himself, "I never do anything right for that guy," he is sowing

Name: John Doe	*Department:* Motor Winding
GOOD POINTS	BAD POINTS
Good winder Always on time Confidence in himself Gets out production	Slides stators from one side to another, often tearing the winding, causing short when assembled into motor

Fig. 1.—An analysis sheet used in preparation for a talk with an employee.

the seeds of antagonism, discouragement, and spoiled work. If criticism must be given, it is well for the foreman to preface his remarks with a few good points about the workman and to wind up with a few more good points. A group of supervisors used the method shown in Fig. 1 to analyze a specific case whenever they found it necessary to criticize a workman. Below is a sample talk based on the analysis illustrated:

"John, you are doing a good job for me around here, and I like the way you handle yourself. You're getting a good reputation for yourself as a motor winder. Lately we have been running into a number of shorts at test. I hate to see your good work going to waste. Do you suppose it's the way you slide your stators across the bench? Look into it, will you, John, and see if we can't get that percentage of good ones up?"

A "CASE STUDY" IN QUALITY IMPROVEMENT

The following is a "case-study" account of a program begun by the Springfield, Mass., plant of Westinghouse Electric & Manufacturing Company to reduce defective workmanship and scrap. It has been kept alive by continuous follow-through over the years and has paid off handsomely. Its objective is to keep before the workman at all times the part that he plays in keeping the organization in which he works a "going" and successful one. It is offered here because it contains useful ideas which a foreman may be able to apply in his own department or which he may want to suggest to his management.

There was such concern about the problem of good workmanship that a careful study of the scrap account was made, which took a period of years to complete. Several important facts came out of this study:

1. At whatever period selected, the defective workmanship account (defective work caused by workman) represented the largest portion of the account, as indicated by the following table.

	June	September	February	October
Defective workmanship, per cent..............	52	56	60	54
All other, per cent......	48	44	40	46

Fig. 2.—Analysis of scrap account.

2. Of this large portion the scrap losses consisted of variable, nonrecurring items of expense, small in value, but making a tremendous total in the aggregate. For example:

| 10 shafts at 0.40 | 3,000 punchings at 0.005 |
| 20 pinions at 0.25 | 5,000 washers at 0.0004 |

3. All other causes, over which the individual workman had no control, were found to be faulty design, materials, processes, or manufacturing equipment, which could be corrected only through design or manufacturing engineering.

4. Other portions of the losses might be termed "epidemic" troubles, or losses due to defects which increased sharply at times, the fault lying with inadequate control of materials, processes, or manufacturing. The problem was an inspection or test function or an engineering function or both.

Thus the problem seemed to divide itself into three major responsibilities, as follows:

25 per cent—responsibility of design or manufacturing engineering

25 per cent—responsibility of inspection or engineering

50 per cent—directly chargeable to the failure of the worker to produce as good a product as could be done

with the materials, equipment, or processes made available to him

Obviously, an important corrective was increased care on the part of the workman, a continued interest and desire on his part to put quality into his work and into the product. The problem of how to get the worker to realize this responsibility and to appreciate that a reduction in scrap losses would benefit him was placed in the hands of the Industrial Relations Department, defective workmanship being regarded as a human problem.

The underlying purpose of the defective workmanship program was to acquaint the entire working personnel with the facts concerning losses and to appeal to their pride in their jobs, as well as to their self-interest, to bring about the exercise of greater care.

The plan was to hold through committee meetings direct discussion of individual faults with the workman involved. The cause of the trouble and the cost entailed were to be investigated, and the workman was to be given an opportunity to present "his side of the story" without fear of reprisal. Then, as a group, the committee would determine how the difficulty was to be eliminated.

The first step was to enlist the support of the local union committee, at the same time giving them an opportunity as a responsible labor organization to make a constructive contribution to the welfare of the plant. Following a meeting, the union officials published an editorial in their news organ, *The United Front*, presenting the facts outlined at the meeting and asking for continued co-operation against the common enemy, *Scrap*.

With this support assured, local departmental committees were established. They included the foreman, the union steward, and the departmental inspector. Depending upon the circumstances, the office of the chairman was held in various cases by the foreman, the steward, or a workman elected by the employees of the department. The office of the secretary, how-

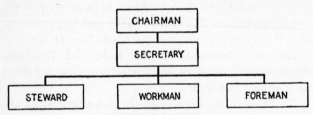

Fig. 3.—Make-up of departmental committee.

ever, was always held by the inspector, for it was he who was responsible to the committee for seeing that subject material, gathered from the scrap tags accumulated and investigated by him prior to the meeting, was available for discussion (see Fig. 3).

The following set of minutes illustrates the contents of meeting discussions.

Date_____ Department_____ Division_____
Present: Messrs. Palmer, Hitt, Goold, Paunoff, Jones
OLD BUSINESS
    An air line has been installed to blow dirt off the contacts while they are being wire brushed. This installation has improved the condition of dirty contacts. Item Closed.
NEW BUSINESS

Item No. 1	*Leaky Center Welds.* Samples displayed and faults discussed with worker. Condition unavoidable insofar as the worker is concerned. Investigation to be made by Mr. Paunoff and report made at the next meeting. Item Open.
Item No. 2	*Bellows.* Dented bellows received in the department caused by poor packing from Department B3. Steward from Department B3 present to discuss the item, present to his committee for correction, and report back to this committee at its next meeting. Item Open.

Item No. 3	*Shafts Undersized*—Workman J. Doe brought into the meeting. Investigation pointed to the fact that he was not aware of the proper tolerances, had not inquired as to the latest drawings, did not know that there had been a later drawing on the part. Committee decided he should not have worked on a prior drawing he had in his bench drawer, even though latest drawing should have come along with the order card. Item Closed.

Divisional meetings with the superintendent as chairman were held periodically. Committee make-up is shown in Fig. 4.

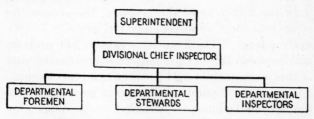

Fig. 4.—Make-up of divisional committee.

The purpose of these meetings was to report the progress of the program, point the need for emphasis along certain lines, give credit where due, and discuss certain problems of interdepartmental committee work.

Occasionally, general plant meetings were called to report progress of the plan. A typical program of one of these plant meetings follows:

OPENING REMARKS
Progress, where are we heading?
INSPECTION AND THE SCRAP ACCOUNT
by an Inspector
THE FOREMAN AND THE SCRAP ACCOUNT
by a Foreman
THE OPERATOR AND THE SCRAP ACCOUNT
by a Workman

Scrap Is Our Problem
  by a Union Steward
We Are on Our Way
  by the Works Manager

Charts showing the progress of the program, sales to the customer, reduction of field-service charges, and other data were on display and referred to by various discussion leaders.

Certificates of merit were awarded to individual workmen nominated by the foreman at meetings such as this.

In the first year of the program, the account for scrap losses was approximately 12.7 per cent of productive labor. The immediate value of the program and its parallel efforts is demonstrated by the decrease of this percentage to 6.34 per cent two years later.

An important point made to plant management by the various committees was that many items were being charged to them for which their departments or workmen were not responsible. In some cases the cause was materials; in some, tools or equipment; and in others, parts received from other departments.

These conditions tended to reduce the feeling of responsibility on the part of the workman, thereby possibly endangering the basic idea of the campaign. To eliminate this defect, subdivisions of the scrap account were set up. Faulty workmanship was given the prefix W; defective materials, M; defective parts from other departments, P; and all expenses due to factors beyond the control of anyone in the plant (such as materials or parts from outside suppliers) were given the prefix U.

This system led to the proper placing of responsibility on the supplying divisions or on the incoming-material-inspection group or on the management group when any item designated *P*, *M*, or *U* reached an appreciable figure.

Publicity

Publicity is most important. After the program had been announced, interest was maintained through the medium of posters, which were changed weekly and distributed through the plant. Many of the

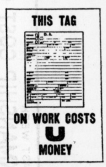

Fig. 5.—Typical posters used to publicize the "No Scrap". campaign. Many slogans were suggested by the employees.

slogans were suggested by the employees. The official news organ of the union volunteered to reprint the posters and slogans which were used. Signs (see Fig. 6) were placed in the departments each week showing the cost of defective workmanship in dollars and in percentage of productive labor.

As the campaign progressed, more information was demanded by the employees. To answer this request, a news letter was published periodically, showing the progress made. Final title chosen for the letter was *The United Front for Good Workmanship*. Figure 7 shows a typical issue. Reproduction was inexpensive. Use was made of cartoons and snappy punch lines.

Ideas for cartoons were presented by employees and

Fig. 6.—Typical sign placed in departments.

committee members. One issue included a statement from the president of the local union, together with letters from satisfied and dissatisfied customers. Many departments continued this idea by placing similar letters on their bulletin boards.

Fig. 7.—Typical news letter.

Figure 8 shows graphically what can be accomplished by a scrap-reduction campaign. The bars show scrap in terms of productive labor lost, using the year the campaign started as base. The successive reductions in scrap emphasize the consciousness of waste drilled into the working force by the drive.

Individual Recognition

Another interesting phase of the program, designed to give recognition to workers who demonstrate good workmanship over a period of time, was the publication of pictures of those employees in a leaflet called "Highlights in Good Workmanship." This leaflet was distributed to all employees in the plant.

Some of the employees who received these mentions were so proud of them that they had them framed and hung in prominent places in their homes. The enthusiasm for these "Highlights" led to the presentation of a certificate to all who were mentioned as highlights during the year. Following the presentation, a letter of congratulation was sent to the home of the recipient by the works manager.

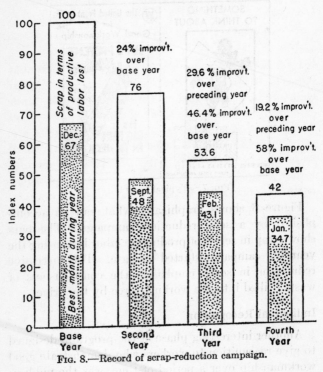

FIG. 8.—Record of scrap-reduction campaign.

It is well to bear in mind that in making such awards the company must be absolutely certain that the award is earned, based on factual records over a period of time; that the performance is above the average; and that all fellow employees are informed of the supporting details.

Part Two—Developments in Statistical Quality Control[1]

By E. H. Mac Niece

It was not until a relatively few years ago that industry in general recognized the fact that 100 per cent terminal inspection, particularly for defects to be caught by ordinary visual observance, is only about 85 per cent reliable because we human beings are, after all, only about 85 per cent reliable. Also, it is now recognized that judgment faculties become fatigued much more rapidly from repetitive inspections than do human muscles from manual work.

It is our purpose here to acquaint the foreman with the high lights of developments in statistical quality control, so that he may have a better insight into management's objectives, and thus be in a better position to co-operate.

DETERMINING THE NEED FOR CONTROLS

It is quite possible to apply scientific waste and quality controls in almost any industrial activity where they do not already exist, and obtain some form of cost improvement.

In each department, the quality level and the waste level should be estimated by actual inspection of siz-

---

[1] Based on the book, "Organizing for Quality and Waste Control," by E. H. Mac Niece, in "Reading Course in Executive Technique," published by Funk & Wagnalls Company, New York, edited by Carl Heyel. Text adaptation and reproduction of charts by permission.

able samples. Existing records may show the extent of scrap and waste. Unfortunately without a sampling there is no knowledge of the outgoing quality level. Customer-complaint records (in consumer-goods industries) cannot be depended upon to present a true picture of unsatisfactory quality because only a small percentage of American consumers will formally register a complaint. It is roughly estimated that for each formal customer complaint there are more than one hundred customer dissatisfactions. Those who do not complain merely purchase another brand. Ignorance of the quality level is too great a risk for any producer.

After an analysis has been made in each department it will be simple to compute the cost of defects and scrap for the whole plant. It will be advantageous to examine carefully a quantity of goods in the shipping department to estimate the actual, current outgoing quality level. This should be compared with the customer-complaint records.

ORGANIZATION

The individual who is to direct the work of quality and waste control is ideally someone with an engineering background, administrative ability, and a specialized training in statistical methods for quality control. (Many of the universities are now offering intensive courses in statistical quality control and industrial statistics.)

Testing stations should be established in the manufacturing areas as close to the actual operations as possible. In many cases these stations need only be a table equipped with dial gauges, burettes, indicator solutions, plastometers, or any of the equipment needed to perform the tests connected with the specific work of the area. If duplicate equipment is needed to cover similar tests in other locations, it should be procured.

Experience has shown that it is best not to establish a central control laboratory. Nothing can defeat the purpose of instantaneous control more than a central laboratory where results are sent to the manufacturing departments too late to do anything about them. The most effective arrangement is one in which the quality-control technician and the manufacturing operator can see each other and signal results instantaneously.

Many manufacturing operations consist of primary or processing operations and secondary or finishing operations. As an example, some surgical dressings start with spinning, weaving, purifying, bleaching, and tentering. These are considered the primary operations. Cutting, folding assembly, sterilization, and packaging are considered as the secondary operations. Furniture manufacture might consider kiln drying, planing, and jointing as primary operations, with sawing, routing, turning, sanding, and painting as secondary operations. Although it may seem strange to start the control activity in the middle of things, the area of primary operations is generally a good place to begin. Establishment of controls in the primary process permits working back to raw materials and working forward to finishing operations.

Possibly work is to be started in the Foundry Department. Numerous quality characteristics will be found which may be important. Strength, hardness, machinability, stability after machining, and the absence of holes or other imperfections may be the important criterion. If these characteristics are not being tested, collection and testing of periodic samples should be undertaken. With the information charted, as will be explained later, the normal variations will become apparent. Also, signals indicating abnormal variations will lead to the discovery of their causes. It may be necessary to specify other raw materials. Formula and method changes may be indicated. A slight increase in an alloy metal may eliminate warping after first machine cuts. A slight change in formula or heat may facilitate machining and increase cutter life.

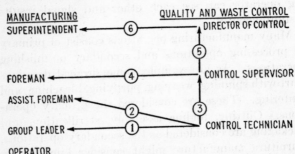

Fig. 1.—Relationship of quality- and waste-control functions to manufacturing functions.

With the data being charted, economic specification limits as well as sampling frequency will soon be indicated. Some characteristics such as hardness may be found to be uniform throughout a heat. Four or five random samples tested for these characteristics per heat or once per shift may be satisfactory to indicate control or lack of control.

Quality- or waste-control technicians should not give orders to the workmen. Good management is based on having the individual report to only one supervisor or head. An arrangement requiring anyone at the working level to serve two masters is impracticable.

In any control program there will probably be three levels in the control department which will parallel certain manufacturing organization levels as shown in Fig. 1.

When quality or waste discrepancies occur at the operator level, the control technician should explain the charts or the data to the operator so that prompt correction can be made. If the adjustments are not made promptly the situation should be reported to the group leader. Further delinquency, in turn, should be handled up through the various levels as indicated in the chart.

PRODUCT SPECIFICATIONS

Too many products are still being made today without any formality of written specifications. If such situations are found it will be important to have product specifications prepared before controls are established. It will be interesting too.

The following form serves well in presenting the information needed in a product specification:

1. *General requirements*
   a. Give a brief description of the product and a brief explanation of its intended use. (Not included should be such indefinite statements as "Workmanship shall be first class and the goods shall be substantially free from defects." These are smilingly referred to by wise production men as the "escalator clauses.")
   b. Briefly describe the basic materials.
   c. Briefly describe the assembly of the basic materials.
   d. If the product is packaged, the general information such as the number of units to be packed in a container should be briefly described.
   e. If shipping containers are used, briefly describe the number of units or packages to be packed in them.

The general requirements should give a thumbnail

description of the product so that it can be identified at a glance without reading through the details.

2. *Detailed requirements*

   a. Specify all product characteristics together with the tolerances allowed. Give dimensions, tensile strength, hardness, density, plasticity, chemical reactivity, or any characteristics *essential* in the product or its components.

   b. Specify all performance requirements. If the product must withstand accelerated aging at high or low temperatures, specify the requirements; specify any drop tests or abrasion tests.

   c. Where possible, specify ultimate consumer-use requirements such as the number of launderings a garment must withstand or the number of operative hours a mechanism must function.

   d. Specify the labeling and packaging in detail. Specify control numbers and markings. Give the package dimensions together with the thickness and construction of the box or carton. Specify the finish and printing of the package.

   e. Specify the shipping container, giving the inside dimensions, construction, and test requirements. Cover the sealing and marking in detail.

3. *Testing procedure*

   a. For each requirement in Section Two describe a test to be performed for its determination, giving the maximum and minimum results allowable.

   b. Include samples of minimum acceptable-quality characteristics when possible. A piece of cloth showing the maximum allowable for ships, bars, slubs, etc., can be placed between sheets of transparent material and included. Slime spots and formation can be shown for paper products. When samples are too large to be included, such as those showing a polished surface, the actual samples should be numbered and located in the manufacturing areas. The numbers should be referred to in the specification.

   c. Drawings of test apparatus may also be included.

4. *Sampling*

   a. The number of samples to be tested for each requirement should be specified, as well as the frequency of sampling.

b. The frequency of examining packages and shipping cases for neatness, correctness of marking, and effectiveness of sealing should also be specified.

c. The recording of the test results should be specified. If average and range charts or "*p* charts" are used, they should be specified.

Such product specifications should be reviewed and approved by Research, Manufacturing, and Sales, before distributing. It may be necessary to issue tentative specifications until control charts indicate the correct limits and frequency of sampling. The preparation of product specification is often delayed because of the contemplation of some future change. It is wise to establish a practice of issuing specifications and amending them when necessary rather than to wait for some expected change.

Specifications should be continually reviewed, using the quality- and waste-control data to strengthen certain requirements which need it and eliminating other requirements which are not meaningful in terms of the product's intended use.

SAMPLING FOR RAW-MATERIALS CONTROL

Raw materials should be covered by specifications. These specifications should be developed co-operatively with the various suppliers. Be sure they are identified by the supplier's lot markings so that sampling can be simplified and lot uniformity can be determined. (See Fig. 2.) As process controls are established, variations discovered in raw materials probably will indicate that modifications to the specifications are needed.

To measure every piece of incoming material or to run chemical and/or physical tests on every drum of

No. 165–262

RAW-MATERIAL SPECIFICATION COVERING
MOULDING COMPOUND NU 67-C

Our Code Nu 67-C   Vendor Code PR 9824

Property	Requirement	Test
1. Granulation	Thru 12 mesh 5% max. Thru 140 mesh 10% max.	ASTM D–392–38
2. Bulk factor	2.7	ASTM D–392–38
3. Moulded sp. g.	1.40 max.	ASTM D–392–38
4. Moulding shrinkage (inch per inch)	.007 max.	ASTM D–551–41
5. Impact strength (Izod)	.24 foot-pounds per inch of notch max.	ASTM D–48–43T
6. Tensile strength	7000 PSI min.	ASTM D–48–43T
7. Flexural strength	9000 PSI min.	ASTM D–48–43T
8. Dielectric strength (short time)	300 volts per mil min.	ASTM D–48–43T
9. Water absorption (max. weight gain %)	.70%	ASTM D–48–43T

All values of limits indicated are inclusive.

Shipping and Packaging Instructions

This material shall be delivered in air-tight, sealed steel containers of 40- to 20-quart capacity, conveying 50 lb net or 25 lb net, respectively. Containers shall be labeled in accordance to contents, net weight, production lot number, inspection control code, and name of vendor.

FIG. 2.—Specimen raw-materials specification.

chemicals or every bolt of cloth received probably would require a receiving-inspection force almost as large as the manufacturing force itself. It is here that scientific statistical sampling can be applied to assure against acceptance of unsatisfactory materials at a minimum of inspection cost, consistent with chosen risks and an agreed-upon quality level.

It must be appreciated that the supplier is also confronted with the same problem of economic inspection and testing of his outgoing products. If the cost of 100 per cent inspection were added to the raw-material costs by the supplier and again added to the final product as receiving-inspection costs by the purchaser, the selling price of the finished goods would probably be prohibitive. Here again, receiving inspection of samples can be utilized to assure an economic and safe acceptance of purchased materials.

In designing or adopting a standard sampling plan, full recognition is given to knowledge that variations do exist in all natural or manufactured material. This requires a down-to-earth decision on a value of outside-limit material which shall not be exceeded, made after due consideration of the many economic factors involved. Such a value is usually described in terms of "per cent defective" and generally is covered in an agreement between the vendor and purchaser. In the case of outgoing product quality, it is usually necessary that the Quality Control Department act for the consumer in establishing the tolerance per cent defective. In acting upon this responsibility, it should give full consideration to whether strict protection is necessary against accepting individual lots of tolerance quality (the concept of "lot-tolerance per cent defective"). Or, it should decide whether it is satisfactory merely to assure against exceeding a maximum average per cent defective over a number of lots in the long run (the concept of "average outgoing quality limit—AOQL"). The latter recognizes that while some individual lots could exceed this average, others of better quality will offset the poor lots to net an average equal to or better than the maximum long-run average.

One very popular source of standard sampling plans is found in the book "Sampling Inspection Tables—Single and Double Sampling" by Harold F. Dodge and Harry G. Romig. Their handbook gives sampling tables which have stood the test of usage, supplemented by descriptions of method, procedure, charts, concepts, and mathematical derivation.

The paramount feature of modern sampling plans lies in their design for greatest inspection economy in terms of the minimum total amount of inspection. In this total is the amount inspected as samples plus an amount covering the remaining portion of lots inspected as a consequence of "nonconforming samples." Obviously, both amounts affect inspection cost. As might be expected, the sample size depends on the lot size under consideration. However, close examination of the tables mentioned in the foregoing paragraph discloses that the ratio of sample size to lot size diminishes with increasing lot sizes, yet constantly maintains a stipulated level of protection.

In contrast to the above is the old-fashioned rule of thumb, "constant-ratio sample size," as in the case where a 1 per cent sample is arbitrarily taken. Such unscientific sampling deserves mention only to be classified as unsound. This is simply because of its varying protection level, relatively less on small lots than on large. Conversely, it provides excess protection on large lots in relation to a considered satisfactory small-lot level. Excess protection will result in excess inspection.

As an example in applying single sampling, making use of standard reference tables, let us assume an agreement between vendor and purchaser to the effect that "the quality shall be such that not more than 2 per cent of the pieces on the average shall be defective." This implies an AOQL sampling plan. It might be that a shipment (lot) consists of 40,000 pieces, all of which are essentially alike, in so far as you know, as determined from manufacturer's lot or date markings. From your records of inspecting the vendor's past shipments you find his quality level (process-average per cent defective) has been quite good, say 0.5 per cent.

Under the above conditions, in accordance with standard tables, you need only inspect a sample of 125 pieces (each piece picked at random from the 40,000 lot). The allowable defect number is four; that is, if no more than four defective pieces are found in the 125, the lot is accepted. If five or more defective pieces are found, the sample is nonconforming. This latter calls for one of several possible actions:

1. The remainder of the lot, together with defective pieces found, is returned to the vendor for detailing (an inspection of each piece remaining) before subsequent return.

2. A detailing of the lot by the purchaser with inspection cost charged to vendor.

3. Some other form of action or adjustment as might be included in the contractual agreement.

In the foregoing, if the vendor's quality level were to be less favorable, a larger sample size and a different acceptance number would be stipulated in the table. Under conditions of no previous history or lack of records it is wise, even for inspection reasons, to assume the worst (highest) quality level covered by the tables until the quality level is actually determined. Since we are interested here in acquainting the foreman only with the general idea of statistical sampling, we are not burdening this chapter with reproduction of the actual tables.

The double sampling plans are quite popular because, by their nature, less total amount of inspection is needed. Particularly is this so when the vendor's quality is generally quite good. Moreover, double sampling has a psychological appeal to the vendor because it seems to give him two chances of having his goods accepted.

As an example of double sampling, assume the same conditions as given in the foregoing example of single sampling: a lot size of 40,000 pieces, a 2 per cent AOQL, and a vendor's past quality level of 0.5 per cent defective. For the first trial, a sample of 47 pieces is inspected. If the number of defectives does not exceed 0, the lot is accepted. If the number of defectives exceeds 0 but does not exceed 6, a second sample of 148 pieces is inspected. If the sum of the defectives in the first and second samples combined (195) does not exceed 6, the lot is accepted. The sample is nonconforming immediately upon finding more than 6 defectives in the first sample, also if more than 6 are found in the combined samples.

CONTROL CHARTS

With control charts, management can very specifically direct its efforts to the process or parts of a process which are out of, or tending to go out of, control. There is no point in spending time and effort on other operations where good control is indicated by the charts. Without such information a production process can suddenly go out of control in one place when efforts are being extended to other areas of activity; looking for trouble where none exists.

The Shewhart Control Charts comprise a scientific yet extremely simple method for charting quality characteristics during production. The charts are a sensitive indicator for that which is currently happening in the process and then, by disclosing trends in the quality characteristic, will foretell what is likely to happen a few hours or a few days later if corrective adjustments are not made. They were originated by Dr. Walter A. Shewhart, who has been termed "the father of statistical quality control." The details are described in the American War Standard Z-1.3, 1942, pamphlet *Control Chart Method of Controlling Quality During Production* issued by the American Standards Association.

A brief discussion of the most commonly used charts, namely, the "average and range charts," is given here to show their simplicity and ease of preparation.

First, consider individual measurements or observations of some quality characteristic, that is, readings on some process factor which is pertinent to the quality of the product. These are to be measurements or readings expressed in terms of numerical values, such as 293 grams, 7.2 volts, 0.005 inches, etc. Secondly, consider a sequence of values obtained by taking successive readings at short-time intervals. Then, consider a small sample or subgroup of successive readings from which its *average* (the arithmetic mean, identified by $\bar{X}$) and its *range* (the difference between its largest value and its smallest value, identified by R) are each computed. It is by this method that data are obtained for establishing charts.

A quality-control chart consists of a sheet of graph paper upon which is plotted the average ($\bar{X}$) and range (R) from each subgroup of a continuing series of subgroups, arranged in the order of occurrence. Appropriate scales are used on one edge of the chart for values of $\bar{X}$ and R, while the other is utilized to identify the subgroup sequence number, *i.e.*, to indicate the time sequence. Also shown are control-limit lines for values of $\bar{X}$ and R. The upper control limit (UCL) and lower control limit (LCL) are located at values computed from simple formulas. The "measure of central tendency for the averages," *i.e.*, the grand average (an average of the averages, identified by $\bar{\bar{X}}$), is usually shown. The measure of central tendency for the ranges (identified by $\bar{R}$) is sometimes shown. (See Fig. 3.)

The use of averages and ranges on a control chart is quite meaningful for quality-control purposes. Plotting of *individual measurement* values has little significance in control work.

The size of subgroups can be "samples" as small as 2, but should not exceed 15. Samples of 4 or 5 are quite generally used. These small-sized samples minimize the inspection effort required for doing the measuring, taking the readings, and recording the clerical results which provide the control; they are preferred also for a technical reason, that of determining the inherent capability of the process by evaluating the "process variability" (lack of stability) for which the average range is the measure used.

From the study of thousands of data from many varied processes, experience shows that 25 subgroups can normally be depended upon for establishing the central tendency and control limits for both averages and ranges. However, instead of elaborating upon the

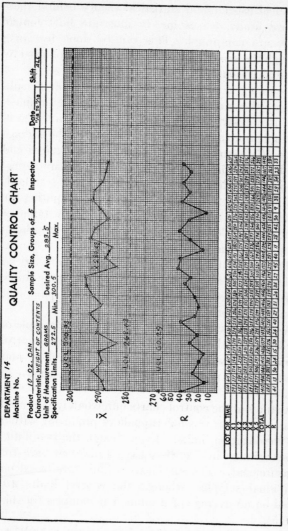

FIG. 3.—Quality-control data based on 25 subgroups of 5 measurements each. Note that upper and lower control ranges are beyond specification limits.

technical aspects and statistical theory behind these control limits, let us merely illustrate how control limits are computed. This can be done by going through the same simple steps as would be followed by the quality-control engineer or technician.

Assuming a series of data consisting of 25 subgroups, the grand average $(\overline{\overline{X}})$ is first determined. This is quickly done by cross adding the average of each subgroup and dividing by 25. Next, the average range $(\overline{R})$ is computed by adding the 25 ranges and dividing by 25. At this point we utilize numerical factors which have been precalculated and standardized in tabular form as the last step in computing the control limits. (Reference is made to a table of "Factors for Computing Control Chart Lines—Small Samples" included in the booklet "A.S.T.M. Manual on Presentation of Data," published by the American Society for Testing Materials, or the same table reproduced in Appendix I of the Z-1.3 pamphlet already mentioned.)

We shall assume here that a subgroup or sample of size 5 was used. Then the upper and lower control limits for averages are calculated. The data and chart may be posted on a single sheet as shown in Fig. 3.

A study of the control charts immediately indicated that the process was not capable of producing within the specification limits. Even though the two limits appear similar in size, they have a different basis for measurement. The specification limits are based on individual samples, whereas the control limits are based on an average of a number of samples (in this case 5).

Demonstrably by statistical treatment not elaborated upon here, the control limits for individuals are larger by the square root of the sample size than the control limits for averages. In this example the variation around the mean would thus be increased by $\sqrt{5}$, or 2.236 times. The natural limits for the process as it is running would then be 247.81 g and 321.15 g, which is considerably greater than the specification limits. In fact, if nothing could be done to the process to reduce the variation, then the specification limits should be increased to these values.

Further study in this case indicated that equipment repairs would not produce the desired results. Modern new equipment could not be procured for 21 months. A study of raw materials showed that with careful sampling, testing for bulk densities, and blending, the finished product could be filled within ± 5 g, which is much better than usual commercial practice.

Occasionally, after application of the tables, situations like the following will be discovered.

UPPER CONTROL LIMIT

UPPER SPECIFICATION LIMIT

LOWER SPECIFICATION LIMIT

LOWER CONTROL LIMIT

Cases like this may be the result of someone hopefully having set tight specification limits. A review of the specification limits must then be made. If it is found that broader limits are satisfactory, the specification requirement should be changed. If it is found that the close specification limits are absolutely necessary, a number of courses of action are required if rejections are to be avoided. First, the equipment may need repair. If this does not correct the situation, machine modifications should be considered. If this fails, then other equipment or better methods should be developed. Raw materials should also be studied.

Manufacturers will always be pleased when the chart shows the following situation.

UPPER SPECIFICATION LIMIT
_____

UPPER CONTROL LIMIT

LOWER CONTROL LIMIT

LOWER SPECIFICATION LIMIT
_____

However, if the average range is unduly large this can give a false sense of security and it is wise to omit the specification-limit lines from the control chart. It should also be understood that if numerous values of range are outside of the range-control limits, it indicates an instability of the process and rather sudden jumps in percentage of product rejections can occur. Also to be kept in mind are the remarks made above with respect to Fig. 3—the natural limits for the process are greater than the control limits based on averages of samples. The natural limits of the process should fall within specifications.

Occasionally the following situations will be found when a control chart is first started.

UPPER SPECIFICATION LIMIT
_____

LOWER SPECIFICATION LIMIT
_____

UPPER CONTROL LIMIT

LOWER CONTROL LIMIT
----

or

UPPER CONTROL LIMIT

           UPPER SPECIFICATION LIMIT

LOWER CONTROL LIMIT

           LOWER SPECIFICATION LIMIT

The foregoing situations do not necessarily indicate a lack of control, but they do indicate a control at the wrong level. The actual spread between the control limits is not bad with respect to the specification tolerance only on a higher or lower level. Such discoveries in applications of control charts will point to and stimulate the needed correction.

When such cases are found in machine-tool work, they may be caused from errors in print dimensions or from improper operator instruction. The correction is likely to be nothing more difficult than a simple adjustment of the tool.

When such cases are found in a process, the combination of causes might vary from simple to complex. Assume a quality characteristic to be moisture content. Adjustment of the drying temperature or time or both would be indicated. If the characteristic were softness in a textile, the system of causes might be a combination of raw material, yarn twist, processing treatment including temperatures and time, chemicals used, yarn sizing, and many other things. This becomes a more complex problem, but well-planned experiments together with control-chart attention can find the cause or combination of causes.

There are many who consider that control charts are most applicable to process work. They consider machine-tool work to be different in that there are bound to be variations from piece to piece as the tool wears and that ultimately all the pieces are given "go–not-go" terminal inspection. This is an erroneous impression. Control charts can actually draw a profile of the tool wear and indicate definite schedules for tool adjustment. What is more important, they can control dimensions so that the outside-limit work at final inspection is at a minimum.

Snap, ring, plug, and other "go–not-go" types of gauges unfortunately do not indicate any degree of variation from the desired value. They only show whether the object just inspected is "good" or "bad" and cannot, therefore, be used for average and range charts.

Dial gauges not only indicate whether or not a dimension is within limits but also permit charting the variations.

Causes for variations in machine-tool work are sensitively indicated by control charts. The chart (Fig. 4) shows that the averages and ranges of a particular dimension on a screw machine are in good control. The same job was later set up on another screw machine. All other conditions—material, tools, and operator, remained the same. The chart (Fig. 5) shows the behavior of the second machine.

As the reader will have already suspected from a comparison of charts in Figs. 4 and 5, the second machine had to be taken out of the line and overhauled.

It is often amazing to see the rapidity with which product characteristics fall into control when the charts are placed right at the machines where operators can see them. It is less amazing to the operators themselves. As one young lady explained it, "When I understood that the idea was to keep between the control lines on the chart, it was easy for

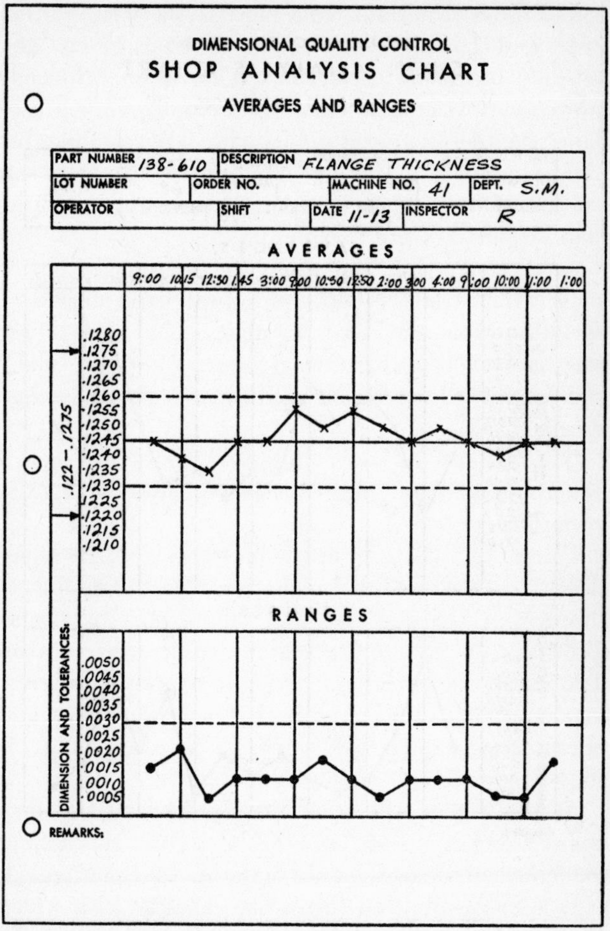

Fig. 4.—Control chart showing that the averages and ranges are in good control for the dimension on a screw machine.

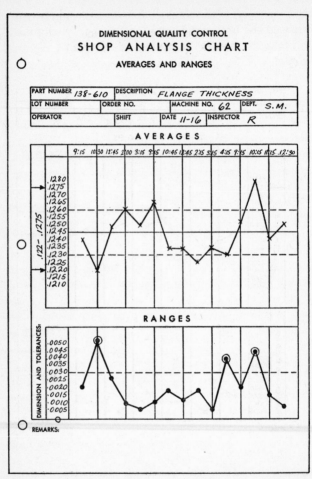

FIG. 5.—Unsatisfactory quality obtained for same setting as in Fig. 4 but on another machine.

me to sense all of the things I did when the points came between the lines and then keep feeling my way back and forth whenever the results come too near the control lines."

p CHARTS

The average and range chart just described serves as a "precision tool" for the control of single quality characteristics measured on *variable* basis. That is, they are measured on a scale which provides numerical values showing the degree of variation from a "central-tendency" value.

However, in numerous industrial activities there is needed a method to evaluate the quality level of characteristics which can be stated only as "good," "bad," or as "go," "not-go." Likewise, a number of assorted kinds of quality characteristics on a single item of product, the same characteristic for a grouping of similar products, or even a combination of both may require a workable quality measure in terms of some common denominator. It is here that "fraction defective," sometimes thought of as "proportion defective" but more commonly called "per cent defective," is used as the measure of quality for subgroups of product, and the *average fraction defective* or *average per cent defective* is used as the quality level.

The fraction-defective chart, known as the "*p* chart," serves as an excellent medium for portraying the results of such inspection, and is quite sensitive in indicating an upward or downward shift in the per cent defective. It can establish whether or not the process is capable of producing at the desired quality level. It can signal when the per cent defective has jumped to a level intolerable to the user. The latter would necessitate immediate corrective adjustments, possibly a shutdown of the machine or process, and a thorough "screening" inspection of the highly defective product already made. If this should occur and the machine or process allowed to continue, the inspection would be maintained for the interim while assignable causes for the jump are sought and corrected. Meanwhile the p chart shows what progress is being made in a return to normal.

In the use of the p chart for waste and quality control, a *defective* is an article (a unit of product, a piece part, an assembly) having one or more defects. A *defect*, in turn, is defined as a single-quality characteristic which does not conform to requirements (standards, specifications, etc.). The quality level (*average fraction defective*, identified by $\bar{p}$) is the measure of central tendency and the deviation from this level is the indicator for quality. As with the average and range chart, control limits are also used, and if exceeded, they provide a prompt warning that corrective action and protective measures should be taken immediately.

The fraction defective (identified by p) of a subgroup of product is the ratio of the number of defective articles found to the total number of articles inspected (examined, measured, and tested).

These limits are relatively simple to calculate. However, for even greater simplicity, standard tables have been prepared for control limits covering various values of per cent defective and sample sizes.

The p chart shown in Fig. 6, covering 18 months' operation, gives a practical application. It is taken from a Second World War case study, because the many dislocations of that period, all affecting quality, highlight the principles discussed. The product

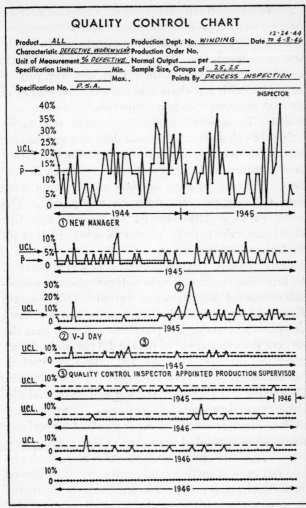

FIG. 6.—*p* chart showing history of quality improvement. At end, more than two months of operation at 0 per cent defective is shown.

involved required critical attention to exacting requirements, ensuring perfect operating-room performance.

With 100 per cent final inspection in use it was at first considered that process control with p charts would be superfluous. Late in 1944, however, process inspection with a p chart was started independent of the 100 per cent terminal inspection which was continued. To maintain a constant sample size, facilitating the calculation of per cent defective and making possible the plotting of points during production rather than waiting until the end of the day, groups of 25 were used. That is to say, as soon as 25 units were inspected, the per cent defective was posted. The last 9 weeks in 1944 showed 13 per cent defective which was substantially what was being rejected by the terminal inspection.

Early in 1945, a new plant manager was appointed. An intensive program for the determination of assignable causes for defectives was started. This program discovered raw-material discrepancies and the need for operator training. It soon was indicated that the per cent defective could be held at 1.3 per cent with an upper control limit at 5 per cent. In July, 1945, it was indicated that 0 per cent defective was possible. Then came V-J Day with the war-end emotional disturbances and personnel dislocations. In September, 1945, a quality-control inspector who had supervisory abilities was appointed supervisor of the winding operations. An inspector trainer was also appointed who followed each defective back to its source, reviewed the method which produced it, and properly instructed the person responsible for it. More than 2 months' operation without a defective (at the end of the chart, Fig. 6) confirms the reasonableness of establishing 0 per cent defective.

Elimination of 13 per cent defectives is an important forward step. However, it must of course be appreciated that the p chart, in itself, did not accomplish this reduction. It did *portray* what was happening and guided everyone's efforts, but the improvement was a combination of good management, good supervision, employee training, and everyone's constant attention to all of the assignable causes for defectives. Much credit goes to the foremen and the operators themselves, for without a lively interest in quality and a sincerity of purpose the improved operation would not have been possible. Here is industrial teamwork at its finest.

CHAPTER IV

PLANNING AND SCHEDULING

By Lawrence L. Bethel

Planning and scheduling of production is the systematic preparation of sequence of operations and the allocation of time for the performance of these operations. In a small company manufacturing a limited number and variety of products, the problem of planning and scheduling production is relatively simple. Most workers in the plant are familiar with the products and the operations through which they must pass for production. In normal times instructions for the various operations can be handed down by word of mouth. The volume of work in the plant is sufficiently small to be easily centralized under the personal supervision of a few men. In such cases formal and detailed records and instructions are apt to become an unnecessary burden.

Today most managements are forced to seek a substitute for the informal procedure of controlling production. The development of a more formal and systematic procedure seeks to accomplish these aims: (1) maximum quality production at minimum cost through even distribution of work to available equipment and personnel, (2) added flexibility in equipment and personnel to meet unavoidable emergencies, and (3) harmony and co-operation between departments.

It is a popular belief that written instructions and elaborate procedures of planning and follow-up make change difficult. If that is true, and it sometimes is, management is guilty of attempting to make the job fit the system instead of fitting the system to the job. Every procedure and every instruction should be planned with the expectation that it must be changed. On the other hand, a foreman and the men under him must realize that they are but a part of a large organization and that a change in operations in one department may disrupt the work of numerous other departments.

RESPONSIBILITY OF THE FOREMAN

The foreman stands as a connecting link between management and the worker. He has a direct responsibility to both. He is responsible to management for getting the work out. He is responsible to the worker for the efficient scheduling of work and the movement of parts and materials in a way that will permit maximum earnings to the worker as well as maximum profit to the organization as a whole.

The foreman can effectively promote these mutual interests of management and the worker through constructive participation in planning and scheduling. If he has the work of his department well in hand, he should be in the best position to advise regarding the combination of orders for more economical runs. His suggestions can cover avoidance of extra setup time, alternative routings of jobs within the department for greater economy and efficiency, and possibilities of freeing equipment that may be needed on an emergency order.

The foreman also has a co-operative responsibility with other foremen in the plant. A planning, or production-control, department of an organization should be looked upon as a service department, which helps in the work of the production departments. It carries responsibility and authority for planning, scheduling, and following up work in production. Yet, it can be effective only if it has the sincere co-operation of those departments which it serves.

If the purposes of planning and scheduling are to be achieved, the foreman must seek *only an honest and fair allocation of time and equipment for the work of a given order.* It is a natural tendency for foremen to ask for extra allowances of time to avoid getting behind schedule. They know that a certain amount of breakdown or delay is unavoidable. Some extra time allowance should be recognized as advisable in efficient scheduling. Yet, the foreman who takes undue advantage of this opportunity is failing in his part of the co-operative effort and is disrupting the planning efficiency of the entire organization.

A foreman has the responsibility for keeping prompt, complete, and accurate records of work scheduled and work in progress in his department or division. The extent to which he may receive assistance in the performance of these duties will vary in different companies, depending upon the organization, the size of departments, and the degree of centralization of departments. But, since he is responsible for the work of his department, he must have at his finger tips concrete information regarding the work in progress and the work which is scheduled for his department.

PLANNING AND SCHEDULING FUNCTIONS

The principal planning and scheduling activities can be divided into four functions: (1) routing, (2) scheduling, (3) dispatching, and (4) follow-up.

1. Routing

Routing of operations for the manufacture of a product consists, first, of the determination of operations through which the product must pass and, second, the arrangement of those operations in the sequence that will require a minimum of handling, transportation, storage, and deterioration through exposure.

Designation of operations and their sequence, in general, is the function of the engineering, development, or methods department, depending upon the organization structure of the company. However, the routing specified by any one of these departments must be subject to alteration as problems of scheduling and actual production are encountered.

It is usually customary in the development of a new product to make up a sample, or trial, run. This trial run may be made in a special department or plant, known as a "pilot plant," or may be run through the regular manufacturing departments. If it is run through the regular departments, all foremen should offer constructive criticisms for improvement of quality, economy, and operating efficiency.

In continuous-manufacturing plants, where departments are devoted exclusively to the manufacture of standard parts or products, it is usually possible to establish "straight-line" production over an established route of operations. However, in diversified or job-order manufacturing, the function of routing becomes much more difficult. An arrangement of equipment for the straight-line routing of one order may be entirely inappropriate for the next order. For this reason departments of such plants are usually arranged according to "process." By this arrange-

DEPARTMENT	DELIVER TO 51	CHARGE TO 51	DATE OF ORDER 7-29	PRODUCTION ORDER NO. Y-2324
CUSTOMER NATIONAL CARBON CO.			DUE DATES — TO BE COMPLETED BY: Three / Two; 14 8/23 / 8/29; 22 9/4 / 9/4; 20 9/20 / 9/27; 56 10/15 / 10/25	SHEET NO. 2
MACHINE NO. 9773 to 9777 GENERAL DRAWING			DATE OF REQUIRED SHIPMENT 10/31 / 11/15	SHEETS
DESCRIPTION FIVE (5) 22" X 60" SPECIAL PLASTIC MILLS				SHIP WITH

THIS LIST IS FOR ONE, MAKE Five ON THIS ORDER

	ORDERED FROM DEPT.	MAKE	MAT.	PATT.	DRAWING	LIST OF PARTS	
1	GP	1	50M	C-2846	156-295	Cut Spur Drive Gear 60.00" P.D., 120 T. 2 D.P.	22 9/4 - 20 9/20 - 9/27 (4751) VBT 10/1 10/3 50 (4710) KW 10/3 - 10/4 - 3 (4932) Mit 10/4 - 10/14 - 110
2						12" Face, 13.506 Bore, 1-1/2" x 5/8" K'way, 61.000" OD	40 - 10/15 - 10/25
3						1/8" radius in bore at shallow end of K'way.	51 10/31 - 11/15
5	44	1	45C		SK-7717	Cut Spur Drive Pinion, 13.10" P.D., 25 T. 2 D.P. 12" F	44 Co 9/30 - 2 - 44 Fg 9/30 - 12 - 44 ANNEAL 10/1 - 3 - (4870) UBT 10/4 - 2 - (5031) Dr for lifters 10/7 - 2
6						5.252" Bore, 1-1/8" x 1/2" K'way. 14.10" O.D.	(4931) Mit 10/14 - 60
7						Pinion is .60" oversize.	(4710) KS 10/15 - 3
8							40 10/15 - 10/25
9	12	1	ST			1-1/2" x 1-1/4" x 12-1/2" Head Key	51 - 10/31 - 11/15
10	12	1	ST			1-1/8" x 1" x 12-1/2" Head Key	
12	89	2	#1100 Sh. St.			Pinion flanges 14-1/2" O.D. 7" ID. Drill Six 7/16"	89 Co 10/2 - 4 (452) Lo (one) 10/8 - 5 - (5030) Dr. in file 10/11 - 8 - 40 10/15 - 10/25 - 51 10/31 - 11/15
13						holes on a 9" Dia. B.C.	
15	12	12	ST			3/8" x 3/4" Hex Hd. Cap Scrs. Hds. cut to 1/4" thick	
16						and drilled for 1/16" Dia lock wire.	
17	12	2	ST			1/16" Dia. lock wire 30" long.	
19	PJ	1	.45C St.		SK-7807	Conn. Gear Block 24-1/8" Dia rough turn.	PU 9/20 - 9/27
20			Forging			10-3/4" Dia. rough bore. 12-1/4" long.	
22	4C	1			"	Use the abovegear blank, cut spur even Conn. gear.	(4871) LBT 10/7 - 10/9 - 20 - (5038) Dr for lifters 10/8 - 10/9 - 2 (4710) KS 10/9 - 10/10 - 3
23						21.96" P.D., 23 T. 3" P., 12" Face, 11.005" Bore	(4932) Mit 10/10 - 10/23 - 100
24						1-1/2" x 5/8" K'way, 23.87" O.D.	40 10/15 - 10/25
25							51 10/31 - 11/15
26	PU	1	.35C St.		"	Conn. Gear Blank 24-1/8" Dia. rough turn 13-1/4" Dia.	PU 9/20 - 9/27
27			Forging			rough bore, 12-1/4" long.	
29	40	1			"	Use the abovegear blank, cut spur even Conn.	(4871) LBT 10/1 - 10/3 - 20 - (5038) Dr for lifters 10/2 - 10/4 - 2 - (4710) KS 10/4 - 10/7 - 3
30						gear 21.96" P.D., 23 T. 3" P. 12" Face, 13.505" Bore	(4932) Mit 10/7 - 10/18 - 100
31						1-1/2" x 5/8" K'way, 23.87" O.D.	40 10/15 - 10/25
32							51 10/31 - 11/15
33	12	1	ST			1-1/2" x 1-1/4" x 11-1/2" Head Key	12 Co 10/4 - 5 (12) - 51 Pl & Fit 10/15 - 10/25 51 10/31 - 11/15
34	12	1	ST			1-1/2" x 1-1/4" x 12-1/4" Head Key	12 Co 10/4 - 5 (12) - 51 Pl & Fit 10/15 - 10/25 51 10/31 - 11/15

FIG. 1.—Typical routing sheet pasted to a parts list (left). Routing sheet not only carries the name of the operation in code, but also shows number of machine on which it is to be done, time allotted, and date due. (NOTE: Headings of first three columns, reduced in this reproduction, read, or are abbreviated to read: ORDERED FROM DEPT.; MAKE; MATERIALS; PATTERNS; DRAWINGS.)

ment, machines of a like kind or machines that are similar in the nature of work performed are arranged in one department. Therefore, we find machining done in one department, grinding in another, and painting in still another. This arrangement usually offers greater flexibility, since a breakdown of one machine may not immediately close down the work on operations to follow. Also, temporary overloading of orders on one operation can be more easily relieved. To facilitate these adjustments, the Planning Department should prepare alternate routings.

In some organizations, the routing is done on a routing sheet pasted to a parts list, as shown in Fig. 1.

2. Scheduling

A production schedule is a budget of time that provides for the beginning and completion dates of a manufacturing order. Preliminary information needed in the construction of a production schedule is obtained from the following sources: (1) the Forecasting and Planning Department, in cases where standard parts or products are being made to stock; (2) date of delivery specified by the customer in the order; (3) minimum time, in terms of past experience, required for production.

Other factors, however, must be taken into consideration: (1) availability of equipment, (2) availability of specially skilled personnel, (3) availability of the necessary parts and materials.

It is usually possible to anticipate the needs for equipment, personnel, and material considerably in advance. Difficulty arises during abnormal rush periods or when unusual conditions have caused shortages. It is at such times that a manufacturer must put forth special effort in order to obtain the maximum work from men and machines.

Master Schedules

There are two principal types of production schedules: *master schedules* and *manufacturing schedules*. The master schedule lists the production of a given product in one or more divisions of the company. In continuous manufacturing, this master schedule may cover a period of a year or more. However, it is usually reconstructed each month to include unanticipated variations in the demand and in the volume of production. For example, a master schedule prepared in January is revised in February to include the 12 months to follow. It would again be revised in March, etc.

In continuous manufacturing, information for the master schedule is obtained from the department responsible for forecasting of sales and production. The information is based on the sales of previous years plus the data obtained from market analyses relative to the probable demand of the current year. Consideration must always be given to the probable reception of new products which are being introduced upon the market as well as to the effect of competing products.

In job-order manufacturing, forecasting future production for a year is next to impossible. Therefore, the master schedule can include only orders which have actually been received. Quite frequently, however, these orders may require several months for completion. This is true particularly in the manufacture of heavy machinery. Since departments of job-order plants are usually organized according to process, several departments will be involved in the manufacture of any one order. The master schedule represents the combined plans for all these departments.

Manufacturing Schedules

The manufacturing schedule is subsidiary to the master schedule in that it breaks an order down into its various parts, according to size, color, weight,

To: Supts.—Foremen—Supervisors and Assts. Apr. 5, 1955
From: Prod. Control (OLW) *Units*—Cases/Day
Subject: Manufacturing Schedule for Week of Apr. 12—Boots

Types	Cs/Day	Final Assembly Conveyer Numbers		
		4	10	20
MB-680	410	410		
MB-508	625	200	425	
MB-420	200			200
MB-810	600			400

FIG. 2.—Typical manufacturing schedule.

material, etc. A separate manufacturing schedule is made up for each division of the order or perhaps for each process through which the product is to pass. A manufacturing schedule may, in fact, become a work schedule. It also includes an assignment of time on assembling units and other special machinery.

Figure 2 is a very simple illustration of a manufacturing schedule covering three final assembly conveyors for a single product for a single week. The illustration, of course, shows only a part of the schedule and is therefore illustrative only of the form used.

Manufacturing schedules may be made by the Production Control Department or may be the responsibility of the foremen of the various departments. In either case, the preparation and revision of manufacturing schedules must be at least the co-operative responsibility of the foremen.

Scheduling as a Co-operative Function

Where a highly centralized system of control exists, two difficulties frequently occur: (1) foremen may feel that, since there is a department to plan and schedule production, they have no responsibility in this function; (2) since the principal responsibility is removed from the foremen, they may not appreciate the problems involved and consequently may be non-co-operative in making and revising schedules.

Quite frequently a constant struggle exists between the foremen of various departments and the Production Office on the one hand and the Sales Department and the Production Office on the other. Foremen are apt to seek as much time as possible on the schedule. They would rather be ahead of schedule than behind. The Sales Department, on the other hand, is interested primarily in satisfying the customer through an early delivery date. The Production Control Office stands between these two points of view and attempts to mediate.

In many companies, foremen meetings are held at least weekly for the preparation and revision of schedules. Under this arrangement, scheduling is considered the joint responsibility of the Production Control Department and the foremen. Each foreman or his representative is called upon to accept or reject time allotments for his department. At these meetings, he is able to gain information regarding the problems of other departments and the effect of change in schedule on other departments as well as his own. He therefore asks for a change in schedule or accepts a time allotment with full knowledge of the scope of his responsibility.

Through this procedure a schedule is the result of the action of the group of department representatives and is usually received quite differently than if it were handed down as an order from the Production Control Office.

3. Dispatching

Dispatch provides official authorization and information for (1) movement of materials to different work places, (2) movement of tools and fixtures necessary for each operation, (3) beginning of work on each operation, (4) recording of beginning and completion time, (5) movement of work in accordance with a routing schedule, (6) control of progress of all operations and the making of necessary adjustments in the release of operations to conform to emergencies.

Dispatching requires co-ordination between all departments concerned. This is usually obtained through varied degrees of centralized control. Under centralized control, dispatch clerks, centrally located, release all orders and authorization for operations, including the movement of materials, tools, and fixtures necessary for the operations. Under decentralized control this responsibility is handled by each department.

One of the factors of greatest concern in determining the necessary degree of centralization is the lack of control which results through a lapse of time between authorization and actual operation. This is of special importance during rush times, when machines are loaded to capacity and special rush orders are more frequent. Under these circumstances, revisions in schedule become more difficult, and consequently the need for up-to-date information regarding the progress of orders is greatly increased.

In continuous manufacturing, under normal conditions, orders may be dispatched to departments a day or more in advance of operations. Each department prepares its own instructions and authorizations and sends duplicates to a central office. Since these duplicates are received by the central office considerably in advance of operations, there is sufficient time for the recommendation of changes.

If it is found that certain orders are being unduly delayed to the point where complications will develop in other departments, a request may be made for adjustments. However, under abnormal conditions, when a company is being pressed by impatient customers and the plant is loaded to capacity, emergency changes are more frequent, and the avenues of action for making a change in schedule must be more rapid. A special rush order may require that operations start immediately and that other orders originally scheduled be held temporarily. Under these circumstances it is apparent that centralized control plays an important role in obtaining speed and co-ordination.

4. Follow-up

Follow-up is perhaps the most important and most difficult of all the planning and scheduling functions.

Planning and scheduling can be of little value unless there is adequate provision for obtaining the necessary information about emergencies which may require changes in schedule in order to maintain an even flow of work. The procedure used in the procurement of materials must include provisions for follow-up to ensure that material will be on hand for a specific job at the time it is needed. Work in process must be checked to determine whether it will be ready for the next operation. A preassembly check must be made to determine whether the necessary parts will be ready on the prearranged date.

Responsibility for follow-up is usually placed in the hands of special follow-up men. Their function is one of obtaining information. They are essentially "go-betweens," who perform a service for the various departments involved. A follow-up man is usually given a specific responsibility in connection with one phase of the follow-up work.

Follow-up of Materials

Follow-up of materials is a function of the Purchasing Department and is one with which the foreman has very little concern. He usually learns of the follow-up procedure only after his department fails to receive the necessary material on the scheduled date and he investigates to discover the reason for the delay.

Although this responsibility is not within the duties of a foreman of a production department, he may suffer the ill effects of a poor follow-up procedure. Therefore, when he is pressed for adjustments caused by shortage of material or when he has to disrupt the personnel of his department because material is not available, he may well feel it within his rights to inquire regarding the follow-up procedure that is being used to obtain delivery of material.   Frequently a group of foremen, collectively, may formulate constructive suggestions and press for the improvement of procedures. The foremen's meeting mentioned earlier in this chapter should provide an excellent opportunity for discussion of this problem.

Follow-up of Work in Process

Follow-up clerks may be assigned responsibility for checking the progress of work, either according to product or according to process. The former method is particularly adaptable to continuous, or line, production. Here the job becomes relatively simple, since the manufacture of a particular product progresses automatically from one operation to the next. One man follows a particular assignment of a product through the various departments until it reaches completion. He is responsible for reporting information about breakdowns and delays, shortages of material, etc.

Follow-up by process is frequently used in diversified manufacture. By this method, the follow-up men are assigned to departments for checking the progress of work passing through the processes of a particular department. When the work passes on to another department, it goes under the responsibility of other follow-up men, who are well acquainted with the supervisors of their particular department and with the equipment of the department. This method avoids the confusion which results when several follow-up men interested in different products are "nagging" at foremen for information regarding the progress of orders.

The foreman should assume the responsibility for the development of understanding and appreciation on the part of the supervisors within the department of the importance of follow-up work. He must also assume responsibility for the training of follow-up men, in order to develop co-operation within the department and to facilitate promptness and accuracy in checking the progress of the work.

A follow-up man has a very difficult role to play. He contacts the supervisor at a time when trouble has arisen and when the supervisor is most apt to be irritated and non-co-operative. If a machine has broken down, the supervisor is most interested in getting a repairman on the job and the machine back in operation as soon as possible. He may have a tendency to be impatient with the follow-up man who comes around asking questions.

The supervisor should be made to understand that the follow-up man is attempting to render a service to the department. He is merely trying to get information. This information, when relayed to the central control office, may prevent work from piling up in the department and may, by rerouting of orders, prevent the stoppage of work in the processes which ordinarily follow the work of this particular machine or department.

Follow-up of work in process should operate on the "principle of exception." Only those orders which are listed as special rush orders or those orders on which difficulty and delay has arisen should be followed up. Automatic controls, which will be discussed later in this chapter, should suffice for the general run of production.

In rush times, there is a tendency for production-control departments to succumb to the pressure of customers and to place orders on a rush basis. Soon the manufacturer finds that 75 per cent of his orders are labeled "rush." The inevitable result is that foremen and supervisors learn to ignore the term and to consider all orders on an equal basis. A definite policy should be adopted on giving priority to any production order.

Follow-up of Assembly and Erection

A common problem in manufacturing, particularly in a job-order plant, is the co-ordination of the manufacture of parts so that they may arrive for assembly on schedule. Frequently subassemblies are necessary before operations can be completed. A delay in the manufacture of a particular part may delay not only the subassembly operation, but future processes and operations in several departments. If parts are let out to other companies or branches on a subcontract basis, the complexity of the problem is increased.

Some companies place one follow-up man in charge of a job or order, with responsibility for keeping a constant check on the progress of the various parts and controlling their arrival for assembly. He sees to it that the work progresses on schedule or that adjustments are made through the rerouting of other orders, so that men and machines will not be idle.

AIDS TO THE CONTROL OF PRODUCTION

A few suggestions of special aids to foremen will be given in this section. It is not expected that these aids will be wholly applicable to any one situation. However, it is hoped that these examples will suggest other possible techniques and devices that can be applied.

1. Load Charts

A foreman who is responsible for the even distribution of work on various machines in his department should have some means of visual control over the loading process. Figure 3 shows a very simple form for recording the load schedule on a unit of equipment —a final assembly conveyer. It shows the order number, type of product, load in the number of pieces, and amount of time on the conveyer scheduled for each item. The chart shows the loading for 1 day only. It will be noted that the conveyer in question has a capacity of 7.8 standard hours and that according to the information filled in, it is now loaded to a total of 6.8 standard hours. Therefore, there remains 1 standard hour available for loading.

FINAL ASSEMBLY CONVEYER-LOADING CHART

Conveyer No. 20   Loading Date 4/17   Capacity 7.8 Std. Hrs.

Types Scheduled:

First Choice	Second Choice	Third Choice	Miscellaneous
MB-420	MB-500	ML-210	ML-108
MB-640	MB-501	ML-215	MH-140
MB-810	MB-520	ML-470	MH-165

Order Number	Type	No. of Pieces	Std. Hrs./C	Cumulative Std. Hrs.	Sizes	1	2	3	4	5
					Quantities					
24-6124	MB-420	200	1.2	2.4		40	40		120	
24-7526	MB-810	400	.5	4.4		50		150		200

FIG. 3.—Simple form for recording load schedule.

Although the illustration (Fig. 3) has been taken from a continuous-manufacturing plant, it is also

DATE________ **CASTERS DAILY SCHEDULE** DATE________

THIRD SHIFT					FIRST SHIFT					SECOND SHIFT				
POTS CAST	CASTER	SIZE MOULDS	KIND OF METAL	FIRE No.	POTS CAST	CASTER	SIZE MOULDS	KIND OF METAL	FIRE No.	POTS CAST	CASTER	SIZE MOULDS	KIND OF METAL	FIRE No.

FIG. 4.—Schedule used in a brass company to record requests for castings from the various mill departments.

applicable to job-order production, where departments are organized according to process. A foreman would have to study the essential characteristics of material or products passing through his department and construct a form which would provide information about these variations in characteristics, enabling him to determine the load in terms of scheduling time.

Records of standard time on the various products that pass through the plant are not always available. In such a case, the foreman can only make an approximation in terms of previous products that were at least somewhat similar in nature. He should have records available to facilitate these approximations.

2. Planning Boards

Planning boards may be used to advantage as a visual aid in the control of production. They may be used in either a centralized- or decentralized-control procedure. In either case, their purpose is to make possible a rapid and accurate check on work in progress and on work that has been scheduled and is ready for operation.

There are various types of planning boards available to meet different situations in companies that vary in size, organization, and type of product. Some companies prefer to construct their own boards to fit their particular needs.

One very simple type has the appearance of a bulletin board. Each work station in the plant is represented by three horizontal sets of hooks. The first set represents work in progress; the second set repre-

---

[1] For additional and supplementary forms for use in recording the loading of equipment, see Bethel, Tann, Atwater, and Rung, "Production Control," 2d ed., pp. 120–124, McGraw-Hill, New York, 1948.

sents work that has been dispatched to the workplace and is awaiting operation; and the third set represents work that has been scheduled but has not been dispatched officially to the workplace. As work progresses through the plant, the dispatch forms are moved up on the hooks in order, or revisions are made to give rush orders priority or to make changes in terms of unexpected emergencies. Pigeonholes or compartments may be built into the board to hold supplementary instruction forms that will accompany the authorization of operations at the various workplaces.

A type of board commonly used employs clips instead of hooks, and will accommodate a considerably larger volume of work. Circular racks can be developed, on which the boards, perhaps 48 by 36 in., can swing like huge leaves of a book, with as many as 60 boards in one compact location. Dispatch forms are held by springs or clips and can be arranged in any order to meet particular needs.

One of the principal criticisms of planning boards is the amount of time that is required to keep them posted. However, some type of planning board will usually facilitate a more orderly scheduling procedure and will provide for rapid flexibility of equipment and personnel during heavy periods of production.

Departmental Procedure

Departmental planning boards may be used as subsidiaries to the central planning board in the Production Control Department or in departments which assume chief responsibility for the scheduling of their own work. In either case there are definite advantages to departmental boards: First, they aid the foremen in the supervision of work, and, second, they increase the accuracy in the recording of beginning and completion times on separate jobs.

When departmental boards are used, jobs are dispatched from the central office to the department instead of to the separate workplaces. Each workman reports to the department dispatch desk to secure his orders and authorization. The department clerk records the beginning time on the job ticket. When the worker completes the job, he returns the ticket to the department desk for the recording of the completion time. Where departmental boards are not used and jobs are dispatched directly to the worker from the central office, the operator may become lax in the recording of beginning and completion times on his job ticket. Or he may purposely misrepresent the situation to establish a backlog of work and to equalize his own working time.

Of course, circumstances within a given company will dictate the advisability of the use of departmental boards. In continuous manufacturing, especially under normal conditions, the use of departmental boards may be an unnecessary duplication of clerical work and may actually hinder the centralization of control and the co-ordination of production through the various departments.

3. Progress Charts

A progress chart will prove advantageous in checking and reporting the progress of work on a particular job or order. The usual practice is to chart only those orders which are falling behind the schedule or which are special either as rush orders or as ones requiring special handling and operations. This practice follows the exception rule previously mentioned.

The best type of progress chart is the Gantt chart,

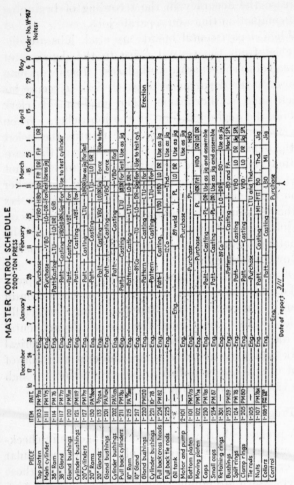

Fig. 5.—Gantt chart.

illustrated in Fig. 5. The numbers at the top of the illustration indicate dates over a 5-month period beginning Dec. 10 and ending May 10. Time scheduled for each operation on each item is designated by vertical lines. It will be noted that the engineering design on the first item, top platen, should be completed by Jan. 21. The casting should be purchased and received by Feb. 11. The planing should be completed by Feb. 25, etc. Progress is recorded by means of horizontal lines for each item. The date on which a checkup is being made may be indicated by a red or dotted line extending vertically across the chart.

Figure 5 represents a checkup which was made on Mar. 11. This date is designated by the vertical dotted line. It will be noticed that operation on the top platen is progressing on schedule, as is the operation on the main cylinder. However, the 38-in. ram is 3 weeks behind schedule. Going on down the chart to the oil tank, we find that it is 4 weeks behind schedule.

The Gantt chart has many variations and applications that can be adapted to meet the needs of a foreman, supervisor, or follow-up man. It may be used either as a paper form or as a progress-control board. In the first instance, the chart may be used also as a reporting device and the original form photostated to obtain the necessary copies for distribution to executives and departments involved. If the Gantt chart is used as a progress-control board, removable markers can be inserted into slots built into the board. This facilitates adjustment in schedule made necessary when certain operations are unavoidably delayed. Such a board, placed on the wall or on a table, is especially valuable in planning meetings of foremen and schedule clerks.

CHAPTER V

TIME STUDY AND METHODS IMPROVEMENT

Part One—Fundamentals of Time Study

By Phil Carroll

Every foreman should know how to study the uses made of time. This applies to his chief concern, production. Whether it is the time of his men, his equipment, or his own, any improvement in utility can be turned into more product.

The originator of scientific management, F. W. Taylor, called the detailed analysis of work "time study." That was about 70 years ago. Today the objectives are the same, and many of the procedures are identical. However, the once-broad term is now applied by some to only the specific work of "rate setting." Other terms, such as "motion study," "work simplification," and "methods analysis," are used in connection with the study of the way work is done. All are constructive procedures directed toward saving time and effort.

Remarkable improvements have been developed for breaking down the job. Moving pictures are used to record in detail the most elementary parts of the job. These can be viewed at reduced speeds. When pictures also include a high-speed clock, the details can be analyzed with respect to actual times taken to perform them.

112

WHY TIME AND MOTION STUDY IS IMPORTANT TO THE FOREMAN

Many plants now carry on training programs designed to teach the foreman how to analyze his operations. One object is to help him to see more clearly what parts of the work in his department can be improved. Another is to help him to train workers.

It follows, then, that a foreman should know "everything" about time and motion study. He could be trained more effectively if he could work in the Time-study Department for a couple of years. Such training would go a long way toward overcoming some of our present difficulties and fortifying industrial managements for the more complicated problems which have yet to be solved. However, the foreman usually cannot take such intensive training. He must be satisfied with acquiring a working knowledge of the principles involved.

The foreman should know the fundamentals of time and motion study for many additional reasons:

1. Too many grievances start with complaints of earning possibilities.

2. Workers want the foreman to become a "better boss" so that he can satisfy their ambitions to get ahead.

3. Requests for higher earnings make it necessary to turn out more production.

4. Increases in production are necessary to provide not only for higher earnings but also for greatly increased taxes.

5. The foreman must be able to see the value of suggestions made by his men.

6. Time can be saved when the foreman can "see" how much of it is actually wasted.

7. Time is the largest single element of cost, assuming reasonable scrap, that comes within the foreman's direct control.

In most plants, the time-study man is given final responsibility for determining the "operation standard time." Further, he is expected to make many suggestions for improving processes. Those two things make up most of his job. Nevertheless, the foreman will not get along so rapidly as he wants to when he sits back and "lets George do it."

Moreover, when the foreman helps to work out better methods, he is too busy making progress to think that "we always did it that way." He does not take time out to resent changes. He is not worried about being asked, "Why didn't you do that before?" When the foreman gets into methods improvement, he helps himself, his workers, his company, and the time-study men.

Another reason for the foreman to learn all he can about time and motion study is that he may be able to explain to his group why improvements are necessary. This is particularly important when wage incentive is used. Many criticisms arise because some men do not receive the pay they think they should. The difficulties are almost always traceable to a lack of understanding of the "system." It is surprising how few criticisms result from actual errors.

THE PRODUCER CAN HELP

The operator can contribute many worth-while suggestions for improvement. He is the channel between output on the one hand and interruptions of all kinds on the other. Moreover, he concentrates most of his activity on a relatively few operations, so that he may make an intensive study of the product and the method used to fabricate it.

However, many have given up making suggestions because they were not well received. Perhaps the foreman is too busy or, what is more frequently the case, is resentful of new ideas advanced by subordinates. To get real co-operation from his men, the foreman must accept their suggestions and remember to give full credit for their ideas. He must not take the credit himself, or he will lose their confidence and help.

THE FOREMAN'S RESPONSIBILITY

The foreman must do his part to step up production by:

1. Increasing employee productive capacity and earnings
2. Lessening the fatigue and strain of working
3. Lowering and controlling manufacturing costs
4. Guiding management in the better operation of industry

The foreman is vitally interested in the effects of method changes when his operations are on wage incentive. Every change in the work content of a job must be followed by a corresponding change in the incentive standards to avoid inconsistency in earning possibilities. The foreman should fully comprehend this phase of labor measurement because he is directly concerned with the complaints which arise from "bad jobs." The maintenance of fair incentive standards requires a revision for each change, irrespective of how small it may be.

All method improvements should be referred to the Time-study Department when incentive standards are involved. This important point of collaboration with the Time-study Department further emphasizes why the foreman should know how time-study standards are determined.

ANALYSIS OF TIME

Simplified and yet constructive observations can be undertaken by dividing time spent into four parts. The general groupings suggested are *lost time, indirect time, handling time,* and *productive time.* These are stated in order progressing from simple to complex.

Lost Time

Time may be wasted because of poor planning or a lack of facilities. "Waiting time" may occur because the blueprint and instructions are not given to the operator. Tools may not be provided, or the employee may have to stand in line waiting for the next man ahead to be served. Time may be lost because the inspector has not got around to checking the first piece. Much of the time lost in these and similar ways can be used productively when the foreman insists upon better planning.

Indirect

Much time is spent before, during, and after the completion of the job. The term "indirect" applies when work of some kind is done, as contrasted with "lost time," which is waiting for something to happen. Indirect includes such things as moving the material to and from the workplace, fixing up the tools, "hunting" the bolts and clamps, and getting the next job. Tool grinding should be considered as indirect because it can be done without holding up the producer and his machine. True, it requires a skilled man to grind tools. However, grinding can be done, without creating delay, prior to the beginning of the operation.

Handling

Handling includes the work done to every piece to get it in and out of position for productive operation. Examples of handling in job analyses are "Pick Up Piece" and "Unload and Aside." All handling and some indirect items may be a part of the standard time. However, the handling times are made the subject of separate analysis, because many changes can be made to lessen the amount. Placing the pieces within easy reach or feeding them automatically by a hopper would be ways to reduce "Pickup" to a minimum. Where no damage would be done, letting the pieces fall into a tote box is a way of reducing "Aside." The classification of handling is made also to point out that, as a rule, the equipment is standing idle during this time.

Productive

The term "productive" is applied to the essential part of the operation. In this explanation, productive is broken down to illustrate the machine time—weaving, winding, plating, milling, drilling, and similar operations which affect the shape or finish of the product. It is separated for another reason. Close analysis by the foreman will bring out the fact that, although the machine is busy during the productive times, the operator often waits.

A BROAD ANALYSIS

A time-study man would make an observation by listing in sequence each element of work and wait time observed. But the foreman need not go to that detail to begin his study of time. As another point of difference, he is certainly not concerned with extreme accuracy in the beginning of his observation. He can start by dividing a blank piece of paper into four columns. Each of the columns can be headed by one of the subdivisions previously described.

Productive	Handling	Indirect	Lost
Drill	Load jig	Get material	Wait for foreman
Pour	Fill ladle	Walk to mold	Wait for heat
Assemble	Pick up piece	Get screws	Wait for parts
Grind	Put on dog	Truck parts	Wait for inspector
Weave	Fill shuttle	Change reel	Machine attention
Paint	Hang part	Clean gun	Wait for dryer

Fig. 1.—The entire time may be divided into four classes for easy analysis. This sample breakdown shows an element illustrating each class of time in six types of work.

From this point on, the foreman might use either of two methods of study. He might follow the customary procedure of a time-study man by concentrating on one or two operations, studying all elements of time. This method is recommended for the study of bottlenecks. For the beginner, it may be simpler to study one element at a time, such as lost time.

Studying Lost Time

Waiting time occurs primarily because work has not been planned. Whether or not a Planning Department exists, the foreman is responsible for starting his jobs. If he fails to provide instructions, blueprints, materials, tools, inspection, and other necessities, the operator cannot start, and time is lost. Time may also be lost between the finish of one job and production of the first piece on a subsequent job. Of course, waiting can occur while pieces are being produced.

The foreman can begin his study by recording all the lost time in his department during the period of 1 hour. If he recorded every minute of lost time he could notice during 1 hour, he might find that there was, for example, a total of 270 minutes lost on all jobs. Lost time of 270 minutes is equal to $4\frac{1}{2}$ hours. Because the example is of a 1-hour study, the total of $4\frac{1}{2}$ hours makes the lost time equal to an idleness of $4\frac{1}{2}$ men for 1 hour. If the hour studied is representative, then the lost time in the department can be regarded as equal to $4\frac{1}{2}$ men for all day.

In a manufacturing department where each operator has a machine, the lost time equivalent to $4\frac{1}{2}$ men also represents down time of $4\frac{1}{2}$ machines. Lost machine time is important at any time because a machine, its floor space, and other related costs may average $5 per hour per machine. Therefore, lost machine capacity is a very expensive waste.

The foreman will be surprised to discover how much lost time actually does amount to. In an average department of 30 men, $4\frac{1}{2}$ lost man-days is a loss of 15 per cent.

When the foreman completes his first study of lost time, he will find notations attributing the causes to many influences beyond the operator's control. A list of these might look very much like the following:

WAITING FOR

Instruction	Foreman	Crane operator
Blueprint	Inspector	Trucker
Order	Setup man	Tool-crib man
Tools	Maintenance man	Timekeeper
Material	Time-study man	Helper

Not all lost time can be salvaged, but the alert foreman can greatly lessen the total once he knows why it exists. He will have to train those in the department who interrupt the operators to think ahead. They must be taught how to anticipate the needs of the producers. In some departments, where correct reports reflect that good supervision has been developed, lost time is often as low as 2 per cent.

Below-standard Operators

Another unsatisfactory loss occurs when incentive operators fail to earn premium. From the standpoint of productive capacity, "fall down" is the same as lost time. Of course, learners are slow, but "fall down" of all kinds can be rapidly eliminated by properly teaching the correct methods.

Analysis of Indirect

The study of indirect time is more difficult to make because, as a rule, the times are of shorter duration. However, some will be long. The foreman can begin by studying the large amounts of indirect time for the department as a whole. Later he can concentrate on the small elements.

Many types of work should be classified as indirect. All the supply functions are in this class. Some may say that these are necessary parts of the operation. Nevertheless, it is not necessary that the productive operator do them.

All of the "get" and "hunt" elements have to be done until the foreman realizes how much more production he can turn out with a given amount of equipment by having a place for everything and everything in its place. Even then he can increase capacity by having certain materials delivered within easy reach of the producer.

Some indirect items are listed here to suggest what to look for:

INDIRECT WORK

Faulty operation	Superquality	Faulty equipment
Poor layout	Poor setup	Excess material
Improper instruction	Inadequate tools	Poor material
Rework	Incorrect methods	Impractical design

Much waste can be eliminated when the foreman pries into the "why" and takes action to remove the causes. Some of his investigations will lead him back to his own doorstep.

Handling

When the foreman studies the handling, he can expect to find that less than half of the total time is spent in performing the actual productive part of the operation. Naturally, in a drilling operation it is necessary to "Pick Up Piece" and "Load in Jig." Then, after drilling, come "Unload the Jig" and "Piece Aside." The handling is necessary to perform the drilling, but the time may be two-thirds of the total. Productivity can be increased, therefore, if the total can be reduced by lessening the handling portion. Perhaps the pieces can be placed closer so as to lower the "get" time. If the jig is examined, some improvements in loading and unloading may suggest themselves. It may be possible to arrange a chute to carry away the finished pieces by gravity.

It may be practical to supply *two* jigs, so that while one piece is being drilled, another jig is being loaded. In this way, the machine will be kept in operation more hours per day. If two pieces instead of one are drilled each cycle, the result is much the same as if there were two drill presses. It must be remembered, however, that these points are suggestive only. One would not order two jigs when production did not warrant the extra expenditure.

Productive

In the really essential part of the operation, some improvements are possible by changes of procedure. Therefore, in the drilling example it may be possible to increase capacity by changing feed or speed, lubricant, drill grinding, thickness of material, or other factors.

The foreman cannot assume that every increase in speed will lessen quality. The facts are very frequently quite the contrary. For instance, on lathe work the foreman should make certain that he is not using feeds and speeds which correspond with carbon tools after he has asked for and obtained high-speed tools. He may be running feeds and speeds suitable for high-speed steel when he has tungsten-carbide tools in the machine.

MORE DETAILED STUDY

If the foreman wants to concentrate on some particular operation that is holding up production, he may separate the times into the same four divisions, as illustrated in Fig. 2. His study will then begin to approach the detail used by a time-study man.

In the simple drilling example the producer picks up piece, places in jig, drills one hole, removes piece, sets aside. At that point, he runs out of material and has to wait for the trucker. When the trucker arrives, the producer assists in getting the parts to his workplace. The simple study outlined shows entries in each of the four columns to indicate the four ways in which the time was spent.

Indirect and Lost Time

Obviously, the foreman would not be content to study one piece. He would study a quantity to get a representative picture of actual conditions. For instance, several hundred pieces might be completed

PRODUCTIVE	HANDLING	INDIRECT	LOST
	1. Pick up piece		
	2. Place in jig		
3. Drill one hole			
	4. Remove from jig		
	5. Piece aside		
			6. Wait for trucker
		7. Get parts to machine	
	1. Pick up piece		
	2. Place in jig		
3. Drill one hole			
	4. Remove from jig		

FIG. 2.—The elements are listed in sequence but in proper columns to show the four classes of time.

between deliveries. In the meantime, the producer might have to wait for the inspector, the timekeeper, or the tool boy.

Again, if there are 50 parts in a box, the operator would have to replenish his supply only once every 50 pieces. And yet, he might have to do other indirect operations such as grind the drill, oil the machine, file burrs, or repair a spoiled piece.

The foreman would have to make his deductions concerning the probable amount of indirect and lost time in terms of occurrence. If there were 50 parts to a box, the indirect time for every part would be one-fiftieth of the time to get one box.

Extra-work Analysis

By carefully scrutinizing the handling elements, foremen may discover that some indirect effort exists because the producer is required to reach too far in performing his operation. Excessive reaching takes

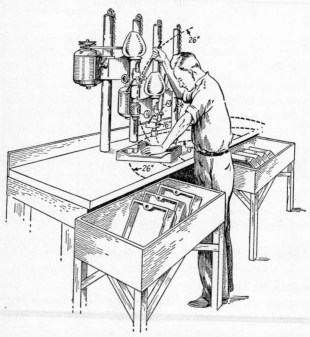

Fig. 3.—Arcs indicate the normal work area in which operations can be done without bending and excessive reaching.

more time than it should. Besides, it causes undue fatigue. Much of the extra time and effort can be saved if the foreman will give some thought to the arrangement of the work station.

He can be guided by the limits indicated in Fig. 3, which was designed to show the range in several directions. This figure illustrates what the motion-study man calls the "circular workplace." Everything necessary to complete an operation is located or performed within the area bounded by the arcs of circles shown. These arcs are determined by the movements of the hands.

Most foremen are familiar with the assembly-bench arrangements using hoppers and trays placed around the arcs. A drill-press operation was chosen for the illustration shown here to point out the need for extending the use of the same effort-saving principles. Perhaps more time has been spent in the study of assembly-bench layout because more pieces have to be handled. But hoppers and trays can be arranged for many other types of jobs to pre-position the pieces for convenience in grasping. Boxes of material can be placed so that parts may be picked up and placed aside without the reaching, bending, stooping, or turning around so frequently observed.

Using Two Hands

Some operations can be improved by changing the sequence of elements so that both hands work together. The same principle can often be applied to working with two pieces of the same kind. This kind of thinking is demonstrated by the progressive foreman when he requests two jigs for an operation. He wants to have one for loading while the other is holding a part being machined. The gain comes through eliminating some portion of the time spent in waiting for the machine. In some instances lower costs would result if the foreman requested one jig to hold *two pieces*, which could be loaded and unloaded simultaneously. Even with but one jig, the foreman can often find ways to utilize two-handed methods by training his operators to load with one hand while unloading with the other.

Saving the "Aside"

Often the foreman can go a step farther and almost completely eliminate the "aside" time. Many parts are not harmed by dropping, so that jobs may be set up to let gravity do the "aside" element. The parts may be dropped onto chutes or conveyer belts or through holes in the machine or bench table.

For work too "fussy" or heavy to drop, the foreman should make certain that the distance moved is a minimum. The box to receive the finished work should be within easy reach. If it is placed on a flat, there should be little walking. It should be remembered that there is no production turned out during walking time.

Charting the Operation

When distances become large factors in the operation, the walking time should be studied critically. In such observations it is well to record both time and distance. This may be done by using charts for diagraming the details to improve the analysis and presentation of results. The details are often classified as to type by symbols, the number and kind used varying according to technique. Figure 4 shows seven symbols sometimes used.

"Delay" signifies a holdup, waiting time for the worker or storage for the material. The latter is of particular importance when the flow of work through the shop is being studied. The other symbols are self-explanatory.

For the analyses which most foremen are called upon to make, only four symbols indicating Operation, Movement, Delay, and Inspection (one symbol) need be used.

Common usage

○ Operation

○ Transportation or movement

◇ Inspection for quality

△ Delay

Additional, for technical usage

▽ Permanent storage

▽ Temporary storage

□ Inspection for weight or count

Fig. 4.—Symbols sometimes used for analyzing operations.

WITH COLUMNS

DISTANCE	LOST	INDIRECT	HANDLING	PRODUCTIVE	ELEMENTS
80		.62			Walk to stockroom
	2.85				Wait for material
		.15			Take tray of parts
80		.55			Return to machine
		.46			Place on table
			.06		Pick up piece
			.07		Load in jig
				.32	Drill 2 holes
			.06		Unload jig
		.14			Inspect
			.04		Piece aside
			.05		Pick up piece

WITH SYMBOLS

SYMBOL	MINUTES	FEET
○	.62	80
△	2.85	
○	.15	
○	.55	80
○	.46	
○	.06	
○	.07	
○	.32	
○	.06	
◇	.14	
○	.04	
○	.05	

Fig. 5.—Charted study of an operation, showing two ways it may be charted.

When a study is being made, the symbols are drawn beside the operation elements, which are listed in sequence. Distances are noted and times are recorded when men and machines are involved. These results are totaled to compare with similar observations made after the cycle has been improved. For effective display, these comparisons may be arranged on the sheet side by side and designated *before-after*.

The foremen who prefer to use columns for their studies will see how to proceed from the outline shown at the left of Fig. 5. In a simpler form, an X can be made in the proper column to indicate the type of element. The X's can later be connected by lines drawn to emphasize the irregularities in work conditions. However, since none of the observations are of much value without facts, the foreman should record times and distances instead of X's in the columns. These can then be totaled vertically to obtain the summary by types.

Better Jigs

As the foreman already knows, tool designers are more apt to build a jig to last 100 years than to give consideration to the rapidity with which it can be used. In addition, it seems that each designer has his own pet ideas about fastening the piece. When more than one method is possible, it follows that some will be better than others (see Fig. 6).

If the foreman cannot discover which one is the best, the time-study man can help determine which holding methods should be used to gain the greatest efficiency, assuming equal quality. From the standpoint of jig design, many suggestions for improvement can be offered.

The foreman must appreciate that a detailed study of a particular job will reveal "wheels within wheels" as the breakdown is made more detailed. For example, "Place in Jig" may be made up of three elements,

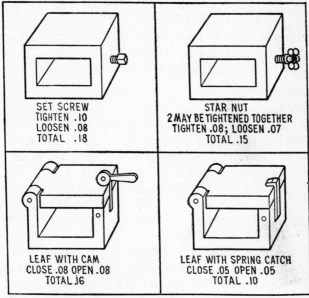

FIG. 6.—Jigs which have different handling times.

namely, "Place the Piece," "Close the Lid," "Lock the Lid." All are affected by design, and the foreman should study these elements when making his recommendations for change. For example, if it were possible to put two pieces in the jig without greatly increasing the closing and locking time, a certain saving would be made in the handling. On the other hand, a certain loss would be created because the machine would have to wait longer.

Combining Operations

Before leaving the handling time, it should be pointed out that machine work may now be called complete and taken to benches for the removal of burrs. Often this is the best practice. However, the foreman may find that the operator who put on the burr can also remove it while the machine is working. Going a step farther, it may be more economical to remove the burr while the piece is rotating in the machine.

Cutting Tools

The effectiveness of cutting tools should be studied. While it has already been pointed out that in many instances the machine is working but a relatively small part of the cycle, nevertheless, opportunities for improvement in machine time may exist. In the first place, the foreman should not be content if tools are operating at handbook feeds and speeds, because manufacturers, in general, are conservative in their recommendations. But in some plants if the foreman will equal the recommended feeds and speeds, he will be able to turn out many more pieces. The point is that the foreman should conduct some experiments of his own to determine what the speeds and feeds can be and still produce the necessary quality.

He should keep in mind, for instance, that when a hole is to be reamed, it may not be necessary to have a fine finish on the drilling. Likewise, when a standard tapping job is to be done, a mirror finish is not necessary in the drilling. If the hole is for clearance only, other conditions of operation are possible. Moreover, everything does not have to be flawless. Several grades of finish may be used in different parts of the operation. The foreman should be on the lookout particularly for high-grade workmanship on surfaces which are to be completely cut away in some subsequent operation.

ELEMENT TIME STUDY

If the foreman wants to go further in the study of operations, his next step is to make an *element breakdown*. Elements are the parts of an operation which must be performed, usually in a certain sequence, in order to complete it.

Elements are of short duration, perhaps averaging one-twentieth of a minute. However, it is necessary to go to this detail in order to see exactly what happens. Elements recorded in sequence are shown in Fig. 7.

The time-study man calls some of these elements "constants" and others "variables." Simplified definitions may serve to explain the difference between the two kinds of elements.

Constants are elements that are practically the same regardless of the part worked. On a certain type of drill press the element "lower spindle" would require the same standard time.

Variables are elements that vary with size and shape or the amount of work done. Drilling time is a variable because it changes with the size of drill, depth of hole, kind of finish, and type of material.

Understanding the difference between these two kinds of elements makes it possible to compare one job with another. For example, the "raise-and-lower-spindle" times should be the same for two different jobs done on the same type of drill press. If the jobs have a different number of holes, the standards allowed for "raise" and "lower" would be multiplied by the respective numbers.

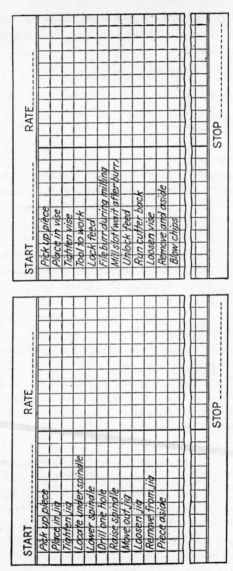

Fig. 7.—Two element analyses illustrating how to begin time study.

However, the times would vary if one piece were larger than the other, or the amount of drilling were different. The times might vary if the jigs used were of different designs. Placing the piece aside might vary if the box into which it is placed were located at a different distance from the operator.

Taking the Time

Having completed the element breakdown, the next step is to see how long it takes. Stop-watch readings can be written beside the elements which occur in sequence, until a number of cycles are completed (see Fig. 8).

It is recommended that on repetitive operations several cycles be studied. When only a few pieces are timed, the information may not be complete because of irregularities which were not observed. The occurrence of such irregularities was illustrated in Fig. 2.

Rating the Time Study

The foreman should remember that what he has written down is actual time taken. This is not necessarily a fair time. Some operators work much faster than others. Most operators work more effectively during the middle of the day than during the "warming-up period" in the morning and at the end of the shift. Over the week there may be a variation, starting with a low on "blue Monday." Obviously, an average of times taken at any one period may be greatly different from a representative time.

To bring such widely varying actual times to a common base representing a fair day's work, it is necessary to judge how much faster or slower than

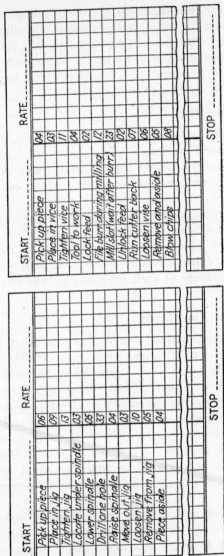

START _____		RATE _____	
Pick up piece	06		
Place in jig	09		
Tighten jig	13		
Locate under spindle	03		
Lower spindle	05		
Drill one hole	33		
Raise spindle	04		
Move out jig	03		
Loosen jig	10		
Remove from jig	05		
Piece aside	04		

STOP _____

START _____		RATE _____	
Pick up piece	04		
Place in vice	03		
Tighten vice	11		
Tool to work	04		
Lock feed	02		
File burr during milling	12		
Mill slot (wait after burr)	23		
Unlock feed	02		
Run cutter back	07		
Loosen vice	06		
Remove and aside	05		
Blow chips	08		

STOP _____

FIG. 8.—Two studies illustrating "watch readings" in decimal minutes for a single cycle.

normal the operator worked during the time study. This appraisal of the operator's performance is called "rating." The rating may be in terms based on a normal of 60 minutes per hour or a normal of 100 per cent, according to the method used in the plant. If 60 is the base, an actual performance at 25 per cent better than normal would be rated as 75 minutes per hour. At about 15 per cent below normal, the time study would be rated as 51 minutes per hour.

The foreman might say that at this stage the time-study man should be brought in. In actual practice, he would be, because the foreman, not being a trained time-study man, cannot be expected to arrive at an accurate estimate of an operator's performance rate. However, it is extremely important that the foreman understand rating. He must train himself in this part of time-study work before he attempts to say anything about the fairness of a standard.

Applying the Rating Factor

In the examples in Figs. 9 and 9a the standards are computed from the actual times by using a rating factor.

Study 1 shows the rating as determined by the Time-study Department to be 70 minutes per hour. The standard time is obtained by using the ratio of 70/60. This raises the low actual times for a good performance to those needed for the normal operator.

Study 2 is taken of a new operator, who is slow. The rating of 35 is used with 60, in the ratio 35/60, to reduce the actual times to standard.

The difference in actual times shown on these examples should indicate how ridiculous it is for a foreman to say, "The standard is too tight," just because the operator cannot make it. It should be

STUDY 1

START ___ 10:12 ___   RATE ___ 70 ___

Operation										
Pick up piece	03	03	04	03	03	03	02	03	04	04
Place in jig	04	04	05	04	04	03	04	03	04	05
Tighten jig	07	06	08	07	08	07	07	06	09	
Locate under spindle	02	03	02	03	02	04	02	02	03	
Lower spindle	02	04	03	03	05	03	03	04	04	
Drill one hole	17	19	18	19	18	17	18	18	16	
Raise spindle	02	02	02	01	02	03	04	03	01	
Move out jig	03	01	02	01	02	02	02	01	02	
Loosen jig	06	06	05	06	06	06	07	06		
Remove from jig	02	03	03	03	02	04	03	04	05	
Piece aside	01	02	02	02	03	02	04	03	03	

STOP ___ 10:17 ___

STUDY 2

START ___ 9:56 ___   RATE ___ 35 ___

Operation										
Pick up piece	06	05	08	06	06	07	06	06	05	07
Place in jig	09	06	08	08	09	09	07	08	10	
Tighten jig	13	14	14	15	14	14	13	17	12	
Locate under spindle	03	06	04	03	02	04	05	04	03	05
Lower spindle	05	04	06	05	06	06	04	06	07	
Drill one hole	33	32	36	35	38	36	37	36	36	35
Raise spindle	03	04	05	04	04	03	05	04	03	
Move out jig	03	02	03	03	03	03	04	04	05	02
Loosen jig	10	09	11	11	10	11	11	12	13	11
Remove from jig	05	05	06	06	07	06	06	08	06	07
Piece aside	04	03	05	02	04	04	04	05	04	03

STOP ___ 10:06 ___

FIG. 9.—Two studies of the same operation, showing very different actual times.

obvious that actual stop-watch times taken by an untrained observer may serve only to aggravate an argument.

Relaxation Is Added

After the normal times are determined, a correct amount of relaxation is added. Using 20 per cent as an example, one can work out the table, Fig. 9a.

Study	Elements	Actual	Rating	Relax, per cent	Standard
1	Tighten jig	.07	× 70/60 +	20	.10
1	Loosen jig	.06	× 70/60 +	20	.08
2	Tighten jig	.14	× 35/60 +	20	.10
2	Loosen jig	.11	× 35/60 +	20	.08

Fig. 9a.—Calculation of standard time.

The foregoing standards should come out the same because the studies were of the same operation on identical parts, and the experience of the time-study man enabled him to arrive at a correct estimate of the rating.

The term "relaxation" is intended to include personal needs, fatigue allowance, incentive, and small unavoidable delays. The amount applied is determined by the type of work. Work performed under restful conditions may have an allowance of 10 per cent. Difficult and heavy work done in the presence of heat or dust may be allowed 35 per cent relaxation.

The factors to be used are determined by extensive studies made by the Time-study Department. However, the foreman should be acquainted with the allowances, so that he understands whether certain

COMPARISON SHEET

	Standard	385	392	405	406	415	417	418
Study number		385	392	405	406	415	417	418
Part number		12281	19312	15221	15560	16110	18147	15441
Material		CRS	CRS	CRS	CRS	CRS	CRS	CRS
Operator		Smith	Black	Jones	Cross	Bowen	Bowen	Brown
Stock length × diam.		5×1	5×⅞	20×2	15×2	5×2	25×1	15×1
Hole - diam. × length		1×1⅛	1×1⅛	1×1	1×½	1½×1¼	½×1	½×1¼
Jig number		3470	3470	3471	3471	3471	3470	3470
Effort rating		70	35	55	60	80	70	75
Pick up piece	Table 1	.04	.04	.12	.10	.06	.13	.08
Place in jig	Table 1	.06	.06	.08	.08	.06	.07	.06
Tighten jig	Table 2	.10	.10	.13	.14	.11	.15	.12
Locate under spindle	Table 2	.03	.03	.06	.05	.04	.05	.04
Lower spindle	.04	.04	.04	.04	.03	.04	.03	.04
Drill one hole	Curve 1	.25	.25	.23	.12	.40	.15	.19
Raise spindle	.03	.03	.03	.02	.03	.04	.03	.04
Move out jig	Table 2	.02	.02	.04	.03	.02	.03	.03
Loosen jig	Table 2	.08	.08	.10	.08	.07	.12	.09
Remove from jig	Table 1	.04	.04	.06	.05	.04	.06	.04
Piece aside	Table 1	.03	.03	.10	.07	.05	.09	.06

Fig. 10.—Studies grouped for comparison.

items of lost time are allowed for in the standard times. Otherwise, delays must be reported by timekeepers to prevent corresponding losses in operator's earnings.

Setting Standard Times

Operation standard times are determined by two general procedures. The *direct method* adds together the element times to secure a total. However, because individual observations include errors in judgment and variations in methods, studies are often grouped together to form *standard data*. Standard data are compiled by grouping and analyzing many time studies. A comparison sheet is started by listing elements of the studies down the left side, as shown in Fig. 10. The standard times secured by time study are then recorded in line with the proper elements. Notice that only standard times are posted to the comparison sheet, because actual times are not comparable. When a number of time studies are thus compared before standards are determined, inconsistencies will be eliminated.

Element Standards

Standards for constant elements are determined in the same manner as one value is selected from a number of readings on an individual time study. Standards for constant elements are used repeatedly in all operations of a given type—"Raise spindle"—.03 is an example (Fig. 8).

Variable elements are analyzed, usually from graphs made by plotting standard times against controlling dimensions. Figure 11 illustrates a number of curves drawn to analyze drilling time. The curves take diameter and depth into account.

HANDLING STANDARDS

PIECE Handling time		Length of stock				
		5	10	15	20	25
Diameter of stock	1	.17	.21	.24	.29	.35
	2	.21	.25	(.30)	.36	.43
	3	.25	.30	.36	.43	.52

JIG Handling time		Length of piece				
		5	10	15	20	25
Drill jig number	3470	.23	.25	.28	.31	.35
	3471	.24	.26	(.30)	.33	.38
	3472	.25	.28	.32	.36	.42

Lower spindle .04
Raise spindle .03   TOTAL R AND L (.07)

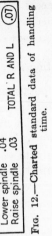

Fig. 12.—Charted standard data of handling time.

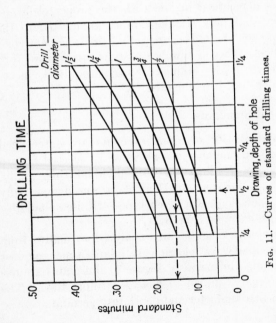

DRILLING TIME

Drill diameter

Standard minutes

Drawing, depth of hole

Fig. 11.—Curves of standard drilling times.

Charted Standard Times

Values obtained from curves may be charted, as shown in Fig. 12. In this way, certain errors of interpretation are avoided and standards can be set more rapidly. Moreover, the foreman and operator can easily understand charted data.

Standard setting can be done more efficiently when element times are grouped. "Raise and Lower Spindle" can be combined because both occur for each hole drilled. For similar reasons, others are combined to lessen the time required to set a standard.

Determining Operation Standards

Standards are set from data by adding together the standards for elements required to do the operation. However, when combinations have been made in charting data similar to Fig. 12, the Time-study Department simply makes a record of the major items allowed. The details would appear somewhat as shown below:

Element combinations	Job specifications	Reference	Standard
Piece handling............	2 in. diameter × 15 in. long	Fig. 11	.30
Jig handling..............	No. 3471	Fig. 11	.30
Drilling 1 hole............	1 in. diameter × ½ in. deep	Fig. 10	.15
Lower and raise spindle.....	Once	Fig. 11	.07
		Total	.82

The standard thus determined is the allowance for a normal operator. It can be equaled by one who has normal skill and exerts normal effort. Since it is an incentive standard, it is expected that the operator will exert more than normal effort and thereby earn extra compensation.

FOREMANSHIP METHODS IMPROVED

Primarily, the foreman is interested in knowing how standard times are developed, in order to explain in an understandable way how incentive standards are determined. He must be on his toes. Perhaps that is why it has been said, "In an incentive department the foreman must be twice as good as in a daywork department." Men do not want to stand around and wait for their next jobs because they lose premium while idle. Premium workers expect the department to be run efficiently. They want a foreman who can take care of their needs and utilize their ideas for increasing production.

To make the most of the workers' suggestions, the foreman must be receptive. He should not "go on guard" by beginning to prove that new ideas are not practical. Even though a suggestion may appear ridiculous in its original form, the open-minded foreman will make the effort to draw out the reasons for the suggestion.

The foreman who understands and uses the fundamentals of time study and methods improvement will completely change his attitude toward that work. In so doing, he will also eliminate many of his reservations toward those who make a full-time job of such work. As he becomes more and more expert in eliminating the lost motion he can see in his department, he begins to look for the help that time-and-motion-study men can give him.

As the foreman progresses along these lines, he begins to look at his department with more of a fact-finding point of view than formerly, when personal feelings played such a large part in his decisions. Many of his personal prejudices disappear, and he looks at his operations more as a manager would. Incidentally, reports on his operations become more understandable and less irksome because they are more favorable. Budgets are less of a headache because the foreman has learned to analyze his difficulties and to remove most of them to produce a more creditable showing. Scrap reports, rejects by inspection, and accident reports contain fewer entries because the methods are better, the interest greater, the morale higher, and the training better.

From knowledge acquired of the workings of the wage-incentive plan, the foreman trained in time study and methods improvement is able to eliminate feelings of distrust on the part of his men and to substitute confidence. Because so many labor-relations problems can arise through misunderstandings, the foreman must make himself thoroughly acquainted with all important details so that he can satisfactorily explain the workings of time study and the incentive plan.

Part Two—Predetermined Time Standards

By Andrews M. Lang

The development of Predetermined Time Standard systems is one of the most fundamental advances in the field of motion and time study in recent years. Also referred to as "elemental standard times" or "synthetic time study," such procedures are really nothing more than a logical extension of the techniques of standard data.

A PTS system may be defined in general terms as a technique for *measuring* work and/or *simplifying* work. Such a definition, however, does not begin to imply the many areas of potential application. An understanding of these areas may be reached only by understanding the principles common to all PTS systems. These are:

1. Any industrial job performed by human beings can be subdivided into a limited number of "basic motions."

2. Every basic motion has a constant value (at the normal or average performance level) whenever it occurs.

3. The total time for any manual operation is merely the total of the times for all the necessary basic motions.

All systems therefore present a set of time values for each basic motion—time values which have been *predetermined* by research workers. With such a set of time values in hand (and the training necessary for their proper use) the time for any manual job can be found in two simple steps:

1. Determine what basic motions are required to do the job.

2. Look up the time value which has been *predetermined* for each basic motion and take the total of all such time values.

Thus it can be seen that the essentials of the procedure are deceptively simple. In actual practice a great deal of attention must be given to step 1, since considerable practice is required in order to determine properly and classify the necessary basic motions.

Although there are a large number of these systems in existence, there are five that have received more attention and use than any others. These are:

Methods-Time Measurement (MTM)
Motion-Time Analysis (MTA)
Work Factor
Basic Motion Timestudy (BMT)
Dimensional Motion Timestudy (DMT)

While the basic principles behind all systems are the same, there is considerable difference in detail. This is because the systems were developed by a number of different researchers working independently.

The system that has received the most attention and which is the most widely used is Methods-Time Measurement (MTM). This system was originally developed by H. B. Maynard, G. J. Stegemerten, and J. L. Schwab, working at the Westinghouse Electric Corporation in Pittsburgh. After carefully checking and testing application of the original research, the results were published in 1948 in the book, "Methods-Time Measurement" (McGraw-Hill Book Company, Inc., N. Y.).

Their policy of making the information freely available served as a stimulant, and the use of MTM spread rapidly. In 1950, Maynard, Stegemerten, and Schwab, together with other consultants, industrialists, and university representatives who had been trained in MTM, formed the MTM Association for Standards & Research—a nonprofit corporation with two primary goals: first, to continue the research work and further improve MTM; second, to carry out a program of standards which would act to sustain quality among those using the system. In an unprecedentedly generous action, the originators of MTM turned over to the Association primary authority for guidance of the technique, including the copyright on the MTM data card. (The MTM Association for Standards & Research is now located in Ann Arbor, Mich. and works in conjunction with the University of Michigan.)

The oldest of the principal PTS techniques is Motion-Time Analysis (MTA). This system was developed by A. B. Segur in Chicago, and it was in 1926 that he set down the basic principle that "within practical limits, the times required by all expert workers to perform true fundamental motions are constant."

Mr. Segur has at this writing made no general publication of the specific details of his system. However, it is known that MTA goes into considerably more detail than most other systems, so that the time required for analysis precludes coverage of all but the most highly repetitive operations.

The Work Factor system was originally developed by J. H. Quick, W. J. Shea, and R. E. Kohler working at the Camden plant of RCA Victor. The system has been used extensively in the electronics industry, although its application is not limited to that field. At the present time, Work Factor is being promoted primarily by the Work Factory Company of Cleveland —a private consulting firm.

In 1951, the Canadian firm of J. D. Woods & Gordon, Ltd., investigated the various PTS systems available and was principally impressed with MTM and Work Factor. However, this organization felt that deficiencies existed in both systems, and so undertook the development of its own motion classification based to a large extent on the MTM and/or Work Factor breakdown. The firm developed new time values to fit its classification, and thus created the system known as Basic Motion Timestudy (BMT).

One of the most recent systems is Dimensional Motion Times (DMT), developed by H. C. Geppinger, Supervisor of Time Study Training at the General Electric Company, in Bridgeport, Connecticut. This system was proposed in order to overcome some of the deficiencies which were felt to exist in the classification of assembly operations by other systems. Its principal contribution is an extremely detailed set of time values for a large number of combinations of "plug-to-hole" ratios. Its use is stated as being limited to highly repetitive operations.

An example of an analysis made using the MTM system is shown in Fig. 1. The analysis is essentially a right- and left-hand chart showing each basic motion by its symbol, its description, and the controlling time value. This analysis covers the operation of riveting clips in a small electric-switch assembly using a foot-operated kick press. The motions (and descriptions) were derived by observing the operation, although they could have been visualized by an experienced engineer. The time values shown (given in "TMU,"

PART PULLOUT ASSEMBLY　　　　PART NO. 432M, 55　　DEPT. ASSY
OPERATION RIVET CLIPS TO BASE　　　　　　　　　DATE 8-5-55

DESCRIPTION LEFT HAND	★	MOTION	TMU	★	MOTION	DESCRIPTION RIGHT HAND
1. GET BASE & CLIP & INTO PRESS						
TOWARD CLIP SUPPLY		(R8C)	15.6		R14C	TOWARD BASES
			9.1		G4B	GET ONE BASE
GET ONE CLIP		G4C	12.9		M14C	BASE TO CLIP
CLIP TO BASE		M14C	16.9		M14C	BASE ON CLIP
CLIP ON BASE		P2NSE	21.0		P2NSE	CLIP & BASE TO PRESS
CLIP & BASE TO PRESS		(M10C)	13.5		M10C	ADJUST GRASP
ADJUST GRASP		G2	-		(G2)	INTO PRESS JAWS
INTO PRESS JAWS		P1SE	5.6		P1SE	ON PIN
ON PIN		P3SD	48.6		P3SD	
			143.2			
2. ACTUATE PRESS						
			11.9		LM10	LEG TO FOOT LEVER
			10.6		AP2	) ACTUATE LEVER
			7.1		LM6	
			14.3		LM2	RETURN FOOT
			43.9		LM12	
3. REMOVE PART, GET 2nd CLIP & INTO PRESS						
OFF PIN		D2E	7.5		D2E	OFF PIN
LET GO ASS'Y		RL1	1.7		RL1	
TOWARD CLIPS		R14C	15.6		(M-B)	ASS'Y CLEAR OF PRESS
GET ONE CLIP		G4C	12.9			

					ASS'Y TOWARD CLIP
CLIP TO ASS'Y	M14C	16.9	(M-C)		ASS'Y ON CLIP
CLIP ON ASS'Y	P2NSE	21.0	P2NSE		CLIP & ASS'Y TO PRESS
CLIP & ASS'Y TO PRESS	M10C	13.5	M10C		ADJUST GRASP
ADJUST GRASP	G2	-	G2		INTO JAWS
INTO JAWS	P1SE	5.6	P1SE		ON PIN
ON PIN	P3SD	46.6	P3SD		
		143.3			
4. REMOVE PART & ASIDE					
OFF PIN	D2E	7.5	D2E		OFF PIN
TO ASIDE POSITION	M10B	12.2	(RLI)		LET GO
LET GO	RLI	1.7			
		21.4			

ELEMENT DESCRIPTION	TMU REQUIRED	% ALLOWANCE	TIME PLUS ALLOWANCE	OCC. PER CYCLE	TOTAL TIME REQ.
#1 GET BASE & CLIP INTO PRESS	143.2	15%	164.7	1	164.7
2 ACTUATE BASE	43.9	15	50.5	2	101.0
3 REMOVE PART, GET 2nd CLIP & INTO PRESS	143.3	15	168.8	1	164.8
4 REMOVE PART & ASIDE	21.4	15	24.6	1	24.6
				TOTAL	455.1 TMU

ALLOWED TIME = 455.1 TMU
= .273 MIN
= .00455 HOUR

SHEET OF SHEETS

Fig. 1.—MTM element analysis.

METHODS-TIME MEASUREMENT APPLICATION DATA

SIMPLIFIED DATA

(All times on this Simplified Data Table include 15% allowance)

HAND AND ARM MOTIONS	BODY, LEG, AND EYE MOTIONS

REACH or MOVE

	TMU
1″	2
2″	4

3″ to 12″ 4 + length of motion
over 12″ 3 + length of motion
(For TYPE 2 REACHES AND MOVES use length of motion only)

POSITION

Fit	Symmetrical	Other
Loose	10	15
Close	20	25
Exact	50	55

TURN—APPLY PRESSURE

TURN	6
APPLY PRESSURE	20

GRASP

Simple	2
Regrasp or Transfer	6
Complex	10

DISENGAGE

Loose	5
Close	10
Exact	30

BODY, LEG, AND EYE MOTIONS

	TMU
Simple foot motion	10
Foot motion with pressure	20
Leg motion	10
Side step case 1	20
Side step case 2	40
Turn body case 1	20
Turn body case 2	45
Eye time	10
Bend, stoop or kneel on one knee	35
Arise	35
Kneel on both knees	80
Arise	90
Sit	40
Stand	50
Walk per pace	17

1 TMU = .00001 hour
= .0006 minute
= .036 second

Copyright 1950

MTM ASSOCIATION FOR STANDARDS AND RESEARCH

620 Penn Avenue - Pittsburgh 21, Pennsylvania

FIG. 2a.—Page 1 of MTM Association's standard card. (This and Figs. 2b, 2c, and 2d reproduced by permission.)

TABLE I—REACH—R

Distance Moved Inches	Leveled Time TMU				Hand In Motion		CASE AND DESCRIPTION
	A	B	C or D	E	A	B	
1	1.8	2.1	3.6	1.7	1.3	1.5	**A** Reach to object in fixed location, or to object in other hand or on which other hand rests.
2	3.7	4.3	5.9	3.8	2.8	2.7	
3	5.0	5.9	7.3	5.3	3.8	3.6	
4	6.1	7.1	8.4	6.8	4.9	4.3	**B** Reach to single object in location which may vary slightly from cycle to cycle.
5	6.5	7.8	9.4	7.4	5.3	5.0	
6	7.0	8.6	10.1	8.0	5.7	5.7	
7	7.4	9.3	10.8	8.7	6.1	6.5	
8	7.9	10.1	11.5	9.3	6.5	7.2	**C** Reach to object jumbled with other objects in a group so that search and select occur.
9	8.3	10.8	12.2	9.9	6.9	7.9	
10	8.7	11.5	12.9	10.5	7.3	8.6	
12	9.6	12.9	14.2	11.8	8.1	10.1	**D** Reach to a very small object or where accurate grasp is required.
14	10.5	14.4	15.6	13.0	8.9	11.5	
16	11.4	15.8	17.0	14.2	9.7	12.9	
18	12.3	17.2	18.4	15.5	10.5	14.4	
20	13.1	18.6	19.8	16.7	11.3	15.8	
22	14.0	20.1	21.2	18.0	12.1	17.3	**E** Reach to indefinite location to get hand in position for body balance or next motion or out of way.
24	14.9	21.5	22.5	19.2	12.9	18.8	
26	15.8	22.9	23.9	20.4	13.7	20.2	
28	16.7	24.4	25.3	21.7	14.5	21.7	
30	17.5	25.8	26.7	22.9	15.3	23.2	

TABLE II—MOVE—M

Distance Moved Inches	Leveled Time TMU			Hand in Motion B	Multiplying Factor		CASE AND DESCRIPTION
	A	B	C		Wt.	Factor	
1	1.7	1.7	1.7	1.5	Up to 5#	1.00	
2	3.6	4.2	4.2	2.7			
3	4.9	5.7	5.7	3.6	10#	1.03	**A** Move object to other hand or against stop.
4	6.1	6.9	7.3	4.3			
5	7.3	8.0	8.7	5.0			
6	8.1	8.9	9.7	5.7	15#	1.05	
7	8.9	9.7	10.8	6.5			
8	9.7	10.6	11.8	7.2	20#	1.08	
9	10.5	11.5	12.7	7.9			
10	11.3	12.2	13.5	8.6	25#	1.11	**B** Move object to approximate or indefinite location.
12	12.9	13.4	15.2	10.0			
14	14.4	14.6	16.9	11.4	30#	1.14	
16	16.0	15.8	18.7	12.8			
18	17.6	17.0	20.4	14.2	35#	1.16	
20	19.2	18.2	22.1	15.6			
22	20.8	19.4	23.8	17.0	40#	1.19	**C** Move object to exact location.
24	22.4	20.6	25.5	18.4			
26	24.0	21.8	27.3	19.8	45#	1.22	
28	25.5	23.1	29.0	21.2			
30	27.1	24.3	30.7	22.7	50#	1.25	

TABLE III—TURN AND APPLY PRESSURE—T AND AP

Weight	Leveled Time TMU for Degrees Turned											
	30°	45°	60°	75°	90°	105°	120°	135°	150°	165°	180°	
Small— 0 to 2 Pounds	2.8	3.5	4.1	4.8	5.4	6.1	6.8	7.4	8.1	8.7	9.4	
Medium—2.1 to 10 Pounds	4.4	5.5	6.5	7.5	8.5	9.6	10.6	11.6	12.7	13.7	14.8	
Large— 10.1 to 35 Pounds	8.4	10.5	12.3	14.4	16.2	18.3	20.4	22.2	24.3	26.1	28.2	

APPLY PRESSURE CASE 1—16.2 TMU.   APPLY PRESSURE CASE 2—10.6 TMU

Fig. 2b.—Page 2 of MTM Association's standard card.

TABLE IV—GRASP—G

Case	Leveled Time TMU	DESCRIPTION
1A	1.7	Pick Up Grasp—Small, medium or large object by itself, easily grasped.
1B	3.5	Very small object or object lying close against a flat surface.
1C1	7.3	Interference with grasp on bottom and one side of nearly cylindrical object. Diameter larger than ½".
1C2	8.7	Interference with grasp on bottom and one side of nearly cylindrical object. Diameter ¼" to ½".
1C3	10.8	Interference with grasp on bottom and one side of nearly cylindrical object. Diameter less than ¼".
2	5.6	Regrasp.
3	5.6	Transfer Grasp.
4A	7.3	Object jumbled with other objects so search and select occur. Larger than 1" x 1" x 1".
4B	9.1	Object jumbled with other objects so search and select occur. ¼" x ¼" x ⅛" to 1" x 1" x 1".
4C	12.9	Object jumbled with other objects so search and select occur. Smaller than ¼" x ¼" x ⅛".
5	0	Contact, sliding or hook grasp.

TABLE V—POSITION*—P

CLASS OF FIT		Symmetry	Easy To Handle	Difficult To Handle
1—Loose	No pressure required	S	5.6	11.2
		SS	9.1	14.7
		NS	10.4	16.0
2—Close	Light pressure required	S	16.2	21.8
		SS	19.7	25.3
		NS	21.0	26.6
3—Exact	Heavy pressure required.	S	43.0	48.6
		SS	46.5	52.1
		NS	47.8	53.4

*Distance moved to engage—1" or less.

TABLE VI—RELEASE—RL

Case	Leveled Time TMU	DESCRIPTION
1	1.7	Normal release performed by opening fingers as independent motion.
2	0	Contact Release.

TABLE VII—DISENGAGE—D

CLASS OF FIT	Easy to Handle	Difficult to Handle
1—Loose—Very slight effort, blends with subsequent move.	4.0	5.7
2—Close—Normal effort, slight recoil.	7.5	11.8
3—Tight—Considerable effort, hand recoils markedly.	22.9	34.7

TABLE VIII—EYE TRAVEL TIME AND EYE FOCUS—ET AND EF

Eye Travel Time = $15.2 \times \dfrac{T}{D}$ TMU.

where T = the distance between points from and to which the eye travels.
D = the perpendicular distance from the eye to the line of travel T, with a maximum value of 20 TMU.

Eye Focus Time = 7.3 TMU.

FIG. 2c.—Page 3 of MTM Association's standard card.

TABLE IX—BODY, LEG, AND FOOT MOTIONS

DESCRIPTION	SYMBOL	DISTANCE	LEVELED TIME TMU
Foot Motion—Hinged at Ankle.	FM	Up to 4″	8.5
With heavy pressure.	FMP		19.1
Leg or Foreleg Motion.	LM	Up to 6″	7.1
		Each add'l. inch	1.2
Sidestep—Case 1—Complete when leading leg contacts floor.	SS-C1	Less than 12″	Use REACH or MOVE Time
		12″	17.0
		Each add'l. inch	.6
Case 2—Lagging leg must contact floor before next motion can be made.	SS-C2	12″	34.1
		Each add'l. inch	1.1
Bend, Stoop, or Kneel on One Knee.	B,S,KOK		29.0
Arise.	AB,AS,AKOK		31.9
Kneel on Floor—Both Knees.	KBK		69.4
Arise.	AKBK		76.7
Sit.	SIT		34.7
Stand from Sitting Position.	STD		43.4
Turn Body 45 to 90 degrees— Case 1—Complete when leading leg contacts floor.	TBC1		18.6
Case 2—Lagging leg must contact floor before next motion can be made.	TBC2		37.2
Walk.	W-FT.	Per Foot	5.3
Walk.	W-P	Per Pace	15.0

TABLE X—SIMULTANEOUS MOTIONS

REACH			MOVE			GRASP				POSITION			DISENGAGE			CASE	MOTION
A, E	B	C, D	A, Bm	B	C	G1A G2 G5	G1B G1C	G4		P1S	P1SS P2S	P1NS P2SS P2NS	D1E D1D	D2			
W	O	W	O	W	O	W	O		W	O	E	D	E	D	E	D	E	D		
E	E	E	E	E	E	E	E		E	E	E	E	E	E	E	P	P	P	E	E	E	A, E	REACH
	E	E	P	E	E	E	P	P	D	E	E	P	P	D	P	D	D	D	E	E	P	B	
		E	P	P	D	P	D	D	D	E	P	D	D	D	D	D	D	D	P	D	D	C, D	
			E	E	E	E	E	E	E	E	E	E	E	E	E	P	P	P	E	E	E	A, Bm	MOVE
				E	E	E	E	E	E	E	P	E	P	P	D	P	P	D	E	E	P	B	
					P	D	E	P	D	D	D	D	D	D	D	D	D	D	P	D	D	C	
						E	E	E	E	E	E	E	E	D	D	D	E	D	D	G1A, G2, G5	GRASP
							D	D	P	D	D	D	D	D	D	D	D	D	G1B, G1C	
								D	D	D	D	D	D	D	D	D	G4	
									P	D	D	D	D	D	D	D	P1S	POSITION
										D	D	D	D	D	D	D	P1SS, P2S	
											D	D	D	D	D	P1NS, P2SS, P2NS	
												E	E	E	D1E, D1D	DISENGAGE
													E	E	D2	

E=EASY to perform simultaneously.

P=Can be performed simultaneously with PRACTICE.

D=DIFFICULT to perform simultaneously even after long practice. Allow both times.

MOTIONS NOT INCLUDED IN ABOVE TABLE

TURN—Normally EASY with all motions except when TURN is controlled or with DISENGAGE.

APPLY PRESSURE—May be EASY, PRACTICE, or DIFFICULT. Each case must be analyzed.

POSITION—Class 3—Always DIFFICULT.

DISENGAGE—Class 3—Normally DIFFICULT.

RELEASE—Always EASY.

DISENGAGE—Any class may be DIFFICULT if care must be exercised to avoid injury or damage to object.

*W = Within the area of normal vision.

O = Outside the area of normal vision.

**E = EASY to handle.

D = DIFFICULT to handle.

Fig. 2d.—Page 4 of MTM Association's standard card.

where 1 TMU equals 0.00001 hours) were taken from the MTM data card shown in Fig. 2.   The total time is given in TMU, hours, and minutes.

Note that in order to get the total time standard for riveting one unit at the average or normal performance level, it is necessary to add a percentage (here 15 per cent) to the basic MTM values.   This percentage covers fatigue and personal and unavoidable delays. All PTS systems give basic time values without allowances, since different percentages may be desired to cover different situations.   (The 15 per cent has, however, been added into the Simplified Data in Fig. 2a.   It is *not* included in Figs. 2b, 2c, and 2d.)

There are many advantages to this approach, both in terms of developing standards and in terms of methods work.   The fact that the stop watch can be eliminated for most purely manual operations has been given such widespread publicity that the value of these systems for methods work is often overlooked. Actually, the return in terms of methods improvements may often be greater than the improvement resulting from better time standards.

METHODS ANALYSIS

There are two basic advantages of Predetermined Time Standards systems for methods-analysis work:

First, in order for this approach to work, there must be a very fine subdivision of an operator's motions. Thus, we automatically get extremely detailed information about how a job is actually performed.

Second, the systems provide basic information relating any conceivable method to the time which will be required to perform it.   Thus, alternative methods of performing work can be compared—in terms of performance times—before the job is even introduced into the shop. This is possible for experienced engineers, since they may *visualize* the basic motions required to do the job, when it is not possible to *observe* the motion used by a worker performing the operation.

The foregoing can even lead to using an analysis of method as a means of evaluating the design of a tool, a company's product, or a piece of equipment being considered for purchase. For instance, a tool designer is often able to provide several different designs for a tool to do a particular job. Yet the design might be equally satisfactory in terms of initial cost, quality of work which would be produced, etc. However, one additional factor which should be considered (although often it is not) is the ease and speed with which the tool may be used in the shop. Using the PTS system approach, an analysis can be made of the motions required to use each of the different tools designed. This would then lead directly to a measurement of the time it would take using each different tool—and would then provide further information as to which design is best. And, best of all, this can be done in the blueprint stage before any of the tools are actually made.

The same basic idea—evaluating in terms of *function*—can be applied whether it be a tool, a company's product, or a piece of equipment being considered for purchase.

TIME STANDARDS

One basic advantage of these systems for time-standard work is that the amount of judgment which must be exercised by the practitioner is minimized. In conventional time study the practitioner must evaluate two things—the motions that are made and the speed of these motions. This evaluation is done using some system of "rating" or "leveling" (as discussed in Part One of this chapter) and relies heavily on the judgment of the practitioner. In the PTS approach, only one thing need be considered—the motions that are made. Once these are determined, the procedure is merely clerical, since the time values (representing a level of "speed") have been predetermined. Because of this, time standards set with a PTS system will be much more consistent than was previously possible. No "leveling" or "rating" is needed in application; the same time values are used for all operations; the work required of every operator will be equivalent, regardless of the nature. (This applies within any *single* system. Although sufficient investigation has not yet been made to provide a final answer, there is some evidence to indicate a difference *between* systems. However, any such difference should be constant.)

It is true that in the original research supporting any PTS system, some form of rating or leveling must have been used. But all this means is that the concept of "average" or "normal" performance for any PTS system is that of the rating or leveling used in the research. It does not destroy the consistency of any system and that is the key to acceptance of time standards by the working force.

A second advantage of the PTS approach for time standards is the speed with which standards may be set. It is not necessary to take repeated observation of a large number of cycles of an operation and then go through the laborious calculation needed in time study. An experienced practitioner can complete a study in an amazingly short period of time, as indicated in the following quotation from the article "The Wheel of Fortune" in *Fortune Magazine* for September, 1949, giving an account of the editors' investigation of the MTM system of PTS:

> Stryker's next assignment was a report of Methods-Time Measurement, a recently developed method of setting production time standards by motion analysis instead of a stop watch. Skeptical of its reception by union men as well as management, Stryker asked the MTM engineers if they would be willing to provide him with a first-hand demonstration of actual operations in a factory. They said they would—and he could pick the factory. He did—American Pencil opened its doors again, and the MTM men went into the plant, studied one operation on the floor, whispered together, made a few calculations, and amazed the company by coming up in 25 minutes with a standard only one-half of 1 per cent above the figure the company had taken hours to establish. . . .

While application cannot be made this rapidly on all types of operation, there is always a substantial improvement over the time for a conventional time study properly made.

A third advantage occurs when standards are being developed for a whole group of similar operations. The techniques utilized in such cases are those of standard data or time formulas where studies made on relatively few operations are used to develop times for all of the operations in the group. With time study, it is first necessary to study several representative jobs throughout the range. This often requires a considerable period of waiting until representative jobs come through the shop. After this, the individual studies must be examined, analyzed, and correlated in order to determine how times vary as the operations vary. There is often difficulty with such items as determining what causes variation in time, separating the elements of the operation into subdivisions affected by a single variable, retaking studies to get proper subdivisions, etc. The complexity of such analysis has hitherto made development of a time formula an extremely laborious job—often so lengthy as to be impractical.

With the PTS approach the situation is considerably simpler. Only a few operations need actually be studied. From these studies, by *visualizing* what will happen to the motion as the operations change, the whole pattern of the formula can be set up and developed directly. In a survey conducted by *Factory Management & Maintenance* ("How Good is MTM?" August, 1950) it was found that by using the PTS approach, time formulas or standard data could be developed in an average of one-fourth of the time previously required with time study.

OTHER USES

In addition to using a PTS system for various types of methods and standards work, there are other valuable applications. One of these is in connection with training new operators. Here the fundamental problem is to get the operator to understand and be able to duplicate each of the motions required to do a particular job. Once again the detailed information about method, provided by a PTS system, can be used to help the operator learn his job. If a PTS analysis is used (written up in terms with which the operator is familiar), it is much easier for the operator to see in fine detail exactly what he should be doing at each point in the cycle. Figure 3 shows a right- and left-hand chart suitable for operator training made up from the PTS analysis shown in Fig. 1 for the riveting operation. Use of this approach has repeatedly led to substantially decreased training periods.

JOB INSTRUCTION SHEET

Part____Pullout assembly____Part No. 432MS5 Dept._Ass'y_

Operation___Rivet clips to base_____

Left-hand motions	Right-hand motions
Reach toward clips	Reach toward bases
	Grasp one base
Grasp one clip	
Move clip to base	Move base to clip
Assemble clip to base	Assemble base to clip
Move assembly to press, shifting grasp as needed	Move assembly to press, shifting grasp as needed
Move assembly between press jaws	Move assembly between press jaws
Put assembly over pin on lower press jaw	Put assembly over pin on lower press jaw
	Move leg to foot lever
	Push down
	Let lever up and return foot to normal position
Pull assembly off pin on lower press jaw	Pull assembly off pin on lower press jaw
Let go of assembly	Hold assembly
Reach toward clips	Move assembly clear of press
Get a second clip	
Move second clip to assembly	
Assemble second clip to assembly	Assemble second clip to assembly
Move assembly to press, shifting grasp as needed	Move assembly to press, shifting grasp as needed
Move assembly between press jaws	Move assembly between press jaws
Put assembly over pin on lower press jaw	Put assembly over pin on lower press jaw
	Move leg to foot lever
	Push down
	Let lever up and return foot to normal position
Pull assembly off pin on lower press jaw	Pull assembly off pin on lower press jaw
Move assembly to lay-aside position	Let go of assembly
Let go of finished assembly in lay-aside position	

FIG. 3.—Right- and left-hand chart for operator training made from the PTS analysis shown in Fig. 1.

Another general use of PTS is in connection with settlement of disputes over incentive standards. With time studies, such disputes do not rest entirely on any factual basis, but to a considerable extent on the judgment of the time-study man. Because "opinion" plays such a large part in determining a rate, it is difficult to arrive at a solution that will be acceptable to all.

With PTS the situation is very much changed. The problem to be resolved depends almost entirely on *facts* which can be determined by answering two questions:

1. Does the PTS analysis include all the motions and only those motions needed to do the job?

2. Is the operator following the method as set down in the PTS analysis?

When these questions can be answered "yes," the dispute will be resolved, since the operator will be able to meet the expected standard.

LEARNING A SYSTEM

We have pointed out previously that the basic idea involved in application of any PTS system is simple. However, in all systems the actual application is not simple, but requires considerable training and practice to ensure proper and consistent motion classification. Most of the systems make available training courses for those wishing to become competent practitioners. Without such training, successful application is most difficult and in most cases should not even be attempted.

It should be noted that many of the systems have developed sets of data which are "simplified" or "approximated" in comparison with the complete data. These can be mastered in a relatively short training period and are particularly useful for foremen who may wish to make rough estimates to check a proposed method improvement or a new tool design, or make any other noncritical application.

For instance, a set of "Simplified Data" in the MTM system is shown in the first section of the data card in Fig. 2a. With only a moderate amount of training, a supervisor can use this to check a proposed improvement in the kick-press operation analyzed in Fig. 1. If the proposed change were to develop a fixture to hold the base unit in the press so that the two clips could be put into it and riveted in one operation, the analysis would be as shown in Fig. 4. This analysis could be made merely by *visualizing* how the job would be done, before any new fixtures were actually made.

Since the MTM Simplified Data already includes a 15 per cent allowance, our calculations are extremely simple, and give a final time standard of 0.145 minute or a saving of 0.273 − 0.145 = 0.128 minute on each part. If we produce 500,000 of these parts per year, and pay our operators $1.30 per hour, our total saving in one year would be

$$(0.128) \cdot (500,000) \cdot \left(\frac{1.30}{60}\right) = \$1,382$$

from which we would have to subtract the cost of the fixture. Thus we can make a factual estimate of savings *before* any time or money is spent in building the new fixture or training operators to use it.

BRINGING A PTS SYSTEM INTO AN ORGANIZATION

Because the PTS system approach is radically different from previous procedures, an integrated program

PART PART NO. DEPT.
OPERATION   DATE

DESCRIPTION LEFT HAND	★	MOTION	TMU	MOTION	★	DESCRIPTION RIGHT HAND
1. ASIDE FINISHED ASSEMBLY & INSERT NEW BASE						
		R4	8	R4		
		D2	10	D2		
		M10 ⃝	17	R14		
		RL ⃝	10	G4		
			17	M14		
			25	P2NS		
			−	RL		
			87			
2. GET 2 CLIPS & IN FIXTURE						
		R14	17	R14		
		G4	10	G4		
		M14	10	M14		
		P2NS	17	P2NS		
			25			
		RL	25	RL		
			−			
			104			

3. ACTUATE PRESS							
		10	LM				
		20	AP				
		10	LM				
		10	LM				
		50					

ELEMENT DESCRIPTION	TMU REQUIRED	% ALLOWANCE	TIME PLUS ALLOWANCE	OCC. PER CYCLE	TOTAL TIME REQ.
1. ASIDE FINISHED ASSEMBLY & INSERT NEW BASE	87			1	87
2. GET 2 CLIPS & IN FIXTURE	104			1	104
3. ACTUATE PRESS	50			1	50
			TOTAL	=	241 TMU
				=	.145 MIN.
				=	.0024 HRS.
ALLOWED TIME	TOTALS				

SHEET OF SHEETS

FIG. 4.—MTM element analysis.

of instructions should be undertaken when starting use in any plant. This should include:

1. Complete training (including opportunity to gain competence through experience) for the industrial engineering staff.

2. General training for all levels of management—foreman to president. This training should include an outline of the technical aspects of the procedure. More important, however, would be to include information covering the possible and proposed uses of the system—emphasizing limitations as well as advantages.

3. Educating the employees about the techniques—through the union if one exists. In this connection, it is desirable to have union representatives participate in both of the training courses listed above.

These above steps, together with other steps needed when introducing any work-measurement procedure, will help to ensure the success of the program.

HUMAN RELATIONS

A PTS system not only provides technical advantages, but also improves the human-relations situation—because it is not the *worker*, but rather the *job* which is studied.

Conventional time and motion study are and will continue to be valuable tools. Yet there is an important difference in worker reaction—and hence in the supervisor's job—when the worker is studied with a stop watch as compared with the job being studied using predetermined time values. With PTS, the engineer does not particularly care if the operator works at a fast or slow pace. Once the worker realizes this—and in addition sees that rates throughout the plant are consistent—his attitude will veer away from hostility toward co-operation.   But the worker must be given the basic information about PTS, through his supervisor as well as his union representative, so that he may realize what the system will mean to him. Without this transfusion of information to all levels of the organization, no installation can be completely successful.   The foreman's job is of maximum importance in providing a firm base on which to support the advantages which can be achieved by using predetermined time standards.

Part Three—The "Standard Minute System"

By George H. Elliott

(*Editor's Note: Although Chap. XI is devoted to wage-payment plans in general, the Standard Minute system is so closely allied to the subject matter presented in the first two parts of this chapter, that it was felt logical to present this specific plan in some detail at this point.*)

Once he has mastered the basic principles of time study, the foreman will do well to familiarize himself with the Standard Minute system of wage incentives and production cost control, since it has become one of the most effective incentive plans in use in American industry today.

An important underlying principle of the Standard Minute system is the expression of all work in terms of "Standard Minutes" of production, instead of so many pieces or pounds or other measures of output. Time thus becomes the common denominator, and the system can be used no matter what a company's product is—mousetraps or automobiles or men's clothing . . . .

Certain other systems using the hour instead of the minute as the basis of calculation—the "Standard Hour" or the "Unit Hour" systems—are the same in underlying concept and mathematical treatment. However, experience has shown that it is much more meaningful to use the minute instead of the hour as the unit. In the first place, most operational cycles in industry are in terms of minutes rather than hours, so that if hours were used, one would almost always be discussing operations in terms of small fractions or percentages of an hour. Second, the foreman will find that talking about operations and output in terms of standard minutes is much more meaningful to workers —they instinctively visualize what is meant by, say, 10 Standard Minutes of production, but would have to do a certain amount of mental gymnastics to get any meaning out of the corresponding 0.1667 Standard Hours.

A Standard Minute is simply the amount of work a person should do in a minute. Specifically:

One minute of work = One Standard Minute

Accordingly, just as there are 60 "clock minutes" in an hour, so should a person produce at least 60 Standard Minutes in a Standard Hour.

Note that in the above sentence, the expression "at least" is used. That is because the amount a person should produce is set at such a figure as to permit the average normal worker who is willing to put just a little extra effort into the job to turn out more than this standard. Specifically, by means of techniques described earlier in this chapter, and in Section Six, the arrangement of work, methods used, availability of tools and materials, and the working conditions are all set up in such a way that the worker can readily turn out 25 per cent more work than the standard, *without undue strain or speed-up*. Thus, instead of turning out 60 Standard Minutes worth of work in 60 clock hours, he should readily be turning out 75 Standard Minutes.

A point to make clear at this time is that by means of objective time studies and "rating factors" or "leveling factors," experienced analysts arrive at the amount of time an operation should take if the worker is working at "optimum or normal incentive" pace. In the preceding paragraph, we mentioned that at this pace he could be making a 25 per cent bonus. That is because it is usual to set the standard times in such a way that the objectively determined incentive time does represent 25 per cent more output than the standard—the standard being taken as 125 per cent of the incentive time. Of course, if a company wanted to be especially generous, it could make its standards quite "loose," so that the objectively determined incentive time would represent 30 or 35 per cent bonus, or whatever other percentage is desired. However, in all cases, given accurate analysis by seasoned time-study men, the normal incentive time should be the same. This will become clear in our example.

Since under this wage-payment system the amount of money the worker receives for a Standard Minute of work is computed by dividing his base hourly rate by 60, it can readily be seen that if he turns out not 60, but 75 Standard Minutes worth of work in 60 clock minutes, and he is paid for 75, he stands to earn $75\!/\!60$ of his base rate in 1 clock hour, or a bonus of 25 per cent. Incidentally, if there is any question about the fairness of the base rate, job evaluation (See Chap. XII) should be done.

Unlike many bonus incentive plans, the benefits of the increased efficiency above 60 in the Standard Minute plan are not shared with the company, or used to reduce the company's direct labor costs. Under this plan, the employee's earnings increase in direct proportion to his production above standard, and he receives not half or three-quarters, but *all* of the incentive benefits. That is why the plan is sometimes called a "100 per cent premium" plan, and represents the best possible incentive plan from the viewpoint of the worker.

DERIVATION OF A STANDARD MINUTE

For any given operation, the techniques of time study or predetermined times discussed in earlier parts of this chapter would be used. Thus, if stop-watch readings are taken, many readings would be averaged before the standard is set. In the present discussion we are not concerned with the techniques of taking times, but rather with the principle on which the incentive is based. Figure 1 is presented to illustrate schematically the concepts involved.

The bar at the top of the chart represents the "stop-watch time" of the operation. This is "raw data," and will differ, depending upon the worker being timed, since obviously a green or lazy worker will be working at a slow pace, while an experienced and conscientious worker will be working at a much faster pace.

To take these differences of pace into account, the experienced analyst applies the "operator's grading factor," as shown at the end of the first bar. For example, if the operator studied was in the analyst's estimation using less time than the average worker would require—less time, that is, than would be needed by the average worker even when working at incentive pace—the grading factor would be used to "loosen up" the observed time to the normal incentive pace of the average experienced operator who would be expected to take a little longer to make the piece. (If, in our schematic diagram, the stop-watch time had been taken on a slow worker, the time would, of course, have had to be graded back, and the operator's grading factor would have been subtracted to arrive at the "adjusted time-study time.") Thus the grading factor assures that a fair standard will be set regardless of the speed at which the worker who happens to be the one studied is working.

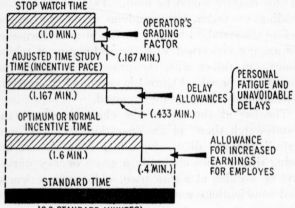

DERIVATION OF A STANDARD MINUTE

STOP WATCH TIME

(1.0 MIN.) OPERATOR'S GRADING FACTOR

ADJUSTED TIME STUDY TIME (INCENTIVE PACE) (.167 MIN.)

(1.167 MIN.) DELAY ALLOWANCES } PERSONAL FATIGUE AND UNAVOIDABLE DELAYS

OPTIMUM OR NORMAL INCENTIVE TIME (.433 MIN.)

(1.6 MIN.) ALLOWANCE FOR INCREASED EARNINGS FOR EMPLOYES

(.4 MIN.)

STANDARD TIME

(2.0 STANDARD MINUTES)

STANDARD
120 SECONDS PER PIECE PER MAN
2 STANDARD MINUTES PER PIECE
30 PIECES PER HOUR

Fig. 1.—Schematic diagram showing derivation of a Standard Minute. *Application of above standard:* Assume that the operator produces 240 pieces in 8 hours—Standard Minutes produced = 240 × 2, or 480; productivity rating per hour is 480/8, or 60 Standard Minutes per hour.

Assume that the operator produces 280 pieces in 8 hours— Standard Minutes produced = 280 × 2, or 560; productivity rating is 560/8, or 70 Standard Minutes per hour.

Assume that the operator produces 300 pieces in 8 hours— Standard Minutes produced = 300 × 2, or 600; productivity rating per hour is 600/8, or 75 Standard Minutes per hour.

The "incentive pace" mentioned above is the pace at which we want the operator to work while he is working—but, of course, the operator could not be expected to keep that pace continuously all day long.

There will always be certain delays which must be allowed for. These delay allowances consist of personal allowance, fatigue, and unavoidable delays.

The *personal allowance* is the time allowed for getting a drink, going to the washroom, and the like, and is usually taken care of by adding 5 per cent to the stopwatch time. Thus, out of 8 hours, or 480 minutes, 5 per cent would be 24 minutes; so one might consider it the equivalent of two 12-minute periods a day.

Fatigue allowances are based upon the actual physical exertion requirements of the job. If a girl is sitting in an air-conditioned factory, sewing or assembling, the fatigue would probably be rather low; whereas if a man is slinging a 50-lb sledge hammer, knocking off gates and risers from heavy gray-iron castings, the fatigue is very high. This fatigue allowance, therefore, varies according to the work performed. However, it is common to lump personal allowances, fatigue, and the unavoidable delays mentioned below into an over-all factor of 15 per cent.

The *unavoidable delays* are those things which occur irregularly during the day, not once every 10 pieces or 50 pieces, nor once every hour on the hour, but nevertheless at some times, and have to be allowed for. For example, in a stitching plant, a girl has thread breaks and has to rethread her bobbin and needle or she may have to change the color of the thread; in a machine shop, a machinist may have to grind a drill or change the cutting angle on the drill; and so on.

After the delay allowances have been added, the total is called the "optimum or normal incentive time." An operator working at this rate of production is said to be working at incentive pace.

The Standard Minute system then adds a 25 per cent allowance to the normal incentive time. That is because, in order to allow him to make 25 per cent increased earnings, the standard time has to give the operator 25 per cent more time than he would actually need when working at normal incentive pace. Thus, if there is a standard of say, 10 Standard Minutes per piece, the worker could say, "Then if I do it in 8 minutes I get 10 minutes worth of pay."

Now on the subject of earning more money: The opportunity is there for the worker to make more money if he wants to put forth the effort. However this incentive opportunity depends entirely on his willing effort as an individual worker. There is nothing forced about it. From now on he can earn 15 minutes of extra pay for every hour he works on incentive. That is a total of 75 minutes of pay for 60 minutes of work, or as we call it—75 Standard Minutes per hour

An Example

To carry the illustration a bit further, let us take as an example an operation which has a standard of 2 Standard Minutes per piece. The first operator completes 200 pieces in 8 hours, the second does 240 pieces, the third 280 pieces, and the fourth 320 pieces per day.

Operator No.	No. of pieces made	Std. Min. earned @ 2 Std. Min. per piece	Actual earnings @ $1.50 per hr. or 2.5¢ per Std. Min.	Actual cost per pc.	Productivity (Std. Min. per hour)
1	200	400	$12.00	$.06	50
2	240	480	12.00	.05	60
3	280	560	14.00	.05	70
4	320	640	16.00	.05	80

Note that in the case of operators No. 1 and 2 the cost per piece is reduced from 6 to 5 cents when the operator's productivity goes up from 50 SMpH to 60 SMpH (Standard Minutes per hour). Above 60 SMpH however, the cost per piece always remains at the same 5 cents, and the operator's earnings are increased proportionately from $12.00 to $14.00 to $16.00 per day. Note also that operator No. 1 was not penalized because he produced less than 60 Standard Minutes in an hour—he was paid his hourly rate of $1.50, or $12.00 for the day. Of course, the supervisor would not allow such a situation to persist indefinitely.

Unlike many bonus incentive plans, the benefits of such increased efficiency over 60 SMpH are not shared with the company or used to reduce the company's direct labor costs. Under the Standard Minute plan, the employee's earnings increase in direct proportion to his production above standard and he receives not 50 per cent or 75 per cent but 100 per cent of the incentive benefits.

STIMULATION AND CONTROL

In addition to opportunities for increased employee earnings, the Standard Minute system affords effective tools for stimulation and control.

Figure 2 shows a Daily Production Report which can be posted on the departmental bulletin board, so that all operators can see where they scored on the previous day. Usually, the report is prepared and posted around 10 o'clock in the morning, or perhaps earlier, in each department throughout the plant.

Reference to Fig. 2 shows that Lyons produced 596 Standard Minutes in 7 hours, at a rate of 85 Standard Minutes per hour. In this case, management wished to post the amount of bonus earned by the individual,

DAILY PRODUCTION REPORT

Client ___ElC/ı1ı2ı\ı MANUFACTURING CO.___

Department ___PRESSES AND SHEARS___ Date ___FEB. 21, 1955___

EMPLOYEE	TIME DISTRIBUTION					Production in St'd Min.	Hours Worked on Standards	St'd Min's. Per Hour	Bonus
NAME OR NUMBER	Total	Non Chargeable	Sup'v. & Indir.	Delay	Day Work				
8 LYONS	8.0				1.0	596	7.0	85	$3.52
65 GOULD	8.0			.3	.5	599	7.2	83	3.34
68 KING	8.0			.2		601	7.8	77	2.66
63 SCOTT	8.0				.6	555	7.4	74	2.22
66 LENGEL	9.0			.6	1.2	520	7.2	72	1.76
86 NEALE	8.0					552	8.0	69	1.54
54 DELSANTO	7.5			1.1		429	6.4	67	.90
88 PELOSA	8.0					536	8.0	67	1.12
7 MELITSKY	9.0			.3	1.0	516	7.7	67	1.08
69 GENTILE	8.0					522	8.0	65	.64
78 DAVIS	5.0			.4		295	4.6	64	.38
71 McCARTHY	8.0				.3	477	7.7	62	.30
50 PICKERING	8.0					496	8.0	62	.12
73 JONES	8.0			.4		464	7.6	61	
77 LAUX	8.0				2.3	366	5.7	58	
70 GRIESEHABER	7.0			.3		382	6.7	57	
5 SHARIN	8.0				.6	408	7.4	55	
81 VAMOS	9.0			.5	1.3	367	7.2	51	
75 THOMAS	8.0				.7	343	7.3	47	
42 GERLACH	8.0			1.7		277	6.3	44	
64 RICHTER	8.0					329	8.0	41	
9 OBERMARK	8.0			.6		281	7.4	38	
60 DALY-FOREMAN	8.0		8.0						4.26
16 WATTS-ASSISTANT	8.0		8.0						2.82
72	8.0		5.7		2.3				.62
Totals	198.5		21.7	6.4	11.8	9981	158.6		

Dept. Rating
64

FIG. 2.—Daily production report posted in department.

although it is not common practice to do this. Gould did 599 Standard Minutes in 7.2 hours and rated 83 Standard Minutes per hour. Going on down the list, we find that Jones hit 61 Standard Minutes which is just above our task level, or standard-day's work. In other words, this is the amount of work that normal, experienced operators should do for the amount of money they receive as an hourly rate. Now looking, for a moment, at those operators who are below 60 Standard Minutes an hour, we find that they run all the way from 58 down to 38—Obermark.

Let us consider Obermark for a moment. He is doing 38 Standard Minutes of work per hour. He should be doing 60 Standard Minutes of work, on the average, throughout the day. If he is paid $1.00 per hour, *he is only earning around* 65 *cents out of the dollar that is being paid him*, and the other 35 cents is simply being thrown away so far as management is concerned. Obviously, this condition would not be tolerated for very long and hence, with such a report as this, plant management and the foreman will direct their efforts to either getting Obermark's production up or getting him out of the department.

The posting of this Daily Production Report furnishes one of the basic accelerative principles of the Standard Minute system through which we may obtain higher production per individual and per machine than one would expect to get from piecework or any other kind of premium or bonus plan. Every man or woman has some pride or ego in his or her make-up. Hence the posting of the scores provides an incentive to the workers to rate high on the list in order to satisfy their own pride and to satisfy their desire to rate well in the eyes of their fellow workers and the company.

Likewise, this scoring principle furnishes management with a means to determine whether or not a foreman is able to operate his department well, and how well by comparison with other foremen in other departments.

Note in the column headed "Delay" in Fig. 2 there was a total of 6.4 hours of delay or waiting time during the day in question. Each time an operator has a delay beyond 5 minutes, he fills out a slip stating what the cause of the delay was. These delays, of course, arise from various reasons such as shortage of materials and supplies to work on; waiting for the foreman to O.K. a setup on a machine; or breakdown of machinery and equipment.

When these delay slips are analyzed for all the departments as a whole for any particular week, it will often follow that there are a surprising number of hours of delay time for various reasons. If one of the reasons is waiting for materials and supplies, this obviously means that the production, planning, and scheduling system is not functioning properly. If the delay hours are high because of foremen not giving prompt O.K.'s on machine setups, the foremen are not on their toes. If there is an excessive amount of machine breakdown and repair time, this means that the maintenance department is probably not doing its job properly. Hence, it will be seen that one of the valuable features of the Standard Minute system is that, by isolating waiting time, management can determine what is responsible and then take the proper corrective measures to eliminate it.

The superintendent also has a daily production report, as illustrated by Fig. 3. (To bring out our point, we show the chart simplified and enlarged, and on the wall in front of the superintendent.) This

SUPERINTENDENT'S CONTROL OVER FOREMEN

FIG. 3.—Weekly report for superintendent's control.

shows the departments, the foremen, and the departmental Standard Minutes per hour ratings for the week ending Jan. 15.   On this day the Yard Department did 69; Lathe 70; Printing 75; Warehouse 45; etc. Obviously, with this type of control, the superintendent knows immediately that the cost of production in the warehouse is much too high, and that either Simms is not doing a good job, or he has too many men, or they are inefficient.

Thus, through these daily reports and similar weekly production and labor cost analyses, labor cost control becomes a reality and everybody knows every day exactly what the labor efficiency of the plant is, what the excess costs were, and what should be done about them.   Likewise, the superintendent can determine the effectiveness of the various foremen in his plant and the chart on his office wall becomes the "Foremen's Daily Production Report," for, as each foreman comes into the superintendent's office, he sees where he stands in the operation of his department relative to the ability of the other foremen in the other departments.

CHAPTER VI

COST CONTROL BY FOREMEN

By Charles Reitell

Modern industrial management realizes that if costs are to be effectively controlled, foremen must do it. Foremen are the finger tips of management touching the thousand and one workers—workers who all too frequently fall down on their jobs, who spoil work, who kill time, who waste materials and supplies, who break tools, and who ruin machines. The purpose of this chapter is to set forth simple, practical methods that will give foremen a tighter and more intelligent control over the production costs that come under their responsibility.

FOREMAN RESPONSIBILITY FOR COSTS

The foreman's department is the logical division for centering the control of costs, because that is the place in the organization where the major portion of costs arise. And costs arise in the foreman's department either badly or well, depending directly upon his caliber as a leader and his understanding in the handling of cost controls.

Amazing but true, foremen are responsible for 65 to 75 per cent of operating costs (excluding raw material) in a typical industrial establishment.

This **high** percentage of costs is due to the large items of expenditure that are lodged directly within the foreman's jurisdiction. Here are the more common outlays that are wholly within a foreman's department:

1. *Direct Labor Costs.* Often very high because of new help inadequately trained, giving slow, off-standard production.

2. *Indirect Labor Costs.* Often too high in terms of direct labor and usually so because of excessive handling charges.

3. *Spoiled Work.* Untrained workers, the worst offenders in producing spoilage.

4. *Tool Breakage.* Likewise caused in great part by new and inexperienced workers, also by too much "rush" effort.

5. *Manufacturing Supplies.* One of the greatest sources of waste and one calling for the tightest of cost controls, in "normal" times as well as when new supplies are difficult to acquire.

6. *Defective Material.* A cost that usually goes back to the vendor; but a smart foreman will catch the defects quicker and thus save waste of labor and overhead.

7. *Power* (if metered to a foreman's department). A cost which if closely watched by a foreman will show as high as a 30 per cent saving.

The above costs are the major ones coming entirely under a foreman's responsibility. There are others, but the above are enough to emphasize the importance of making cost controls one of the foreman's chief functions.

A cost condition worse than useless is one under which a foreman is given cost data over which he has no control and about which he can do nothing. (Cost data supplied to foremen have even been known to include a share of advertising, selling, and administrative expense!) A foreman should not be confused with costs that are alien to him and to his department. *He should be made responsible only for those costs that are entirely and exclusively within his department and upon which he has the authority to act.* Once this policy is clearly established, useless and wasteful "buck passing" is avoided.

Of course, it is not within the foreman's power to establish the type of cost control to be used in his company. However, by familiarizing himself through study with the main features of a modern cost system designed to bring home to the foreman those elements of cost within his control, he will be in a better position to:

1. Understand his own company's cost-control objectives, even if the particular system in use differs from the one studied.

2. Co-operate more helpfully with those functional departments which are responsible for cost control in his company.

3. Be more alert to cost-control possibilities, that is, be "cost-control conscious," even if his company, at the moment, has no well-designed method to "feed" cost information to him.

The remainder of this chapter will therefore be devoted to a description of a modern cost-control system, making use of "flexible budgets," designed to furnish foremen with up-to-the-minute cost information.

ESTABLISHING THE COST CONTROLS

The *first step* in building the control features for foremen is to make certain that the plant is organized into well-defined departments. Under such an organization, each foreman knows where his responsibility begins and where it ends.

An attractive result of sharply defining the field of activity is the feeling of proprietorship that is quickly built in the foreman's mind. When the foreman has a clear-cut department and when he gets costs that measure those activities that are entirely within his department, he is certain of developing into a real manager—no "alibiing," no split responsibility, no overlapping of authority.

The *second step* in building the cost controls has to do with the plant accounting. The cost accounting must be so divided and coded as to make certain that the costs flow easily into the various operating departments. When this is accomplished, costs will go down through well-grooved channels to each of the foremen who are to receive them. The result is that the foreman quickly realizes that he will be considered either a "good" or a "bad" supervisor on the strength of how well he does his work as measured by the cost records that come to him.

The *third step* in controlling costs is to gain an understanding as to how costs behave—what happens to them under different conditions of operation.

This phase of cost control is extremely important, and every foreman should try to set such "cost pictures" for his own department. As an example, the behavior of the spoiled-work account of a machine-tool company, covering 26 weeks of operation, is shown in Fig. 1.

This cost graph shows the spoilage costs in relation to the amount of standard productive hours worked in the department. Each dot represents the spoilage cost for a week and the corresponding number of standard hours of direct labor.

This record is from a plant which shifted suddenly to new production. Over 60 per cent of the labor force at the time of this study was composed of relatively new workers, and it is this fact that accounts for spoiled work costing only 1.6 cents per standard hour at the previous low volume and 15.0 cents per standard hour when 6,700 standard hours are worked. The

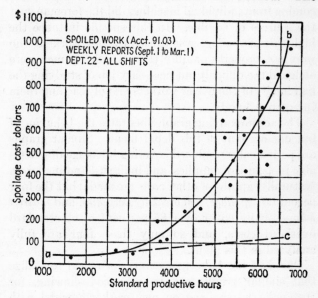

Fig. 1.—Cost graph.

normal volume of activity in this department before the new work was between 3,000 and 4,000 hours a week. At the time under consideration the capacity was about doubled.

The chief foreman in this department drew the curve *ab*, representing the trend of spoilage costs as new volume of work was encountered. He also plotted line *ac*, showing what the cost would be at the different volumes of activity if the new workers did as well as his experienced workers.

The graph showed this chief foreman how serious was the problem of spoiled work. What was he to do about it? This graph but emphasized and drew attention to the seriousness of the problem; it did not solve it. Only by carefully analyzing the scrap reports coming from individual machines did the foreman spot the sources of trouble. In this specific instance the high cost of spoilage was caused by new workers who were not properly or fully trained. Setup men were assigned the difficult but necessary job of studying the bad habits of the newer workers and of teaching them the correct habits.

The accompanying graph illustrates the behavior of but one account in this department. Similar graphs are periodically produced covering breakage of perishable tools, use of supplies, and indirect-handling labor. Naturally, graphs of other costs are made; but the four accounts—*spoilage, tool breakage, supplies,* and *indirect help*—usually cover over 85 per cent of off-standard overhead costs, and so only these four are fully analyzed in this plant.

One does not have to see very far ahead to realize that similar graphs can be produced showing, for instance, the spoilage on new work compared with spoilage of routine production. Likewise, spoilage conditions of the different shifts can be charted.

The knowledge of cost behavior within a foreman's department quickly teaches him that there is no constant relationship between standard hours of direct labor and the cost of a given account. At one volume of capacity, indirect labor costs may show a ratio to direct labor of 1:4, while at another volume the ratio may show a 1:2 relationship. Different ratios of allowances for costs are necessary for different volumes of work.

This truth brings to the fore two important principles that are basic for the adequate control of costs by the foreman:

1. The operation of flexible budgets
2. The development of cost standards

THE FLEXIBLE BUDGET AND COST STANDARDS

The Meaning and Use of Flexible Budgets

The flexible budget gives the foreman the standard allowances for each item of cost over which he has control *at any volume of productive work* that goes through his department. These budgets are set up before the beginning of a period and therefore become cost targets or bogies that the foreman tries to hit and beat in actual performance.

The following table (Fig. 2) shows a typical flexible budget, which has been built for Chief Foreman Stub Gridley. The Cost Department, the Planning Department, and Gridley made up this budget at the beginning of the year. It should be carefully studied.

From the illustrative flexible budget, the foreman should note the following:

1. That Stub Gridley is the named responsible person in seeing that these cost standards are met. He is cost manager of the department.

2. That the different volumes are expressed in standard productive hours.

[NOTE.—A standard productive hour is measured by good units produced. If the standard time calls for six pieces per hour, and in an 8-hour day 54 pieces are produced, then nine ($5\frac{4}{6}$) standard productive hours' worth of work have been produced in the 8 hours.]

Dept. 8 Mould

FLEXIBLE BUDGET

Chief Foreman, Stub Gridley

ITEMS						VOLUMES of ACTIVITY						
	70%	75%	80%	85%	90%	95%	NORMAL 100%	105%	110%	115%	120%	125%
STD. PROD. HOURS	16,940	18,150	19,360	20,570	21,780	22,900	24,200	25,410	26,620	27,830	29,040	30,250
DIRECT LABOR ALLOWANCE	$16,093	$17,243	$18,392	$19,542	$20,691	$21,841	$22,990	$24,140	$25,289	$26,439	$27,588	$28,738
DIRECT OVERHEADS:												
Chief Foreman's Salary	$ 560	$ 560	$ 560	$ 560	$ 560	$ 560	$ 560	$ 560	$ 560	$ 560	$ 560	$ 560
Ass't Foremen's Salaries	340	340	340	680	680	680	680	680	680	680	680	680
Indirect Labor	1,860	1,980	2,100	2,230	2,350	2,470	2,560	2,690	2,820	2,950	3,000	3,150
Spoiled Work	510	650	810	870	980	1,195	1,352	1,580	1,845	2,190	2,500	2,880
Perishable Tools	300	350	375	400	500	650	800	1,000	1,250	1,550	1,850	2,150
Manufacturing Supplies	840	900	960	1,020	1,080	1,140	1,200	1,260	1,320	1,380	1,440	1,500
Power	700	715	730	745	760	775	790	805	810	815	820	825
TOTAL DIRECT OVERHEADS	$ 5,110	$ 5,495	$ 5,875	$ 6,505	$ 6,910	$ 7,470	$ 7,942	$ 8,575	$ 9,285	$10,125	$10,850	$11,745
TOTAL BUDGET	$21,203	$22,748	$24,267	$26,047	$27,601	$29,311	$30,932	$32,715	$34,574	$36,564	$38,438	$40,483

Fig. 2.—A typical flexible budget.

3. That all costs are set in relation to a given amount of standard productive hours.

4. That only those costs over which the foreman has full jurisdiction are listed on his budget.

5. That when volume falls between the 5 per cent divisions, *e.g.*, 82 per cent, then two-fifths of the difference between 80 per cent and 85 per cent is added to the 80 per cent budget in order to get the current 82 per cent allowance.

Viewed in the large, this flexible budget is the road map charting the path that costs should follow. Thus the budget acts as a target of accomplishment.

Being in the nature of a target, it adds enjoyment to the foreman's endeavors. Just as a target gives sport to the gunner and also improves his marksmanship, so does the flexible budget make a game out of cost activity and at the same time improve the cost control of the foreman.

Setting the Cost Standards

Who sets these cost allowances? They are established by the co-operative endeavor of the Cost Department, the Methods and Time-study Department, and the foreman. It is a joint undertaking. Many different sources are used for setting the cost standards. The experience of a given cost item, as shown on the behavior chart, gives the past performance. The results of time studies furnish assistance. The plans of the foreman in suggested improvements are considered, and the judgment of the group also is brought to bear in arriving at specific amounts.

This setting of cost standards improves greatly with experience. As time passes, it becomes a very useful factor in plant management.

VARIANCES

Measuring What Is Done against What Should Have Been Done

The co-operative setting of cost standards means that a foreman must think ahead of the work to be performed. He must make plans. By following this procedure the cost standards are very well known and understood by him before the operating period. Then, when actual experience takes place, he immediately compares the actual against the standard—the performance against the plan.

This means that the foreman is following the "exception principle" of scientific management. Under the operation of this principle the foreman need concern himself only with the amount and the cause of the off-standard conditions—*the variances from the known norm*. Most of the work will pass through his department at the cost-standard pace, which is known and understood before the operations take place. Only the exceptions stand out in bold relief, and it is these that require careful analysis and adjustment.

When such a method is followed, no out-of-line costs can long endure. Bad variances are flagged at once, and, forthwith, policies are (or should be) started to right matters.

COST REPORTS FOR FOREMEN

The foreman, of course, must make every effort to understand thoroughly the cost reports he receives and should immediately question points that are not clear. Where management is doing its part in securing foreman co-operation in cost control, it considers the careful setting up of clear, simple

MARCH	CURRENT MONTH		ITEMS		YEAR TO DATE
		24,200	Budgeted Std. Productive Hours		72,600
		26,620	Actual Std. Productive Hours		74,954
		110.0%	Department's Activity		103.2%
VARIANCE (Bad in Red)	ACTUAL	CURRENT ALLOW-ANCE	ACCOUNT		VARIANCE YEAR TO DATE (Bad in Red)
			NO.	NAME	
$−453	$25,742	$25,289	9.01	DIRECT LABOR	$− 647
				DIRECT OVERHEADS:	
$− 12	$ 372	$ 360	91.12	Chief Foreman's Salary	$− 27
	480	480	91.13	Ass't Foremen's Salaries	− 40
−126	2,946	2,820	91.15	Indirect Labor	− 432
−202	2,047	1,845	91.03	Spoiled Work	− 544
14	1,236	1,250	91.18	Perishable Tools	− 83
373	947	1,320	91.21	Manufacturing Supplies	212
66	744	810	91.23	Power	219
$ 113	$ 8,772	$ 8,885		Total Overheads	$− 695
$−340	$34,514	$34,174		Total Department	$−1,342

Remarks:

DEPT. 8   FOREMAN Gridley   MONTH OF March

FOREMAN'S COST CONTROL REPORT

FIG. 3.—Typical foreman's variance report.

reports for foremen as important as the data the reports convey. In such reporting, the following nine principles are applied:

1. The report should be so shaped as to meet the specific needs of the foreman.   Thus it helps to solve his particular problems.

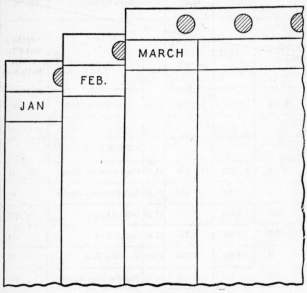

FIG. 4.—"Shingling" of reports.

2. The report should be simple in form and in terminology.   Shop language should be used.

3. The report should present only the cost data that are under the jurisdiction of the specific foreman.

4. The report should be "hot."   Stale figures are of little value.   Sometimes it is advisable to give daily-variance cost reports if a serious condition exists.

5. The report should show both the standard allowance and the actual expenditure for each cost coming

under a specific foreman. Likewise the variance in each account should be shown.

6. Each cost report should be clearly identified with the foreman's name and department. If only a few departments exist, different colored sheets may be used.

7. Reports should be carefully bound in "shingled" form. By shingling, a progress report on the variance of each cost from one period to another is obtained.

8. A follow-up analysis should accompany each cost report. Each bad variance should be carefully followed until the proper corrective work has been accomplished.

9. Cost reports should be in such shape as to provide one of the major matters for discussion at foremen's meetings.

A typical foreman's variance report, from a large manufacturing plant in New Jersey, is shown in Fig. 3. This report goes to the foreman monthly. (Because of the bad variance conditions, however, this report can be given to the foreman weekly.)

Note how this report embodies every one of the nine basic principles.

The shingling method (Fig. 4) is to bind one month's cost report over other months so as to leave an overlap on the left margin, an overlap just the width of the variance column.

The punched holes at the top of the sheets are so spaced that when the report is placed in the ring binder the shingling is obtained automatically.

Closely linked to the cost report is a program of follow-up. No bad variance is allowed to continue without attention and a close checkup. The follow-up report used here (Fig. 5) is suggestive.

COST CONTROL—FOLLOW-UP REPORT

MONTH OF   March

NAME OF ACCOUNT	NO.	VARIANCE	CAUSE OF VARIANCE	PROCEDURE FOR REMOVING BAD VARIANCES	PROGRESS CHECK-UP DATES				
					3/3	3/10	3/17	3/24	
Direct Labor	9.01	$-453	Fall-down and High-rated Workers	1. Have setup men handle training Fall-down men.	X	X	Improvement shown.	Got the broaching work licked.	
				Keep daily records of improvement.			Most fall-downs on broaches.		
Spoiled Work	91.03	$-202	New Workers	Training and closer watching by Foreman. Have inspectors show at what elements of the operation spoilage takes place.	X			Better spoilage condition than 2 weeks ago. Still lots of room for improvement.	

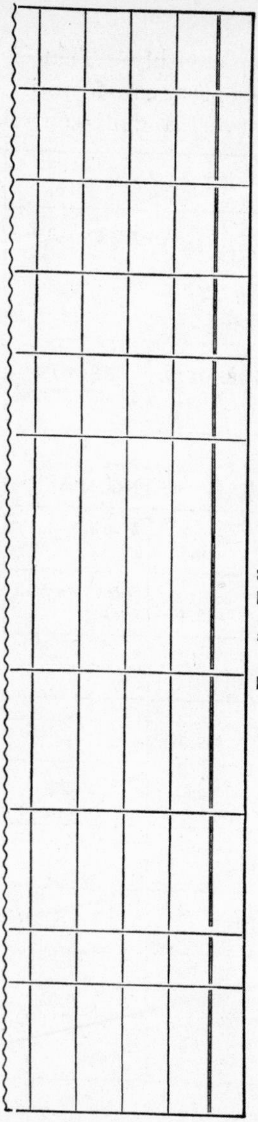

Fig. 5.—Follow-up report.

Daily Reports

The reports illustrated are monthly. That is sufficient if operations are moving along satisfactorily. When variances are bad, however, a daily-control

DAILY COST REPORT				
DEPT. 8				FOREMAN Gridley
DIRECT LABOR DATE—MARCH 17				
NO.	OPERATIONS SHOWING BAD VARIANCE	ACTUAL COST	SHOULD COST	REASON FOR EXCESS
17	Rough Bore and Face	$12.18	$10.80	Slow operation. New Man
26	Drilling	8.74	6.12	Man in Woman's job.
42	Mill	16.85	12.40	Substitute Mill used.
	TOTAL FOR THE DAY	$37.77	$29.32	
	BAD VARIANCE	$ 8.45		

FIG. 6.

report suggests itself. Such a report is illustrated in Fig. 6.

MANAGERIAL FOREMANSHIP

A sharp tool in the hands of an untrained worker is dangerous. A cost-control report in the hands of a foreman untrained as to the report's meaning and use likewise is dangerous.

Foreman training in cost-control and budgetary procedures is essential if proper results are to be accomplished. Where such training is designed to get the best results from the techniques just described, it embodies the following steps:

1. The foreman is made to understand the place of his department in the plant organization. An organization chart is prepared, including both the Production and Service Departments.

2. Every supervisor is given a typewritten list of his responsibilities. This procedure is a definite part of standard instructions. The building of sharp lines of responsibility removes much confusion and misunderstanding, and authority flows more smoothly throughout the plant.

3. The feeling of departmental proprietorship on the part of foremen is encouraged. Each foreman is trained to treat his variance reports as the profit and loss statement of his department. He is made to feel that it is *his* department and that he is responsible for the results shown.

4. The philosophy of performance control by use of cost standards is emphasized. This training covers methods, time studies, expense standards, cost behavior, and flexible budgets.

These training suggestions carry the foreman one step nearer to being a true manager in every sense of the word. After all, one can do most anything when there are no limits on the purse strings. A real manager must execute policy and be measured by a monetary yardstick in so doing. *It is controlled expenditures that make for management.* And only as foremen become responsible for doing definite amounts of performance within definite outlays of cash can they really be termed managers.

In the past, foremanship was involved in handling men, materials, and mechanical equipment. Usually foremen were averse to anything that smacked of accounting or financial figures. They felt the place for accounting was in the accountant's office, and inasmuch as foremen were hired to see that workers produced, they saw little reason why they should get into the bookkeeping business.

But today we realize that the confining of costs to the main office is injurious both to the foremen and to the accountants. By keeping costs away from foremen, the plant operates without the best controls, and as a result definite savings in time and money are lost.

Section Three

THE FOREMAN'S DIRECT
PERSONNEL RESPONSIBILITIES

CHAPTER VII

THE FOREMAN'S TRAINING RESPONSIBILITIES

BY GLENN GARDINER

The foreman's training job takes on special importance in any period of extreme production needs. By the very nature of most of the jobs for which industrial workers must be trained, not less than 90 per cent of all the training that is to be done will of necessity be done right *on the job*. The speed and effectiveness with which the great army of industrial workers will be trained is dependent upon the ability of foremen quickly to pass on their know-how to new workers and to old workers on new jobs.

Relatively few jobs can be reproduced in a schoolroom or a training center. The only place where the tools, machines, materials, supplies, and processes are available is right where the work is being done. The man who supervises the work must also take responsibility for the major part of the job of training workers.

WHAT TRAINING MUST THE FOREMAN DO?

The training which the foreman must do includes the imparting of all the information and knowledge of operations which a worker must possess in order to carry out the functions of his job efficiently and intelligently. This means that training done by foremen must include the following:

1. Job rules and regulations
2. Safety
3. Quality standards
4. Knowledge of material working properties
5. Material and equipment conservation
6. Waste prevention
7. Output expectation
8. The actual operations of the job

Until the worker is fully informed regarding all these points, he is not capable of doing his job efficiently and intelligently.

The foreman's result will depend upon his ability to develop a working force that will carry out his departmental work program. If he does not train his men well, they cannot be expected to perform well.

WHO NEEDS TRAINING?

Everyone under a foreman's supervision needs training. The training job is never done.

We think immediately of the new employee as one who needs training. It is a mistaken assumption, however, to take it for granted that the main training job is completed when new workers have been instructed.

Older employees are constantly being moved on to new operations. They, too, need training when new jobs with different or higher skills are to be performed.

The Second World War demonstrated forcibly that top-skilled workers are not available in the labor market when production for the entire country is tremendously expanded; and postwar reconversion also had to take place amid a shortage of many skills. When men of top skill are needed, the foreman will usually be required to select the man who comes nearest to possessing top skill and to give him the necessary training to develop top skill in him.

A foreman should think of every person whom he supervises as a man or woman in training. Until each worker has been developed to his highest skill capacity, there is still need and room for training. This training the foreman must constantly give.

Training Lessons Learned during the War

During the Second World War, *time* was the most important factor in America's industrial-production program. Our very national existence depended upon the speed with which we trained an industrial-production army. Total war thus created the need for "blitz" training methods. There was no time for the old "absorption" training, where men were "exposed" to a job with the hope that they might pick up enough knowledge and skill to be able to hold the job.

Most of the techniques of training learned by industry during the Second World War are applicable to the highly competitive conditions of peace. The need for flexibility and lower overhead will not permit foremen to put one man after another on a job until he strikes one who seems to "get the hang of it." The training job in most plants requires that a foreman take the men and women available and train them quickly to the highest level of skill which they are capable of attaining.

It was demonstrated during the war that the use of proper instructing methods by foremen can cut the training time by 20, 40, or 60 per cent. The rapidity with which we can bring workers to peak productivity is a critical factor in determining the total output of American industry. Our industrial foremen have the know-how, and if they are good instructors they can quickly pass this on to their workers.

TRAINING AND INSTRUCTION

The terms "training" and "instruction" are often used interchangeably. Their meaning is much the same. When we think of training, however, we usually think of the whole process of taking a man from the point of little or no knowledge about a job to the point where he has fully mastered the job. We bring this about by instruction. Instruction is the tool with which we "build" a trained man.

Training may be the result of many bits of instruction. The trained mechanic has been instructed on numerous specific operations. He has been instructed regarding various pieces of related information necessary for him to do an intelligent job.

Training is a process that goes on and on. Instruction may be intermittent. A foreman may give a man 50 pieces of instruction before he has developed him into a fully trained man. Instruction may be given in a few sentences. It is a part of training. We think of training as the all-around development of a man on a job, while instruction consists of the various steps in the training process.

SUPERVISION AND INSTRUCTION

Instruction consists of giving a man an understanding of *what* we want him to do, *when* we want him to do it, and *how* we want him to do it. Instruction includes giving the man the reasons why we want him to do it in a specified way.

In defining supervision, one must conclude that supervision aims to do these very same things. Supervision and instruction are inseparable, since so much of supervision *is* instruction. Conversely, practically all instruction is supervision, in a sense.

Because supervision and instruction are so bound together, no foreman can be a good supervisor unless he is also a good instructor. When a foreman is successful, an analysis of the basis of his success will usually reveal that he has succeeded in getting over to his men a clear understanding of what he wants them to do, how he wants them to do it, when he wants them to do it, and why he wants it done in a certain way. Accordingly, the first objective of every foreman who is ambitious to succeed should be the development of instructing ability.

Instruction is something of a trade in itself. Many foremen are selected for supervisory jobs because they have demonstrated high ability as workmen. It is assumed that they will be able to get others to work as efficiently as they have worked. But it does not necessarily follow that an efficient workman will make an effective foreman. One reason why the expert mechanic frequently fails when promoted to foremanship is that he has not recognized the necessity of learning the instructing trade. He cannot get results from others unless he is able to instruct them effectively.

QUALIFICATIONS OF A GOOD INSTRUCTOR

To be a good instructor a foreman must possess certain qualifications. The foreman-reader should check his own qualifications against the following list to determine wherein he most needs improvement.

1. Thorough knowledge of the job to be taught
2. Ability to put himself at the worker's level of knowledge about the job
3. Sincere interest in learners

4. Great patience
5. Friendliness
6. Knowledge of the basic steps of good instruction
7. Ability to express himself clearly
8. Ability to plan and prepare for instruction before giving it to the worker

In addition to the possession of the foregoing qualifications, a foreman must have the right attitude. He must appreciate that "if the learner has not learned, the instructor has not taught." He must not have the attitude of the foreman who said, complainingly, "I've told that dumbbell how to do that job at least a dozen times, and still he goes and does it wrong!" The foreman must recognize that every learner failure is in reality an *instructor* failure.

WHO SHOULD DO THE TRAINING?

Some foremen may feel that they are too busy to take time to instruct and train men. Pressed with many responsibilities, foremen are often too ready to delegate responsibility for training to an assistant or to an experienced worker.

No foreman can afford blindly to delegate the responsibility for training. He must know beyond any question of a doubt that every man he supervises actually gets correct instruction.

Merely turning a new man over to an experienced worker does not ensure proper instruction. If the experienced worker has certain work habits which are not right, he will pass the bad work habit on to the new worker. Or he may not have patience to bother with the new worker. Or he may be the type who likes to assume a bossy, domineering attitude toward the new worker. As a general rule, instruction of workers on new jobs should be done by the foreman himself or by an assistant who has been properly trained and coached in the correct method of good instruction.

The foreman is the one responsible for departmental results. He may be handicapping himself unless he makes sure that proper instructions are being given to men learning new jobs. One of the reasons why so many foremen are constantly rushed is that so many men have been improperly instructed. Their mistakes keep the foreman in "hot water." There are very few foremen who cannot well afford to spend some time on the instruction of every new worker. In fact, foremen cannot afford *not* to take a hand in the training of each of their men.

This early training period affords the foreman an unusually good opportunity to size up a new man. He gets to know exactly what the new man knows. He has an opportunity to impress the new man with his own friendliness and interest in him. The foreman should be jealous of this opportunity to spend the first period with a new man. This is the very starting point of good relations between the foreman and the worker.

BEFORE THE FOREMAN GIVES INSTRUCTION

Even though a foreman may be thoroughly familiar with a job on which he is going to instruct a man, it still is necessary for him to make some preparation for giving instruction.

To begin with, he must carefully decide what must be taught to the learner. He must review in his own mind the information which must be imparted. He must check to be sure that the method he has in mind is the method now being used. He must be sure that he is ready to teach the best way of doing the job.

Before giving instruction, the foreman should make certain that the workplace is in proper arrangement. He should see that all tools and materials are ready and in place. He must see that the workplace is arranged in exactly the condition he will expect the worker to keep it.

Part of the worker's first impression of the job is formed on the basis of the arrangement of the workplace. If all is confusion, he will find it more difficult to "catch on" to the job. Untidiness will create in him immediately a lack of respect for tidiness and quality work.

Before giving instruction, the foreman should break down the job into its details, so that he will be sure to give instruction on every necessary point. Overfamiliarity with the job makes it easy for a foreman to leave out certain essentials. He must remind himself to get down to the worker's knowledge level before starting to instruct.

JOB BREAKDOWN FOR INSTRUCTION PURPOSES

Anyone who has ever asked directions on how to get to some place he has never been to before knows how confusing a well-meaning instructor can be. He gives detailed instructions; he tells what turns to make, how far to go before one must turn right, what landmarks to look for, and he suggests how to keep you on the right road. Then the stranger starts out. He may make the first turn or two correctly, but after that everything is jumbled in his mind. The informer gave what he believed were simple instructions. They were simple to him because he knew the route so well. But to the stranger, the instruction seemed complicated.

When the foreman starts to give instruction to a man on a new job, the learner's mind experiences the same difficulty in grasping all the details. If the foreman gives him too much instruction at one time, he gets very little of it. However, if the foreman carefully breaks down the job into the detailed steps in its performance and decides how many points should be "put over" to the learner at one time, it helps the learning process greatly.

Let us consider another example. Suppose a man were going to learn a poem with 12 verses of four lines each. If he read through the entire 12 verses and then tried to repeat the poem, he might not be able to repeat even the first line. No matter how many times he read the entire 12 verses through, he probably would not be able to memorize it. However, if he took the first four lines and learned them one line at a time, it would take only a minute to memorize the first verse. Then he would go on to the second verse and learn it line by line. Then he would repeat the first two verses. After that he would pass on to the third, the fourth, and through all 12 verses, learning one verse at a time and repeating it until he had it thoroughly memorized.

Jobs must be taught and learned in much the same manner. A job must be broken down into all the points to be taught. If there are more than six or seven points, the job should be broken into more than one instruction lesson. Six or seven points are about all that can be "put over" effectively in one instruction unit.

If a foreman were going to instruct a man on how to use a micrometer, he would probably need to break the process down into about three instruction units. The first instruction unit would consist of teaching the learner the parts of the micrometer and the care he should exercise in handling it. The second instruction unit might properly consist of the reading of the micrometer. The third instruction unit might consist of teaching the learner how to make measurements and actually apply the micrometer to parts to be measured.

The foreman should not get the impression that making a job breakdown is a complicated process. It requires only 5 or 6 minutes to jot down the steps taken in doing the job. This should serve rather as a reminder list for him to follow in giving the instructions. It will help him make sure that he does not omit any essential points. It will also help him to size up the job to determine whether it should be taught in one, two, three, or four instruction units.

THE FOUR BASIC STEPS IN INSTRUCTION

No matter what job is to be taught, the instruction should follow these four basic steps of good teaching. These steps are as follows:

Step 1. Preparation of the learner

Step 2. Presentation of instruction matter

Step 3. Performance tryout

Step 4. Follow-up

By these, or similar, terms the basic steps of good instruction have long been designated. They were most effectively demonstrated and utilized in connection with the Job Instructor Training Program of the Training Within Industry Division created by the United States government for on-the-job training of war-production workers in the Second World War.[1] Thousands upon thousands of foremen were coached in the effective use of these four basic steps in thousands of war-production plants of America.

[1] This program, formulated in the New Jersey district of the Training Within Industry Division under the direction of the

Preparing the Learner for Instruction

This first step, preparing the learner for instruction, is very important. Unless it is properly taken, the learner cannot be expected to learn.

The first thing for the foreman (or other instructor) to do is to put the learner at ease. A nervous, "jumpy" worker cannot concentrate. His mind is in no condition to receive new ideas. The learner can be best put at ease by a friendly attitude on the part of the foreman. The foreman should make the new man feel that he will be sincerely helpful. He should not "rush him." Calmness on the foreman's part will make the learner feel calm.

Another factor in preparing the learner is arousing his interest in the job. The foreman should tell him something about the job that will make him want to learn it and should point out the opportunities that mastery of the job will open up to him.

Next, it is important to find out how much he already knows about the job. The foreman should check into what he has been doing. He should ask questions about his past experience and learn what work he may have done which might help him to understand his job. When the foreman knows what the new man knows about the work, he will be in a position to start in at the right point or level with his instruction. Finally, it may be important on certain jobs to position the worker properly. He should be placed in a position where he will be looking at the work from the same angle from which he will view it when he performs the job. If the operations on the

---

author, was based upon material previously compiled and prepared by him and published in "How to Instruct" by the Elliott Service Company, New York.

job are demonstrated while he stands looking at it from the opposite side, he will be seeing it backward.

All of these points are important in properly preparing the learner for instruction. When he is at ease, his interest aroused, his knowledge of the job appraised, and he is properly positioned, he is ready for instruction.

Presentation of Instruction Matter

In the second step of instruction, the foreman will present the knowledge and information to the learner which he will need in order to perform the job. This presentation will be accomplished by a combination of methods. Mere *telling* alone usually will be insufficient. Mere *showing* is not enough. The proper use of telling, showing, illustrating, and questioning will put over the instruction most effectively.

By combining, telling, showing, illustrating, and questioning, the foreman will impress the instruction through his senses of sight, hearing, and feeling. By asking him questions beginning with *how*, *when*, *why*, *where*, *who*, or *what*, the foreman will be able to determine, as he goes along, whether the learner is absorbing the ideas he is presenting. Questions beginning with those words cannot be answered by a mere yes or no. They must be answered by a sentence which will reveal whether or not the learner really understands.

Instruction matter should be presented one step at a time, slowly, clearly, completely, and patiently. The steps should be repeated as often as is necessary. The foreman should make sure the learner really understands before he proceeds. When he is satisfied that the learner has really learned, he is ready for the performance-tryout step.

Performance Tryout

In the performance-tryout step, the learner is given an opportunity to demonstrate whether he has actually learned the job. This is a testing step in which the foreman has the learner perform the job under his observation. It is easy to determine whether he has mastered the manual parts of the job by watching his performance. His understanding of the informational side of the job can be determined by making further use of the questions beginning with what, why, when, how, where, and who.

As the learner performs the job, the foreman should watch him closely and correct any mistakes as soon as he makes them. Where necessary, instruction should be repeated. It may even be necessary to go back and repeat the presentation of part or all of the job.

The purpose of the performance-tryout step is to make sure that the learner really knows the job and is able to handle the job by himself. He should not be left alone until the foreman is certain that he has mastered the job.

Follow-up of Instruction

When the foreman is satisfied by the performance-tryout step that the learner is ready to go ahead with the job, the time has come to "put him on his own." The learner needs this opportunity to develop confidence in his own ability to do the job. The foreman should come back after a short interval to check up, to be sure that he is following instructions. If he needs correction, the foreman should make his corrections patiently and in a friendly manner. He will have to be checked up rather frequently at the start so that he does not stray away from the method he has been taught.

The follow-up step continues until the worker is able to proceed on the work with the normal amount of supervision. At that point the actual instruction on the job or operation in question is completed. Thereafter the foreman will have to give only the normal supervision he would give to any qualified man on the job.

DEPARTMENTAL TRAINING PLAN

Every foreman should have a departmental training plan. He should make an inventory of the skills of the men he has under his supervision. Here is how a foreman can go about it:

He can write the name of each of his men on a separate card. He can then take one individual's card and list on it the different jobs or operations in the department which that particular person can perform. Next he should jot down the several jobs for which that man is best qualified to receive instruction, listing them in the order in which he intends to instruct him. It should be his object to have each of his workers trained to perform more than one job. The more jobs each man can perform, the more flexible will be the working force.

When the foreman has listed the present skills and the skills which he expects to teach each man, he will have a simple inventory of the skills the men in his department already possess. He will also have in elementary form a program of training ahead, because he will have listed several jobs which he intends to teach each man as the opportunity presents itself.

To complete the departmental training plan, the foreman should make a study of the expected labor requirements for his department, in accordance with the volume of work that is likely to be assigned to it.

Depending upon whether or not expansion is planned, he will need few or many additional workers of certain specified skills. One way to arrive at some conclusion as to the number of men needed for certain operations is to make a list of the labor requirements if production were to be increased 25, 50, or 100 per cent. When these projected requirements have been listed, they can be matched against the skills of the present work force. In this way the foreman can relate the training he expects to give each worker to his expected needs. He will also be able to determine how many new men will have to be brought in at the lower skills to be trained to take the place of present employees who may be moved up when expansion of the department takes place.

It is very important for every foreman to have some fundamental training plan for his department. It is a bad mistake to wait until the actual need is on top of him. Then it is usually too late to do the kind of training job that must be done.

UPGRADING

When the supply of top-skilled workers is limited, the need for them must be filled by training the men most nearly qualified for these top-skilled jobs. Training men for higher skilled jobs is generally spoken of as upgrading.

Upgrading offers hope to workers that they will have opportunities for advancement. The worker who feels that he is on a "dead-end job" finds it difficult to maintain interest in his work. The general morale of any work force is dampened when men do not see opportunities ahead. The very fact that a foreman is interested in training men for higher skilled jobs gives them enthusiasm. It is evidence of the foreman's personal interest in them, and appreciation of this attitude on the part of the foreman will be manifested in better work and more efficient all-around performance.

TRAINING AN UNDERSTUDY

In addition to training of men in the ranks, each foreman should give careful consideration to the selection and training of one or more understudies, depending upon the size of and expansion plan for his department. Inasmuch as the selection of a man for an understudy places that man on the first rung of the ladder of supervision, it is very important that the selection be made with care.

Very often a foreman selects as his "right-hand man" some worker who has certain qualifications along mechanical lines. Too often insufficient consideration is given to the fact that eventually this man will probably step into a full-fledged supervisory job. Therefore, many of his personal qualifications should also receive consideration before he is lifted from the ranks.

Unless he has the qualities of leadership that will qualify him for later supervisory responsibility, he should not be selected as one who is likely to be in line for the foreman's job if the foreman is promoted.

In training an understudy, one of the first things to do is to give him careful coaching as a job instructor. If he can be trained to use the four basic steps of good instruction, he can be of great help to the foreman in sharing some of the training load of the department. Since instruction and supervision are so inseparable, it logically follows that the developing of instructing ability in an understudy is one of the best kinds of preparation for ultimate supervisory responsibility.

In training an understudy, the foreman should share his information with him and "let him in" on departmental plans. Foremanship problems should be placed before him to give him an opportunity to exercise his judgment and ingenuity. He should be given responsibility for certain functions in the department. He should not be pinned down to one function so closely that he does not develop the breadth of view which a supervisor should have.

Some foremen are slow to appreciate the value of training a good understudy. In some cases foremen fear that the development of a good understudy may build up a rival for their own jobs. The foreman who is qualified to hold his job, however, need have little fear of being replaced by his understudy. More often foremen lose opportunities for promotion themselves because there is no one prepared to take over their jobs.

The development of a capable understudy will release the foreman from many details and enable him to spend his time in the solution of the major problems of the department. The foreman is judged by departmental results. The stronger the organization he can develop in his department, the more successful his departmental results will be. If his department succeeds, he can hardly escape his full share of credit.

CHAPTER VIII

WHAT TO DO ABOUT SAFETY

BY ROGER WILLIAMS

In normal times the loss of productive manpower and materials is an economic hardship. In time of war or threat of war, such losses can be a matter of life and death to a nation.

The National Safety Council reports for 1953 a staggering number of accidents causing 95,000 fatalities and 9,600,000 injuries, with motor vehicles the largest single factor. The total economic cost—direct and indirect wage losses, medical and hospital, administrative and claim settlement, and property— is estimated at $9,600,000. Accidents were the leading cause of death among males between the ages of 18 and 37 years, normally the most productive and useful span of life. Of the total, work accidents caused 15,000 deaths and 2,000,000 injuries.

At the start of the Second World War, the rising national accident toll was so serious that President Roosevelt, in August, 1941, issued a proclamation calling "upon every citizen, in public and private capacity, to . . . do his part in preventing wastage of human and material resources of the nation" through a program of accident prevention. Happily, later statistics have shown that the nation did take some heed; for 1941 proved to be a peak year in industrial accidents with 1953 showing a good reduction in rates from the base average, as indicated below. Unfortunately, this improvement was offset considerably by continued high accident rates for motor vehicles.

If a worker is injured in an accident, his production is lost until he returns to his job whether the accident occurred at work or away from work. In 1953, man-days lost from accidents to workers when away from work amounted to 60,000,000, while losses from work accidents, including indirect losses, totaled 250,-000,000 man-days.

Accident-prevention work has become important in every industry, and the accident-frequency rates have been substantially reduced. In 1953, 5 of 36 industries reporting to the National Safety Council reduced frequency rates 20 per cent or more from 1952 and 13 had decreases of 10 to 20 per cent. The average decrease for the 36 industries was 11 per cent. A good accident-prevention program, consistently carried out, will yield a substantial reduction in the accident rate. This is shown by the record of the reporting industries, whose total frequency rate for 1953 was only 57 per cent of the 1935–1939 base period, and whose total severity rate was 54 per cent of the base.

Faith and confidence in the ability to reduce accidents is justified by the knowledge that many industries, such as communications, iron and steel, railroads, rubber, automotive, paper and pulp, electrical equipment, and underground coal mining, have carried out safety activities faithfully and reduced accident frequency by 40, 50, and even 70 per cent over a period of years.

Nor is the need to control accidental injuries confined to the so-called "hazardous" occupations. A large commercial organization, which has a great many office employees in addition to field representatives, reduced its occupational injuries two-thirds in

4 years by a systematic accident-prevention program, in which representatives of all departments participated.

SAFETY FOREMANSHIP UNDER STEPPED-UP PRODUCTION

The accomplishments in accident prevention have largely been the result of engineering leadership. Naturally, the foreman has had a leading part in the movement. He is the head man, the overseer, the leader in directing men. He is the one responsible for the most effective use of manpower and materials. Departmental safety records readily indicate how efficiently the foreman discharges those responsibilities.

It is difficult for the foreman to maintain good safety records under conditions of rapidly expanding production.

At such times, many new employees enter industry. The foreman cannot assume that they are qualified for a given task, regardless of their credentials. The only sure proof of qualification is a safe and efficient operation on the job.

When production is stepped up to the point where it crowds capacity, old-style machines are put into use again. Perhaps they have been stripped of important guards. They are unfit from a production or safety standpoint until they have been reconditioned, safeguarded thoroughly, and proved by tests, over an adequate period, to be wholly reliable.

Additional machinery and personnel require expert planning to assure a smooth flow of product. It is important to place both men and machines properly. Other factors such as lighting, ventilation, more frequent removal of product and debris, and sanitary facilities must be adjusted. Farsighted planning will eliminate many bottlenecks and hazards that otherwise would prove costly.

Economic and social readjustments bring worry, fear, and other distractions to workers. Such tensions are the cause of many occupational injuries. Troubles at home, other job opportunities, higher costs of living, and similar personal problems prevent the concentration and alertness demanded by the job.

Older employees try to maintain the pace and physical effort of former years. They do not realize the normal limitations which time brings to eyesight, muscles, tissues, and vital organs. Foremen must anticipate these changes and place older employees so that they may work productively but without injury. Younger employees must be trained not to sacrifice safety to speed.

Industry generally has not maintained an adequate training program for the development of new supervisors, despite the emphasis on this subject in recent years. There continues to be a serious lack of foremen qualified to train and supervise new employees. Many experienced foremen, too, have forgotten much of their earlier experiences and fail to explain fundamental facts soon enough for the benefit of the inexperienced employee. The safety-minded foreman enlists the understanding co-operation of all his employees. It may seem to take more time at the beginning than can be spared, but it will save a greater amount of his personal time in the long run by eliminating accidental stoppages in operation. Prevention is more economical than cure.

Women in Industry

Women and girl employees are somewhat more aware of the misfortune of physical handicaps such as dismemberment and disfigurement than are men and have a tendency to adopt safe practices more quickly and maintain safe work habits more permanently. Nevertheless, the absorption of women into industry creates additional problems for the male foreman. The special arrangements of sanitation and rest rooms must be planned in advance by management. Male employees should be informed and instructed as to deportment and co-operativeness with respect to the new working environment. The foreman himself must adopt an understanding patience to gain the confidence of and establish his leadership with these new employees.

Slacks have generally been found to be the most satisfactory work garments for women. They automatically remove the hazards of loose, flowing garments. A reasonable uniformity of style, material, and color also offsets most quickly the distraction effect upon male employees.

Hair nets or lightweight caps are absolutely necessary to prevent serious head injuries on machine work. The wearing of jewelry on fingers and wrists or around the neck must be strictly prohibited.

Proper footwear may cause more difficulties for the foreman. Work shoes with reinforced metal toe box are now available for feminine wear, and employees should be urged to adopt them. In any event, the foot should be enclosed completely, and low heels are equally essential. A patient explanation and demonstration should convince the new woman employee that proper footwear not only affords better protection, but reduces fatigue as well. Provision also may often be necessary for women to be seated while work-ing. This will also permit alternate foot operations.

The foreman should also anticipate the fact that women employees must not be permitted to lift or handle heavy materials. The maximum weight to be handled is frequently specified in state labor laws.

RELATED FUNDAMENTALS

Every foreman, as the representative of the em-ployer, is subject to the provisions of the labor law of his state. The basic purpose of the law is to assure the health and safety of workers by requiring minimum standards in the construction of buildings, installation and operation of machinery, and working conditions. Representatives of the administrator of the law make periodic inspections to verify compliance and can be very helpful to foremen by giving advice regarding correction of unsatisfactory conditions. In some instances, the law requires employees to use safe-guards, which it demands that the employer provide.

Nearly every state now has a workmen's com-pensation law. It provides for the payment of compensation for injuries to employees or for death of employees resulting from occupational injuries. Usually, employees or their dependents may be denied compensation only if the injury or death resulted from the willful intention of an employee or from the intoxication of the employee while on duty. The employer is required to keep a record of injuries to his employees and to report those involving medical expenses or loss of time under specified conditions. These claims are passed upon by a board or commis-sion in accordance with prescribed schedules of benefits in proportion to normal earning capacity.

The funds from which compensation benefits are paid are derived usually through insurance rates levied upon the employer's pay rolls. Insurance carriers report regularly to a designated agency the amount of pay rolls on which insurance premiums were collected and the actual or estimated cost of the injuries reported for the same period. These reports are separated according to the type of industry or operations involved. Many different operations therefore have a different insurance rate, reflecting the relative frequency and severity of occupational injuries. In addition, many employers who have a specified minimum or larger amount of annual insurance premium are compared with the over-all experience of their industry and may receive a percentage deduction or charge in relation to the industry rate. The final rates are usually issued annually and must generally be approved by the state insurance department.

From the above, the foreman will realize the economic necessity for employers to adopt a policy of accident prevention. An employer can no more afford to pay substantially more than he should for his compensation insurance than he can to pay too much for merchandise or labor. The employer who qualifies for a percentage deduction in his rate fares better in competition and is more likely to maintain steady employment.

No foreman need be apologetic or hesitant in requesting co-operation in accident prevention from employees, because it is one of the few employer-employee relationships in which there is no personal advantage for either at the expense of the other. Actually, the injured workman and his family are the principal sufferers from accidental injuries. Even the financial shock can be relieved only in part by workmen's compensation benefits. In addition, the injured employee may be barred from continuing in his occupation because he is permanently crippled or may have to forego promotion or wage increase, and he may never experience the full enjoyment of life.

In addition to the legal and humane considerations, it is a well-demonstrated fact that safe operations invite the most desirable workmen, raise the morale of employees, and create good will and public esteem.

CAUSES AND TYPES OF ACCIDENTS

Critical studies by the National Safety Council of large numbers of industrial accidents over many years have shown that more than 95 per cent are avoidable. Of these avoidable accidents, 20 per cent are the result of faulty conditions, another 20 per cent are due to faulty behavior, and 60 per cent result from a combination of these two causes. Control of environment and behavior is thus the underlying purpose of accident-prevention programs.

The "human element"—in management, foremen, and workers—has been at fault. It is impossible to install a mechanical guard on a man's actions; the guard must be created within himself, so that he will habitually think and look before acting. Only through sustained education and supervision can this "mental guard" be created and maintained. These, more than all else, can halt the widespread wake of human misery and economic waste that follows accidents.

Because a cross section of industrial accidents shows a very consistent uniformity in the relative frequency of certain types of accidents, the evidence points to consistent faults in behavior. Naturally, the relative severity varies to reflect relative hazards. For instance, a man may trip or slip on the ground and not be seriously injured by the fall. Another man, however, may trip or slip under similar circumstances on a scaffold and fall to the ground, meeting serious injury or death.

There is no certain control of the injury resulting from an accident. A heavy object may fall without striking anyone, may cause death, or may result in only minor injury, depending upon the factors of time and distance. Two persons may incur identical injuries, and yet one may recover quickly and resume work, whereas the other may suffer permanent impairment as a result of former injury, which has been aggravated, or constitutional weakness. *Therefore the emphasis must be upon the prevention of all accidents, so that there will be no injury.* The foreman should not be overconcerned with "industry averages." *His goal should be zero.*

The following discussion considers common "primary causes," as classified by the National Safety Council and widely used in analyzing accident statistics.

Handling Objects

This type of accident accounts for some 22 out of 100 average industrial accidents. The person is handling material or an object other than a tool and sustains personal injury or injures another workman. Splinter in any part of the body, strain, sprain, and hernia are typical injuries. They generally occur in the processes of sorting, piling, loading or unloading, lifting, carrying, or packing materials.

Most of these injuries can be prevented by proper instruction in correct practices. Employees must be shown how to lift safely by stooping down to grasp the object and then lifting by the use of leg muscles rather than to bend down and put all the strain upon the muscles of the back and abdomen. They must be taught to take a firm, secure grip of the object and to ask for help if it appears to be too heavy for one man. Material should be lifted—not dragged—from a pile.

a   *b*

Fig. 1.—A sprained back can easily be caused by wrong lifting. Three simple rules should be enforced by the foreman: 1, keep the back straight, at about a 60 deg. angle; 2, get down to the load by bending the knees; 3, lift slowly, evenly, using leg muscles. (*a*) Right way. The foreman should tell his employees to let leg muscles bear the strain. (*b*) Wrong way. By lifting this way, weak muscles are strained.

When long material is carried, the front end should be kept higher than the rear to avoid injuring others. Material should be so carried as to permit clear vision ahead. Gloves or hand leathers should be used to protect hands, and shoes with metal toe box should be worn to reduce the possibility of injury. The need for precautions of this sort should be obvious to the alert foreman.

Falls of Persons

A person falls and sustains injury in some 17 out of 100 average industrial accidents. The fall may be to the same level or to another level. Fractures of arm, shoulder, leg, ankle, or skull result far too frequently. The proportions of falls on the same level and to another level are nearly the same. Most of them can be prevented by the maintenance of safe equipment for working at an elevation and of secure footing under all circumstances.

Stairs which are worn or broken, without handrail, poorly lighted, or with objects piled on them are a very frequent cause of falls. Too often persons will use a poor substitute, such as a box, barrel, or chair, instead of a ladder when reaching or climbing. Then too, ladders may be weak or broken and may not be lashed or held in place while being used. Scaffolds or platforms should be so constructed as to be secure, whether they are to be used for only a few minutes or for a long period of time.

Floor or elevator openings should be guarded to prevent falls. Broken, splintered floors and those with uneven surfaces should be repaired promptly. Spillage or wastage of liquids or slippery materials should be cleaned from the floor to prevent slipping.

Adequate and orderly workplaces, well-defined passageways without interference by materials or equipment, and the elimination or clear marking of blind traffic points will remove many common hazards.

Machinery

About 16 out of each 100 average industrial accidents occur in connection with moving machinery. They do not include tools carried in the hand, such as power-driven drills, grinding wheels, riveting or welding and similar tools. In most instances they result in punctures, crushing, or severance of a body member. The continued high frequency of these accidents also indicates the human willingness to take chances, despite the serious attention which regulatory agencies have given to guarding mechanical hazards.

Guards for dangerous moving parts have by now been incorporated in the design and construction of most machinery. Where they have not, standard guards can be purchased or constructed at relatively small cost. To safeguard workers, however, the foreman must insist upon safe work habits. Guards must be in place when machinery is in operation. Power must be off when workmen clean, oil, or adjust moving parts. The common practice of stopping a moving part by hand pressure must be forbidden.

Loose clothing, such as long sleeves and neckties, jewelry on fingers or wrists, and long hair, is extremely hazardous around machinery. Distraction of many kinds can easily divert the attention of an operator or change his timing, so that an injury will occur.

The effectiveness of starting and stopping devices and of other safety devices on machines must be verified periodically. Often the employee himself puts them out of action in the mistaken belief that they interfere with production.

The attempt to operate any machine, including elevators, by anyone who has not been instructed and authorized to do so must be prohibited.

Vehicles

Although we might think of vehicular accidents as occurring only on the highway, 7 occur among the 100 average industrial accidents. Enforcement of the well-known rules for the safe operating condition of the truck or other vehicle, use of adequate warning devices, and observance of speed limitations will assure effective control of this hazard and will place proper responsibility upon the operator.

Hand Tools

Eight among each 100 average industrial accidents involve hand tools. These include all types of portable tools, whether driven by power or manually, as well as such usual equipment as hand trucks and wheelbarrows. Foreign bodies in the eye or other parts of the body are often caused by the faulty use of these tools. Injuries occur principally to the hand, face, or foot. Lacerations from knives are very common, and screw drivers, wrenches, and hammers contribute a large proportion. Too often the employee considers an injury of this type to be minor, and infection develops.

Employees should be provided with the correct tool for a specific purpose, and it should be in good condition before use. A monkey wrench is frequently used instead of a Stillson, and an improper grip results in injury to the knuckles or causes a fall. The heads of tools become mushroomed and should be dressed to prevent particles from flying. Screw drivers are often used for chisels. The edges of blades may often be faulty. Wooden handles may be splintered or cracked and may be missing entirely from files. The hammer head may be loose and fly off to injure another workman or to damage property. Sharp knives may be used without handle guard. Knuckle guards on shovels and hand trucks may be ineffective because of the incorrect position of the employee's hands.

It is especially important that the foreman insist that, after use, every tool be returned to its proper location in a safe place.

Falling Objects

Approximately 10 of 100 average industrial accidents are of this type. They include objects falling, flying, or being thrown off in various operations, or any objects not being handled which fall, tip over, shift, or move from position. Tools or material may be dislodged from a scaffold, platform, or shelf. Material may fall from a load in transit or from an improperly placed position. Rock or dirt may fall from the roof or sides of a tunnel, quarry, or other excavation. Fatalities, fractures, and suffocation are the most serious results.

Toeboards on scaffolds and platforms, adequate shoring and bracing, secure piling and support of material, careful placement of tools and material at an elevation, keeping workmen clear of material being moved over their heads, and the prohibition of undermining will prevent most of these accidents.

Men using air to clean debris from machine or workbench should be made to take care that particles are not blown onto other workmen. Naturally, when more effective prevention is not practicable, helmets should be provided whenever workmen are exposed to the hazards of objects falling from above.

Workmen should be required to wear suitable eye protection whenever flying particles cannot be controlled at the source. Too frequently a workman will dress a tool on a grinding wheel without using eye protection, because the operation is momentary. Even the smallest fraction of a minute is sufficient time for a flying particle to destroy eyesight.

Dangerous and Harmful Substances

This type of accident involves substances of an explosive, corrosive, or irritating nature; explosions from pressure; electricity; hot substances; chemicals; fumes; gases; and dusts. No recent statistics are available, but earlier estimates indicate approximately 7 out of 100 average accidents.

Worn electrical wiring, improper insulation, defective switches, and inoperative fuse plugs cause many serious injuries and fires. The improper storage and handling of explosives and inflammable materials, the nonsegregation of dangerous operations with a minimum of human exposure, and failure to control inflammable or harmful dusts, gases, and fumes at the source have caused many catastrophes. The use of protective clothing, such as noninflammable suits, gloves, boots, aprons, goggles, respirators, and protective ointments, and insistence that exposed employees thoroughly wash face, hands, and arms before eating and at the end of the day's work have reduced occupational injuries of this type.

On many kinds of work, clothing must be cleaned and changed frequently to prevent it from catching fire or causing skin irritation.

Stepping on or Striking Objects

Here the object is not one being handled at the time. Again, no recent statistics are available, but earlier estimates indicate 7 out of 100 average industrial accidents. Striking objects, such as bumping into doors, machinery, piled material, moving objects, office equipment, and overhead equipment, constitutes the majority and usually results in bruises. Stepping on objects causes more serious injury. Stepping on nails and sharp objects is likely to result in a puncture of the flesh with a greater likelihood of infection. Stepping on rough objects more frequently causes sprains, strains, and fractures.

Clear vision before stepping or moving, clean and clear passageways, good footwear with steel insoles where necessary, removal or bending over of nails, and thoughtfulness in removing dangerous objects when observed, will help control this type of accident.

The remaining average industrial accidents include many miscellaneous types. It has been effectively demonstrated that effort concentrated on the leading types of accidents will accomplish a reduction in all types. Development of a proper safety consciousness among employees makes them alert to all types of hazards.

CONTROL MEASURES

The fundamental principles of successful safety measures are the same, irrespective of the size or type of a business. There is no "magic" that will ensure results. There is no short cut. Short-lived campaigns will produce short-lived results. Effort must be unremitting and intensive. Results must be checked and rechecked.

The success of any safety program depends primarily on the safety-mindedness of the owners and executives of the company. Safety consciousness cannot be maintained in employees if they see no interest being taken in their efforts and accomplishments. Executives and foremen should demonstrate sincerity and, especially, set the proper example themselves by safe practices.

If the company employs a safety supervisor, the foreman should co-operate with him and always be ready to accept his help. In any event, the foreman should assume full responsibility for a good safety record. Efficient operation and safe operation cannot be separated.

Employee Training

No matter what selection and placement methods are employed by his company, the foreman should make it his business to find out what qualifications a new or prospective employee has for the work to be undertaken and make sure to the best of his ability that the employee is suited physically and temperamentally for the work. He should also find out what disabilities the employee may have incurred during previous employment and whether he received compensation payments for any injury. With this knowledge a foreman will not unwittingly expose a workman to hazards which may aggravate a pre-existing condition or place him at work which he cannot be expected to perform efficiently.

Even though the employee may have received general safety instructions, the foreman should instruct him in the safe methods of the specific task. He should remind him of the advantages to all concerned which are derived from accident prevention and encourage him to submit suggestions for the correction of hazards. The new employee must be watched frequently until he has demonstrated his aptitude for the work and has formed the habit of safe and efficient operation.

Older employees, too, must be reminded frequently of the fundamentals of safe performance and alertness to hazards, because they often form unsafe habits without realizing it.

Inspection

It is physically impossible for any foreman to be in enough places at appropriate times personally to verify safe conditions and behavior. He should therefore require each employee to verify the proper conditions of his workplace and of his equipment and tools before a task is begun or resumed. Furthermore, he should require each employee to maintain orderliness and to keep equipment and tools in first-class condition at all times. He must be patient, but firm and positive, in instances of noncompliance with safety regulations, just as he would be when poor workmanship is demonstrated. The foreman should also take advantage of periodic inspections by the safety supervisor, representatives of the insurance carrier, and regulatory agencies.

Accident Investigation

Every employee should be required to report to his foreman any injury, no matter how minor it may seem at the moment, so that the foreman may correct the cause to prevent recurrence, as well as make sure of necessary medical attention.

Prompt removal or guarding of hazards found by accident investigation is an urgent necessity. The foreman's responsibility does not end by requisitioning necessary action. He cannot be relieved until the correction has been made. Moreover, co-operation of employees is discouraged when practical safety suggestions are not carried out so promptly as possible.

Accident Records

Every foreman should know whether his record of occupational injuries shows progress in comparison with the previous experience of his department. It is often not fair or effective to compare one department with another, because of differences in operations and in numbers of employees working. It is immaterial whether the record be maintained at a central office for all departments or whether each foreman maintain his own record with other operating records.

Classification of the actual numbers of lost-time and minor injuries by type of accident will focus attention and corrective action upon the more urgent situations. Knowledge of the employees who have repeated injuries will stimulate closer observation of their surroundings and work methods, so that the underlying faults may be remedied. Faulty vision or other physical impairment may be suspected, and the suggested physical checkup may be had in time to prevent a serious injury and loss in the production line.

A day-to-day record to show the absence of lost-time injuries during a month or during longer periods will stimulate competitive interest among the departmental employees. Long operating periods without any lost-time injuries should be recognized, to encourage co-operation. This may be accomplished by a short talk of appreciation by the foreman and by a personal note of appreciation or other recognition by the executive in charge of all operations.

Whenever accident frequency does not decrease, the foreman and the operating executive, if necessary, should assemble employee groups on work time to explain the lack of progress and to invite open discussion of the causes and their correction.

Injury Rates

The American Standards Association has approved a standard method of compiling industrial injury rates, which affords the most reliable comparison of injury frequency and severity.

The *frequency rate* is the number of injuries per million man-hours of exposure. To obtain the frequency rate, multiply the number of injuries by 1,000,000 and divide by total work hours.

The *severity rate* is the total days lost per thousand man-hours of exposure. To obtain the severity rate multiply the days lost by 1,000 and divide by total work hours. (A fatality counts as 6,000 days lost.)

The work hours of exposure may be compiled actually from time records or estimated from the average number of employees and average hours of a work week. For example, an average of 100 employees on a 40-hour week would total 4,000 man-hours per week, or 200,000 work hours every 50 weeks. Assume too that there were three disabling injuries, which caused a combined loss equal to 180 work days during the 50 weeks.

$$f = \frac{3 \times 1,000,000}{200,000} = 15$$

This result means that the three actual disabling injuries are at the rate of 15 injuries per 1,000,000 work hours.

$$s = \frac{180 \times 1,000}{200,000} = 0.9$$

This means that nearly 1 work day has been lost from production during each 1,000 work hours.

Whenever these formulas are used, the factors should be on an accumulated basis up to 12 months, because a small total of man-hours worked, such as weekly or monthly, will distort the resulting frequency and severity rates. An accident may occur during a particular week or month, but there may not be another with loss of time for many more weeks and months.

The wide variations of injury rates of different industries reflect the relative hazards and effectiveness of accident-prevention measurers. General progress, however, is shown by the reduction in the average industrial accident-frequency and -severity rate of plants reporting to the National Safety Council alluded to at the beginning of this chapter. Injury rates of smaller employee groups are substantially higher than those with greater numbers. The best individual and industry records confirm the opinion that safety is a sign of good management.

The accompanying chart (Fig. 2) shows industry rates representative of current experience.

Safety Committees

A foreman should always be willing to serve his turn on a general or executive safety committee of the company. Brief meetings should be held at regular intervals, and minutes kept to record the subjects discussed and action taken. A small committee is more likely to reach decisions on necessary action. The accident record should be reviewed, together with the findings from accident investigations and inspections. Recommendations to management and foremen should be followed up for early completion. Programs to further the safety education of employees should be formulated by this committee.

In addition, a foreman may find it necessary or desirable to form a departmental safety committee to create greater interest and secure more energetic cooperation from his immediate employees.

1953 INJURY RATES

FREQUENCY RATE
DISABLING INJURIES
PER 1,000,000 MAN-HOURS

Industry	Rate
COMMUNICATIONS	1.22
ELECTRICAL EQUIPMENT	2.88
AUTOMOBILE	3.39
AIRCRAFT MANUFACTURING	3.58
CEMENT	3.81
STEEL	3.90
TOBACCO	4.37
CHEMICAL	4.53
RUBBER	4.61
SHIPBUILDING	5.33
TEXTILE	5.51
MISC. MANUFACTURING	6.26
STORAGE & WAREHOUSING	6.45
PRINTING & PUBLISHING	6.54
RAILROAD EQUIPMENT	6.77
MACHINERY	6.92
GLASS	6.96
SHEET METAL	7.07
ALL INDUSTRIES	7.44
SERVICE	7.75
NON-FERROUS METALS & PROD.	8.00
IRON & STEEL PRODUCTS	8.75
WHOLESALE & RETAIL TRADE	8.85
PETROLEUM	9.00
ELECTRIC UTILITIES	9.43
PULP & PAPER	9.54
MEAT PACKING	9.98
LEATHER	10.75
FOUNDRY	10.94
AIR TRANSPORT	12.80
GAS UTILITIES	12.92
FOOD	13.42
TRANSIT	13.54
CLAY PRODUCTS	13.74
QUARRY	14.93
CONSTRUCTION	15.68
WOOD PRODUCTS	17.55
MARINE TRANSPORTATION	22.15
MINING, OTHER THAN COAL	22.95
MINING, COAL	25.81
LUMBER	33.71

* FIGURES IN PARENTHESES
SHOW AVERAGE TIME
CHARGE (IN DAYS) PER CASE

• ALL RATES COMPILED
IN ACCORDANCE WITH
THE AMERICAN
STANDARD METHOD OF
COMPILING INDUSTRIAL
INJURY RATES,
CODE Z16.1-1945

SEVERITY RATE
TIME CHARGES (DAYS)
PER 1,000 MAN-HOURS

	Industry
(85)* .10	COMMUNICATIONS
(36) .17	TOBACCO
(77) .22	ELECTRICAL EQUIPMENT
(44) .27	MISC. MANUFACTURING
(44) .28	STORAGE & WAREHOUSING
(34) .30	WHOLESALE & RETAIL TRADE
(85) .30	AIRCRAFT MANUFACTURING
(25) .31	AIR TRANSPORT
(30) .32	LEATHER
(111) .38	AUTOMOBILE
(76) .42	TEXTILE
(70) .46	PRINTING & PUBLISHING
(66) .46	GLASS
(47) .47	MEAT PACKING
(107) .49	RUBBER
(70) .49	MACHINERY
(79) .61	SERVICE
(46) .62	TRANSIT
(106) .75	SHEET METAL
(86) .76	IRON & STEEL PRODUCTS
(116) .79	RAILROAD EQUIPMENT
(59) .79	FOOD
(179) .81	CHEMICAL
(111) .83	ALL INDUSTRIES
(157) .84	SHIPBUILDING
(67) .87	GAS UTILITIES
(93) .89	PULP & PAPER
(95) 1.05	FOUNDRY
(120) 1.08	PETROLEUM
(278) 1.06	STEEL
(62) 1.09	WOOD PRODUCTS
(150) 1.20	NON-FERROUS METALS & PROD.
(66) 1.46	MARINE TRANSPORATION
(110) 1.51	CLAY PRODUCTS
(157) 1.55	ELECTRIC UTILITIES
(422) 1.61	CEMENT
(131) 2.06	CONSTRUCTION
(175) 2.62	QUARRY
(137) 3.14	MINING, OTHER THAN COAL
(116) 3.90	LUMBER
(85) 4.79	MINING, COAL

FIG. 2.—Injury rates based on reports to National Safety Council.
(*From Accident Facts, 1954 ed., National Safety Council.*)

Personal Protective Equipment

The need for protective equipment was mentioned in connection with various accidents. Whenever it is needed, the foreman should set the proper example by using it himself. Also, he should be sure that suitable equipment is furnished. Manufacturers or distributors of safety equipment will usually send a representative, and appropriate samples will be made available. Whenever possible, the employees should be permitted to indicate their preference of types, since such choice is usually effective in securing co-operation.

Despite personal selection and fitting of goggles and respirators, there may be some personal discomfort in the beginning. That is natural, and the foreman should urge the employee to be patient until he becomes accustomed to it. Wearing these protectors is like adopting bifocal glasses or false teeth, which may be troublesome and uncomfortable at the start but which reward patience finally by enabling one to see more accurately and to enjoy food more thoroughly.

Provision should be made for the occasional cleaning and sterilization of goggles, respirators, and similar devices. This is necessary not only when such equipment is to be used by another, but also after it has been used steadily by the same employee.

Education

No one person or small group of persons can carry on successful safety work alone. All employees must feel that they are essential partners in the program. Educational work must be carried on continuously to make all employees safety-minded.

Safety posters and pamphlets should be displayed one at a time in suitable locations to remind all employees of the safety fundamentals they are expected to follow. When several posters are displayed together, none receives proper attention. It is effective to remove posters frequently and display them again when the accident record indicates that specific need.

Accident charts posted in suitable locations usually attract individual interest. House organs, exhibits of safety equipment which show new developments or which have effectively prevented personal injury, manuals of safe practices, and local newspaper publicity concerning progress in accident prevention are effective in maintaining interest.

Equipment for illustrated safety talks and demonstrations, speakers on appropriate topics, safety literature, and record forms are usually available through the facilities of insurance carriers. Personal representatives will spend the necessary time to assist foremen in learning the most effective method to apply control measures and further educational work.

Safety-minded persons have fewer accidents in their homes, in automobiles, and in public places; they lose less time from their work. The loss of production time which outside accidents cause should be of equal concern to foremen.

According to the records of one insurance carrier, approximately one of each eight industrial employees sustains an injury during the year, and only one of twenty employees is sufficiently injured so that he loses productive time. The injured employee is not the same person each year. Therefore training and education together with adequate supervision can be expected to help the other 19 employees to avoid an occupational injury in the future. That is the purpose of accident prevention. Accidents are the evidence of failure and therefore are the signal for prompt remedial action.

CHAPTER IX

INDUSTRIAL FATIGUE

By Howard W. Haggard, M.D.

There are a great many definitions of fatigue, and this fact in itself indicates that none is completely satisfactory. The most widely accepted definition may be stated as "Fatigue is the sum of the results of activity which appear in diminished capacity for doing work and as a feeling of tiredness; it is relieved by rest." This definition is satisfactory for our purposes here if the word "activity" is understood to include not alone the work a person is performing, but also all conditions under which he performs the work, and if the word "rest" is understood to include not only physical rest, as in stopping work, but the relief from conditions unfavorable to activity.

Defining fatigue in this way does not simplify but instead complicates the problem of industrial fatigue. However, this complication is desirable. The solution of the problem has been greatly impeded by narrow definitions based wholly upon the fatigue that occurs from violent exertion, such as everyone has experienced in running or swimming. In such exertions, energy is expended at a rate greater than the body as a whole is capable of maintaining. A man becomes progressively out of breath, the rate at which his heart beats increases until it becomes very fast, and he has more and more difficulty in moving his arms and legs. In exertion of this sort, the heart cannot pump enough blood, even when working at full capacity, to maintain an adequate supply of oxygen and nourishment for the muscles and the nervous mechanism which controls them. The ability of the muscles to carry on the work diminishes and is finally lost. During rest after the exercise, the deep breathing and rapid rate of the heart continue for a time, and then restoration to normal conditions occurs. The man then recovers from his fatigue; he is rested, although his muscles may ache for a time and he may feel tired, sleepy, and disinclined to any mental activity.

The feature which has caught attention in this familiar type of fatigue is the decreased ability to perform work. In moderate and light industrial occupations, a decreased ability to do work, seen as decreased production, may also occur. The decrease is taken to indicate fatigue, and this fatigue, by reasoning backward, is assumed to be simply a milder form of the acute variety occurring in athletes and due to the same overexpenditure of energy. In consequence, it has seemed to follow logically that the one prevention of fatigue is less work and the one cure is rest.

This erroneous view, when applied to ordinary industrial fatigue, has guided attention in the wrong direction. The facts in the matter appear to be these: (1) Ordinary industrial fatigue from light and moderate occupations does not result from overexpenditure of energy; (2) it is not centered primarily in the muscles, but in the general nervous system; (3) it is mainly psychological rather than physiological; (4) it is an expression of the man's unfavorable reaction to all conditions surrounding his activities; (5) rest is not necessarily a cure, and diminished work is not necessarily a prevention.

There is no evidence that industrial fatigue from moderate and light occupations is due to the gradual accumulation of waste products or poisons from the exercising muscles. It is certainly not due to the expenditure of energy at a greater rate than the body's capabilities. Instead, it may be considered as a physical, nervous, and mental reaction of the man as a whole to the *total* of the strains put upon him by all unfavorable factors—physical, physiological, and psychological—in and surrounding his activities. Although attention has been mainly directed to the work performed, the work is only one of the strains.

It would help in obtaining a truer conception of industrial fatigue if the word "fatigue" were limited to the condition resulting from violent exertion and some other term such as "impairment of productivity" were applied to the so-called "fatigue" resulting from light or moderate industrial occupations. Such a term would help to direct attention away from the idea of fatigue as something occurring as the result of overexpenditure of energy.

WORK AND REST

The various activities of the body are carried out by the energy liberated from the foods that are eaten and stored in the body and continually brought to the active tissues by the circulating blood. The liberation of energy takes place in chemical reactions, which are ultimately in the nature of an oxidation; the food is oxidized, or burned, by the oxygen taken in through the lungs and carried to the tissues by the blood. The liberation of energy takes place in the tissues at a time when and a place where it is needed, and the liberation is under the control of the nervous system. Most of the energy liberated is in the form of heat; the muscles are the only tissues capable of liberating energy as movement. If the contraction of the muscles results in a movement against resistance, as in lifting a weight, work is done in the engineering sense of the term. But the same amount of energy may be liberated even when no "work" is done, as when the force of the muscle is insufficient to overcome the resistance and the effort results in straining. This is called "static effort." Only a portion of the energy liberated in the muscle can be used to perform work or to make static effort; three-fourths or more of the energy, depending upon the efficiency of the particular muscles, appears as heat. It is this heat which causes the sensation of warmth during vigorous exercise.

The term "rest" is commonly used to mean the opposite of work. But in reality, the body, including the muscles, is never at rest and never ceases to work so long as it is alive. The heart continues to beat, the muscles of the chest continue to move, and various organs carry out activities necessary to the maintenance of life. In addition, the muscles attached to bones, as in the legs and arms, are continually making a static effort. These muscles are arranged in pairs, or groups of pairs, one of which moves a bone in one direction about a joint and the other in the opposite direction. Thus the biceps muscle on the upper side of the arm pulls up the forearm, and the triceps beneath the arm pulls it back again. When the arm is at rest, both muscles pull gently and evenly and hence pull against each other. This pull is known as "tonus." In cold surroundings, tonus may be greatly increased and the arm become stiff from the heightened pull of the muscles; as the muscles "warm up" with exercise, the arms become limber as the tonus decreases. Likewise, tonus is increased by emotional conditions and by concentration of attention; a man can become rigid with fear and tense with concentration. The important feature here is that even at rest the muscles are continually doing "work"; they are simply doing less than when they are exercised.

The amount of energy liberated during rest, as in bed, from the various basic activities described above varies with the size of the individual, but for a man of average size it is about 80 cal. per hour. (One calorie is approximately 4 B.t.u.; in physiology both heat and work are ordinarily measured as calories.) In the most violent exertion a man can perform, even for a few minutes, as in a rapid sprint, the rate may rise to thirty or fifty times that of the resting rate. Nearly all this energy is liberated in the muscles and at a far greater rate than the body is capable of maintaining for more than a short time. From this type of exertion, as was pointed out, physical fatigue results.

In vigorous manual work which can be continued for 8 hours a day, as in the heavier jobs in farming, mining, etc., the average rate of energy expenditure may vary between four and eight times that of resting. Taking 80 cal. an hour as the resting rate, the rates of energy expenditure for heavy work would then range between 320 and 640 cal. per hour, or expenditures of 2,560 and 5,120 cal. respectively during 8 hours. In the remaining 16 hours in the 24 the man would expend, on the average, some 1,600 additional cal., thus bringing the total daily expenditures in round numbers to 4,200 and 6,700 cal. The latter figure approaches the limit of the ability of a man of average size to eat and digest enough food to supply this much energy. If these limits of eating and digestion are exceeded, the man will gradually and continuously lose weight.

In doing heavy manual work, as described here, the rates of the heart beat and of breathing are increased. However, if the man is in good physical condition, both rates, after a few minutes of the work, reach steady states well below their maxima.   There is no strain upon the circulation of blood or upon breathing, and any symptoms of fatigue which develop cannot be attributed to the high rate of energy expenditure, as in the violent exertion of running or swimming.

In light and moderate industrial occupations, the rate of energy expenditure is less than three times the resting rate.   In an occupation such as typewriting, the total energy expenditure may be only 50 per cent more than that of resting.   Often in the "rest" period intended to relieve the feeling of fatigue from such occupations, the activity of the worker is actually considerably increased by walking about.   Often, too, after a day spent working, the factory employee may expend a greater total amount of energy in gardening, athletics, or dancing.   Obviously, in light and moderate industrial occupations there is little strain on the circulation of the blood and the other general functions intimately concerned in the expenditure of energy. The work done by the muscles is such as could be continued for a virtually indefinite period without the development of unfavorable changes in the muscles. In spite of these facts, several hours at a continuous light or moderate occupation are followed by a feeling of tiredness and an impairment in productivity—the symptoms of fatigue.

Such fatigue results from the sum total of what has here been called "strain."   The principal strains from light and moderate industrial occupations lie primarily in their continuity. They are tiresome, just as listening to a serious lecture several hours long is tiresome to the listeners, even though they are sitting in chairs and doing no "work." This feeling comes from the effort to maintain continued attention and is a form of boredom.

The nervous system, including the brain, regulates all bodily conditions and influences all feelings; it, in turn, is influenced by all conditions in the body. Persistent strain put on any function may influence the whole nervous system and radiate its effect to every part of the body. A familiar example of this is eyestrain; the eye is a small organ, and its internal muscles are minute; but persistent strain on this single organ may lead to such remote effects as irritability of disposition, a feeling of tiredness, and headache. Again, the act of standing erect requires only about a 25 per cent greater expenditure of energy than rest, but it soon becomes very tiring. The muscles holding the body erect work at a disadvantage, and the circulation of blood to them is poor when there is no movement. The strain may produce severe tiredness and even pain in the legs, but in spite of these sensations the muscles can move and do work, and the movement actually brings relief from the feeling of fatigue.

Relief from the fatigue of continued strain can often be best obtained not by rest, but by changing the nature of the task performed. Fatigue from one light task influences the fatigue from another only to the extent in which the tasks are similar. If they are actually different, the change of work is beneficial. Varied work can be continued without tiredness for a much longer working day than can a single variety of work. It is one of the misfortunes of the modern factory system that a wide variety of tasks for each worker is rarely possible.

A repetitive act which requires continued concentration of attention and which at first leads to fatigue may, with practice, become so nearly automatic as to require only occasional attention and permit conversation and pleasant social relations. The task then largely ceases to cause fatigue.

SUSCEPTIBILITY TO FATIGUE

Fatigue is always the product of two factors: (1) the strains which tend to cause fatigue and (2) the susceptibility to strain. Susceptibility varies from man to man, and in each individual from day to day. It is influenced by the constitution of the individual, that is, his physical strength and health and his psychological stability. Poor physical condition, as from ill-health, inadequate diet, or chronic infection, in itself constitutes a strain, which is added to those from the occupation; it increases the intensity of the total strain and hence the susceptibility to fatigue.

Diet especially is a point which deserves greater attention in industry than it now receives. Inadequacy of diet, particularly of protective foods such as vitamins, is said to be widespread among industrial workers. Such inadequacies may be a cause of tiredness, inattention, and lack of vigor and well-being.

The psychological make-up of the individual, his personality, and his temperament are also important factors in determining the extent to which the nature of a given strain will affect him. A man who is "easy going" may be little affected by certain strains which, on the contrary, may strongly affect and greatly add to the tiredness of a man who is by temperament excitable, anxious, or irritable. In considering the likelihood of any occupation as a cause of fatigue, attention must be given to the susceptibility of individuals engaged in it. Much can be done to avoid unnecessary fatigue by the careful selection of men for different sorts of occupations.

In athletics and in military activities, the importance of selection and training in reducing susceptibility to fatigue is well recognized. This selection and training do not by any means consist entirely of developing more powerful muscles or greater capacity of the heart. They consist, first, in excluding from active participation those individuals who are definitely unsuited, physically or psychologically, for the work to be performed and, second, in conditioning the total physical and psychological qualities of the men selected to the occupations which they are to perform. The men are kept in as good health as possible; their diet is designed to supply all the essentials of good nutrition; they are practiced at their occupations until they are almost automatic in their skill in the procedures which they carry out; they develop a sense of co-operation and group integration; they are rewarded for achievement; their officers carry the major responsibilities; and every effort is made to maintain confidence and high morale. The benefit from proper training of this sort is a marked decrease in susceptibility to fatigue. Obviously all these conditions cannot be fulfilled in industry, nor would it be desirable to do so.

PHYSICAL SOURCES OF STRAIN

In heavy manual occupations, the influence of physical strains, other than those of the work performed, on the development of fatigue can often be clearly seen. In hot surroundings, men tire more quickly than in cool surroundings. The dissipation of the heat produced by the exertion places an added burden upon all activities, and there is a disinclination to work. The strain of hot surroundings is not limited to those men doing heavy work, although it is most evident in their activities; it also affects sedentary workers. For them, cold surroundings may also increase fatigue because of the strain and discomfort of such conditions and the stiffness of the tensed muscles. The minimum strain from temperature is experienced when the air is adjusted to the degree of physical activity so as to permit free operation of the body. Movement of the air is desirable, since this has a bracing and stimulating influence on all activities.

Connected with the dissipation of heat under hot surroundings is the excessive loss of salt in sweat. Salt is necessary to the normal operation of the body; when the amount in the body becomes deficient, there is increased susceptibility to fatigue and even cramps in the muscles and stomach. When a man loses more than 3 quarts of water by sweat in a day— and he can easily do so in performing heavy work under hot surroundings—the amount of salt carried away may not be replaced by ordinary amounts taken in the diet. To help prevent this condition, it is advisable to administer salt either in the drinking water or as salt tablets.

Inadequate or improper lighting in the factory or office may add appreciably to susceptibility to fatigue. Eyestrain from insufficient light, from glare, and from moving shadows may definitely contribute to the strains which cause fatigue. The awkward and strained position which the worker may be forced to take to avoid indirect glare may cause a muscle strain which contributes to the fatigue. This same feature may also develop if the arrangement of the work, and of levers or treadles on the machines, are not advantageously placed, or if the benches and seats are improperly designed so that it is necessary for the worker to hold his body in a strained position.

If work can be performed with a natural rhythm of the body, this assists in decreasing the strains which contribute to fatigue. In occupations which permit it, music has been used advantageously to set the rhythm of work and avoid the strain of initiating and maintaining this rhythm. The assistance of this stimulation to rhythm is clearly seen in dancing with and without music.

PSYCHOLOGICAL AND SOCIOLOGICAL STRAINS

Any psychological or sociological factor which is unfavorable and unpleasant, particularly if it disturbs the emotions and arouses anxiety, may be considered as a strain which contributes to fatigue. Many such factors lie beyond the factory and are centered in the home and social life of the individual and in family and financial troubles. Although these are beyond the direct scope of managerial control, any procedure which tends to lessen them contributes correspondingly to relief from fatigue.

Insecurity, frustration, pressure, and lack of adjustment to the particular job are strains which may increase fatigue. One such feature in particular is ill chosen and unsuited supervisors whom the employees do not like or respect and who create irritation and a sense of injustice. In the same class are policies of management which create similar unfavorable impressions and give rise to discontent. Similarly, an attempt to alter a habitual rate of production by penalties may lead to increase of fatigue, even though the speed-up of the physical work might not, in itself, do so.

On the other hand, any favorable attention by management which gains the approval and co-operation of the employees adds an incentive to work and relieves fatigue. In fact, it has been shown that almost anything management does that attracts the favorable interest of the workers or indicates interest in their welfare may be followed by improved productivity without increasing fatigue. It is psychological features such as these that make it extremely difficult to evaluate the specific benefit of any measure which is applied with the intention of increasing production. It is always uncertain whether improvement follows from the measure itself or from the interest created.

REST AND RECUPERATION

In very heavy work in which actual physical fatigue develops, periods of rest may be necessary to allow for recuperation from the physical strain. The worker himself is rarely the best judge of the most advantageous distributions of work and rest, and usually they can be determined only by trial. In moderate and light exertion, rest periods are not needed for physical recuperation, but they may be needed to relieve the continuity of strain. Again, the actual time of rest and the frequency of rest periods cannot be set by some theoretical formula.

An important feature is the attitude of the employee toward the rest periods. If they are desired, and particularly if they are looked forward to as pleasant and social breaks in the routine of the day, they are undoubtedly beneficial. They become especially so if opportunity is given to eat some food during such periods. The pause may give considerable relief from the feeling of fatigue, but there is no direct relation between this relief and the output after a rest period. If rest periods are given, they should be continued on an established and enforced plan of regularity.

During long periods of work, rests are usually taken, whether approved or not. It has been found, however, that approved rest periods have a far greater recuperative effect than do those taken without permission. It has also been shown that rests due to breakdowns of machinery or an inadequate rate of supply are less valuable than voluntary rests.

All these factors indicate that psychological rather than physical factors are predominant in the benefits from rest periods. Habits of work in relation to rest periods are rapidly acquired, and breaks in the habit have an adverse reaction. The time off for luncheon may be considered as a rest period and is often unnecessarily long, particularly if food is taken during a midmorning period, and hence a smaller lunch is eaten than if no food were taken earlier.

FATIGUE, ACCIDENTS, AND SPOILAGE

One of the first signs of developing fatigue is a decrease in the alertness of the worker. Attention becomes more and more restricted to the immediate occupation, and there is decreased speed of response to situations in the surroundings. The attention, although restricted to the work, is not so alert as in the period before the beginning of the development of the fatigue. The result of these changes may appear first not as a decrease in the quantity of work produced, but as an increase in errors and spoilage and also in an increase in accidents.

ACCUMULATIVE FATIGUE AND STALENESS

The length of time required for recuperation after a day's work has never been definitely determined, and likewise the nature of the changes occurring during recuperation has never been established. This fact is not surprising, since in all man's experience no certain explanation has ever been given for the need of daily sleep or of the recuperative changes occurring during sleep. However, no one will deny the need for sleep.

One of the important questions in respect to fatigue is the length of time that one sort of employment can be continued daily, and for how many days, without accumulative effects developing. The answers that can be given to these questions are only those gained from experience. A man may work 8 hours a day in a factory and then put in 3 or 4 hours of even more strenuous work doing home gardening or carpentry, as well as devoting his Saturday afternoons and Sundays to these or other occupations, and return to the factory rested and refreshed each morning of the working days. If, however, his factory workdays are increased to 7 a week and 12 hours a day—the same total hours as his factory and diversified work before the change—he will usually show definite impairment of his productivity, of his attitude, and eventually also of his health.

The reason would appear to lie in the continuity of one type of work rather than in work in general. Where work is highly diversified—as it rarely is in the modern factory—it is probable that with suitable incentive the working period could be greatly increased without the development of accumulative fatigue. It is possible also that an additional factor is operative:

The occupations carried after factory hours not only give diversity but they are also usually self-supervised and voluntary and interesting—all features that have important psychological advantages. Men may work long hours and with great vigor at occupations which interest them and in which they can take pride in the success of their accomplishments, without suffering from ill-health. They may become despondent and develop ill-health, however, when interest is lost in the work or they become frustrated from their lack of success.

CHAPTER X

SPECIAL PROBLEMS IN SUPERVISING WOMEN

By Lydia G. Giberson, M.D.

To do his job well, the foreman must be able to project himself into the worker's position, feel with that worker the difficulties of the job, both mental and emotional, and determine just what direction and instruction are necessary. He must see and feel with the workman and yet retain his dignity and authority as a foreman.

These responsibilities of foremanship do not change when the employee is a woman. The foreman's objectives remain the same, even though some of the factors in his problem differ vitally. A few of those differences follow:

1. The skill of the woman worker, while possibly comparable to that of a male worker, is not backed up as his is by years of varied industrial experience and know-how; she has no comparable "language."
2. The physical endurance of women, comparable to and in some ways superior to that of men, exhausts itself in a different manner, renews itself more readily, and requires a different kind of working rhythm.
3. A woman has a tendency, not altogether regrettable, to live her full life wherever she happens to be. If she could bring her children to work with her, she probably would be completely happy! Normally, she is unwilling to pare herself down to one aspect, the way the male worker automatically does when he enters a factory.
4. The foreman, while perhaps an excellent judge of men, may forget a great deal of his judgment when dealing with women. He may be hampered:

    a. By a false conception of women's being somehow "different" and, in the struggle for a living, obscurely "inferior."

    b. By a failure to hold women to a reasonable approximation of the standards set by male employees.

    c. By sheer ignorance of the few health- and morale-maintenance problems which differentiate women from men employees.

5. New industrial-group problems arise where large numbers of women are employed:

    a. The husband-wife units employed by the same company, especially when the wife's earnings are higher.

    b. The all-female working group, with its excess of emotion and sharp rivalries much more intense than those of all-male groups.

    c. Double promotion and pay standards, one for men, another for women.

The simplification of machine design for operation by women and other newly trained employees has progressed rapidly. While this has simplified the training problem, it has sometimes created a corresponding increase in machine operators and a heavier demand on the foreman's ability to keep a unified production schedule working smoothly.

There is also a further complication of the apprentice system and a further extension of "in-plant" training to include new women employees and thus a much heavier drain on the teaching capacity of the industrial foreman.

THE ROLE OF WOMEN IN INDUSTRY

The role of American women in our industrial civilization was until recently a relatively minor one, but the Second World War brought the realization that women may be an essential source of supply for skilled and unskilled labor. When a great expansion of new and old industries coincided with the formation of a

10,000,000-unit armed force, new and untapped sources of industrial labor had to be found. Oldsters were called back to work, but the main source necessarily had to be women.

British aircraft plants operated efficiently with women making up nearly 50 per cent of the personnel, and the drain on manpower in Germany and Russia placed great numbers of women in low- and high-level industrial positions. Women thus proved that they could perform jobs that were once reserved for men and perform them soberly and competently under the most trying conditions.

Even more important than the huge numbers involved was the character of the women coming into American industry. These new workers were quite different from the women employed in Russia, England, and Germany. They were the products of different social surroundings and social habits. They were not "lower class" working women. They were definitely American middle class, and they entered industry by request. They brought with them the standards and independence of action which marked their activities in previous years outside that sphere.

This entry of millions of middle-class American women into industry effected widespread and *permanent* changes—for many changes remained as they did after the First World War. There were permanent effects from the replacement outside industry, too. The feminine streetcar conductors, taxicab drivers, service-station attendants, etc., raised the tone of these occupations and shut off some employment of marginal male labor.

The nature of the changes in industry itself reflected two forces: first, the middle-class character of the women themselves and, second, the skill of the industrial foreman in working out the human problems involved. It would seem logical, then, that the supervision of women in industry should not be rigidly based on personnel practice that originated in conditions prior to the Second World War.

SUPERVISORY PROBLEMS

With great numbers of women engaging in industry, the development of female supervisors of women workers seems inevitable. However, for the present and for the immediate future, the male supervisor has decided advantages in technical efficiency and control of general shop conditions.

Though there is considerable debate on the point, women workers are probably more efficient under male supervision. The authority which the foreman represents is less open to unfavorable comparisons. The distance between the two sexes helps to maintain discipline. There are apt to be fewer cliques. Favoritism is more easily found out than in female supervision of an all-female group. And even if these matters are disregarded, women in general have not yet given proof that they are willing to assume the heavy responsibility and long hard hours which most foremanship entails. Yet, if the American woman is at all comparable with English and Russian women, she will also emerge as a competent, hard-headed worker capable of filling almost any industrial post.

Perhaps the most immediately helpful approach for the present male foreman to take toward the problem of mass female employment in industry is to carry over to this problem the kind of thinking he has been doing with respect to new employees in general. Most foremen have received training in dealing with new and green employees. The woman new to industry is a very green employee indeed. She has not had even the training in mechanical dexterity which every American boy goes through in his teen-age years of tinkering in school and out. Her schooling, habits, and frame of mind have been far distant from the industrial facts of sweat and grease and concentrated attention on a mechanical process. Quite obviously she has some difficult adjustments to make, and she will need plenty of time to make them in.

It is fairly clear that she should have an induction and training period of great care and considerable length. She needs adjustment to the industrial climate. Women should receive specially adjusted lectures on fatigue, personal hygiene, safety, production theory, and other topics. They should have supervised machine instruction and the instruction kept alive and stepped up by, perhaps, some version of the flying squadron used so effectively in the rubber industry. During the middle section of the training period the new women should be assigned as helpers to older workers, who would act as tutors. Minor stockroom and clean-up duties would absorb some of their time until they were assigned to specific machines. In the later stages of their training, they might profitably be used as relief workers for the short periods when trained workers must be away from their machines. In any case, extended time is essential; women workers need to grow into the shop climate.

The foreman should remember that what is commonplace to the industrial male is quite often stirring, strange, and daring to the new industrial woman. The noise, the huge machinery, the great dimensions, the impersonal activity, the long hours of disciplined action, the startling new idea (to most women) that one is to be judged by what she does and not by who she is or how she looks—these are some of the things which are vastly disturbing until the new woman employee learns to fit herself into her job. She rebels instinctively at the impersonality and the lack of privacy.

The point should be made here that women who have worked in industry before coming into a particular department are not likely to cause much new trouble to the supervisor. The real problems are those who go from their homes to the factory for the first time. That is a difficult transition: the "boss" of a household must change into a disciplined member of an industrial group!

PHYSICAL FACTORS

Once thoroughly established on the job, the female worker presents only a few practical problems, solutions of which must be worked into present good shop practice. There are first the matters of physical strength and endurance. Other factors being equal, the degree of these two in women is more apt to be underestimated than not. The healthy, mature female is a superbly equipped specimen, strong and resilient—full of "bounce." Given a chance to adjust herself to the new demands, she can expend without harm as much energy as the male worker, though at a slower rate and with more frequent rest periods. The energy potentials of both are not dissimilar. The male is more explosive; he can summon greater strength for a short period. But the healthy female has great reserves of endurance and recovers very rapidly from fatigue; the fact that she is more subject to worry and other emotional drains on her energy obscures but does not alter these physiological generalizations.

This reserve of strength is not present, naturally, in immature women or in those who are "run down." Nor will the generalizations apply to healthy women who adhere to a fashionable semistarvation while attempting physical labor. The presence of such physical subnormals involves a revision of selection procedure, job placement, and educational programs in physical hygiene.

Wherever women are now employed in industry, care is very sensibly taken that the heavier lifting and handling are performed by men. Chain hoists are provided and proper worktable levels set. Tensions on controls and foot levers are adjusted, lighter weight tools have been designed, and chairs, stools, and hand rests are more in evidence. There is better housekeeping and more efficient waste disposal. It has been realized, too, that lighting, ventilation, and noise reduction are closely connected with working efficiency. Of course, these improvements represent merely a hastening of advances already under way for male employees.

Frequent rest periods increase women workers' efficiency. Perhaps the best form for these is to have alternates, or relief workers, who can step to the machine for 5 or 10 minutes while the permanent operator takes a breathing spell. The more advanced apprentices could be used for this purpose. In addition to this feature, common practice has tended toward adoption of a 10-minute stoppage in the middle of each work period, that is, in the periods before and after lunch. It is being more generally admitted that the nonstop, no-lunch shift of 7 to 8 hours is unwieldy and inefficient, especially in view of the unofficial and often unconscious rest periods taken by the worker. Rest from fatigue is inevitable; it is either involuntary or supervised. By supervision it can be allotted and controlled.

Closely allied to these matters of endurance and recuperation are the necessary medical and safety precautions. Medically, the woman in industry presents new problems only for two reasons: periodic illness and a habitual neglect of her health. Her apparently greater sensitivity to fatigue, worry, and emotional upsets is due largely to these two factors, though often enough she gives the conventional female response to a situation because such is expected of her.

Most women eat poorly and ill advisedly; it is something of a medical contradiction to see a strapping female nibbling daintily at a lettuce and banana salad. An underfed, unsatisfied body feeds on itself, with a correspondingly lowered resistance to "nerves" and fatigue. In such a condition women are more apt than men to rely upon patent medicines for physical relief, and that is a dangerous thing. Unusual strains on their energies and undue usage of drugs go hand in hand—and form a vicious circle. The plant nurse or physician ought to warn women employees away from laxatives, headache powders, sleeping mixtures, and "cold tablets" which have not been specifically prescribed by a physician. In most cases where self-medication is resorted to, a hot bath and rest would have met all requirements, and recurrence could be prevented by continued rest and proper food.

Vitamin and mineral deficiencies are quite common among women; the conditions they induce are readily diagnosed and corrected. But let the plant doctor do it! A physical examination is indicated at the first sign of malnutrition, excessive fatigue, or undue nervousness.

In plants where it is humanly possible to do so, a canteen or lunchroom service ought to be inaugurated, and on a scale sufficient for the purpose.

The American Medical Association's Council on Foods and Nutrition has declared that what working-men need (and what working women need) are nour-ishing, vitamin-rich snacks between meals to still hunger pangs, keep up their blood-sugar level, and provide energy:

1. Since meals in company cafeterias are often inadequate in vitamins, these should be planned by dietitians.

2. Workers who need extra energy should be served "Oslo meals" in midmorning and afternoon. Origi-nally given to Norwegian school children, Oslo meals (also used in British factories) consist of whole-meal bread, cheese, half an orange, half an apple, a raw carrot, a little less than a pint of milk.

At first sight these suggestions may seem ambitious. However, there is little doubt that over-all and long-term efficiency in industry would be increased by the introduction of proper rest periods and a better use of our superabundant food resources. Certainly, women will need some such help if they are to be really effec-tive in industry.

SAFETY

When considering the safety of his women employ-ees, the foreman will find that most of his problems will come under one of these three headings: (1) ignorance and inexperience, (2) unsafe clothing and unmodified machine design, and (3) momentary illness of periodic, early pregnancy, and fatigue origin.

The first of these, inexperience and ignorance, can be guarded against readily through organized instruction, safety education, and continuous inspection. The effort is bound to be trying to the foreman, for he will feel that he is writing his rules on water. Women new to industry just do not take in quickly the dangerous results of inattention and carelessness, and the foreman will have to draw heavily upon the experience he has had fighting the male die-hards of the old school who pooh-poohed the modern safety campaigns and who were so difficult to train in safe practices.

There is one consolation, however; women will accept a conventional way of doing things and adhere to it rigidly. The delegation of inspection and safety instruction to a few older women in the shop may do much to make the program acceptable.

In the matter of unsafe clothing, the foreman will immediately run into the tangled problem of womanly vanity; he would do best to sidestep it if he can. Some uniformity of dress should be established, to include, if possible, the wearing of slacks. Dangling jewelry and adornments should be forbidden, and loose, full-cut sleeves should be frowned upon. Those women with long hair should be required to wear caps or strong hair nets. It is perhaps too much to expect most women to wear the ugly "safety shoe," but the supervisor can insist upon stout, low-heeled oxfords and place a ban on all open-work shoes. The habit of stuffing handkerchiefs up the sleeve of a dress should be discouraged, and the use of vanity cases restricted to the dressing rooms. Most of the reluctance toward wearing proper clothing will vanish if management will provide attractive lockers and rest rooms where the women can change comfortably into their street clothes; if they can do that they will not care unduly how unfeminine they look while working in the shop.

War industries employing women performed a pioneering job in evolving a type of attire which protected the girls from industrial accidents and de-emphasized their biological allure without sacrificing feminine charm entirely. Conventional working clothes fell far short of the ideal. Patch pockets, flaring trouser legs, belts, and wide sleeves were grave accident hazards; tight sweaters, snug slacks, and feminine artifices of color and style were distracting influences involving equal hazards to the men.

An example of what is possible to overcome problems of this sort was furnished by the Allis-Chalmers industrial-relations department. It developed suits to fit the wishes of the girls and the special needs of their various jobs. Slacks, worn with back-closing safety shirt, were designed with trim waist-line pleats for hip fullness, rear pockets, and jersey tuck-in. Coveralls were created with action back, inserted belt, fly-front closing, short sleeves, hip pockets, and tapered trouser legs. The girls were also persuaded to wear an elastic-back safety cap, safety goggles, and safety-toe shoes.

Monsanto Chemical Company solved the charm-vs.-safety problem by providing cap-blouse-slacks outfits in three color selections—white for laboratory workers, blue for mechanical, and khaki for operating departments. Piping on collars and cuffs added the feminine touch.

The modification of machine design is not directly within the foreman's province, but, as noted before, there are many things he can do to make the work safer and less fatiguing. Wooden platforms for women of short stature will bring the controls within easier reach, and extensions of levers will reduce the manual effort necessary to move them. Safety guards can be readjusted, and illumination sources lowered. Wastage and debris can be kept cleared away, and the electrical switches and wiring either locked or tightly covered over. An active foreman will think of these and a dozen more.

In the dangers rising from momentary illness, the foreman must depend upon the medical staff, that is, if he has one. If the working force is trained to alertness in detecting fatigue in themselves and in others, there will be few accidents from this source. In the fortunate shop which has relief workers and rest periods, they are not apt to occur at all. It is perhaps best to caution the foreman against a too ready suspicion of malingering, or "soldiering." It is a relatively rare thing. The medical department and especially the other women employees will keep a sharp check on it. A momentary faintness is not unusual even among healthy women, and usually it is not at all serious. Here, again, the answer is a convenient and attractive rest room where, given the female's marvelous ability to recover quickly, 10 minutes and a cup of tea or coffee will produce a thoroughly rested and competent employee.

In general, statistics show that trained women employees are very little more susceptible to industrial accidents than are male employees. If the necessary changes in routine and procedure are made, and if educational steps are taken, the women workers will not constitute a threat to the foreman's safety record.

EMOTIONAL FACTORS

Problems of morale affecting women industrial workers are so numerous that the foreman will be called upon for considerable ingenuity and even more considerable humanity. He will find that many of the problems of the local community have moved right in on his shop floor. Getting and keeping a husband, for instance, is still the prime business of women; no industrial supervision will stop it. Although the changed economic status of women has lessened their need to marry for a living, the institution of marriage is a rather durable thing and not apt to be replaced or discontinued. Women, as usual, will seek out husbands while giving the illusion of doing just the opposite. And, if the woman is unhappy in industry, she will escape through marriage, the method she knows best.

All this is understandable and even admirable, but it does bring the supervisor a set of behavior problems for which he must work out his own solutions. The foreman, presumably, is not a moralist, but efficiency demands that sex be removed from the working area. Flirtation and familiarity in mixed groups cannot be tolerated, and even respectable courtship cannot be indulged in on company time. Even mild exhibitionism should be repressed immediately. An absolute ban must be placed on alcohol.

Most of these behavior difficulties will disappear if an interesting recreational program is organized. In a social gathering each person has a name and a responsibility and cannot risk group disapproval. Perhaps a very simple minimum code of social behavior could be worked out and included in the instruction courses for new workers and in the rule books of each employee organization. The women themselves would then enforce it.

A word must be said of the foreman's own attitude. Familiarity with women employees is likely to be a costly affair for the male supervisor. He should maintain at all times the dignity of his authority; it is his retreat from and protection from loose emotion. If he is the only male present, he becomes the focal point of a great deal of feeling. The foreman can be friendly; he can be helpful; he can even be cordial. But he cannot be familiar and still control his group. He need use his authority quietly and only as a last resource, but that authority must be definite, clear, and sharp.

Behavior has its medical aspects too. In the last analysis good shop morale is dependent upon good mental and emotional health; normal behavior cannot be expected from sick people. There are always a few mentally ill persons in every large group, a considerably larger number of people whose thinking and emotions are out of balance because of physical disease, and a great number of people whose emotions are temporarily upset.

One must also remember that mental and emotional tension fluctuates in any one individual; there are pretty well marked stress periods in which he is not "himself." Shock, the age of thirty, the fifth year of employment, the male and female "change of life," or menopause, anxiety, sudden fear, and grief—these are a few. The important thing for the foreman to recognize is that such periods are possible, probable, natural, and temporary, and that he should avoid giving the impression of harshness which might be the last straw necessary to "break" a personality into active and dangerous illness.

When external strain is added to internal stress, the two may add up to an explosion. It is always surprising to a nonmedical person what disastrous results can come from apparently trivial causes. An ounce of sympathetic understanding before the "break" can do more good for the employee and the industry than tons of medicine, doctors, and labor committees can do afterward. Impersonality is probably the cardinal sin in dealing with human beings. Men and women are not machines; they are susceptible to shock, to fear, and to emotional crises of age and development. Brutality or callousness during any one of these states may cause permanent injury. Clear cases of shock, uncharacteristic mental vagueness, and repeated near accidents should be referred immediately to the medical department, and in any case the employee should be excused temporarily from active duty. All this applies equally to men and women employees. The women do not constitute a special problem, and if cases of this sort are more frequent among that group, it is chiefly due to their lack of industrial experience and neglect of their physical health.

Women new to industry will be slow to learn that they have added something more than a new feather to their caps. It will take some time for them to realize that they have entered into a new phase of living, with corresponding radical changes in their personal and family lives. It is a basic point that industrial work must not be considered by either the foreman or the woman worker as merely something tacked on to an existing pattern of living. It is an extremely bad attitude in general just to add an industrial job to an already full life; the woman must be ready to give up knowingly some of her duties and privileges in order to compensate for her added activities.

It is almost impossible to be a competent housewife and a competent industrial worker too. A woman can rarely be successful in both at the same time; she must skimp one way or the other, and the very act of skimping is bad physically and mentally. Transportation difficulties, shopping problems, care and training of children, sewing repairs, laundering, preparation of food, house cleaning, arrangements for rent, bills, and installments, care of sick and aged relatives—these are some of the things which take too much energy from the industrial woman worker. Obviously there is a need for co-operation and aid from those within the family and from outside social groups. There is not much the foreman can do about all this, except in extreme cases, to make clear to the employee that she must choose between working in industry and working at home.

DISCRIMINATION

One of the sorest points with women employees has been, and probably will continue to be, the discrimination against them in wage scale and in opportunity for advancement. War conditions sharpened the resentment, for women filled many previously held male positions at less than male pay.

The national demand for trained workers in the last few decades opened up many opportunities for advanced training for women both inside and outside the plant, including government-supervised courses, colleges, and private technical schools. The training ranges from light assembly through toolmaking to technical engineering and production management. Apparently the question of women's technical equality has just about been settled. Russia has women engineers, machine designers, production experts, toolmakers, airplane mechanics, and shop-maintenance crews; and in dozens of other classifications women contribute a sizable portion of that country's actual and reserve industrial (and therefore military) strength. Soon it will be commonplace for the industrial foreman to extend his function of picking likely material for advanced training to include women as well as men. He will put such women employees in contact with the proper training facilities and keep an open mind about the results.

POINTS IN SUMMARY

The foregoing pages have presented some of the trends affecting women workers. How much deeper they may go, and what other changes may yet be attributable to our experience during and after the Second World War, it is impossible to say. The social patterns in this country have altered greatly during war and postwar years, and out of this "boiling over" has come a new attitude toward women, which the supervisor must take into account. Yet there are not many specific rules at present for the foreman to follow in his supervision of women employees. What few there are he is apt to know from his experience in handling men under similar circumstances. Manner, however, counts for a great deal; in handling women the foreman needs to apply his rules with perhaps just a little more tact and finesse. Here are a few special points for consideration:

1. Do not let shop manners grow up like Topsy. Avoid pushing new women employees into a social vacuum. Work out a simple, short, clear code of social behavior, see that it is understood, and stick to

it. It might be a good idea to organize a small committee of older women employees to see that it is observed, and in cases of open violations have the committee recommend corrective action.

2. If possible, keep the women in groups to themselves and shift the personnel occasionally to avoid cliques and favoritism.

3. Few people of spirit take kindly to a reprimand, especially a public one. Reprimand women workers in sober judgment and never in anger or irritation. Always give the woman an "out," and, if humanly possible, allow her to have the last word. Do not let the trap close around her, no matter how just the charge.

4. Sidestep and refuse every invitation, however innocent, to place the supervising function on a man-to-woman basis. Keep the distance of your authority.

5. Be free in your praise of work when the work deserves to be praised, but do not praise the individual woman worker who produced it. Keep to an impersonal standard of values and avoid comparisons to other workers.

6. Try to keep control of spontaneous group action.

7. Keep an open mind about the abilities of women employees. Watch for individual differences and mark for advanced training those who show greater efficiency and superior ability.

8. In general, treat the women the same as you would the men. Any woman who has faced childbirth can overcome lesser dangers without hysteria. If possible, see that women, too, have something specific to do in case of an emergency.

The essential consideration, however, about these suggestions is that women employees, *once they have been carefully inducted into industrial responsibilities,* must receive no special privileges. They are mature citizens, responsible in every degree for their actions. They would not have it otherwise; the women of other nations have not set a standard of achievement too high for American women. And the foreman may be reassured that the millions of American women who have entered industry have brought with them enough of the positive middle-class virtues of order, kindliness, and sanity to make industrial living in general, and the foreman's job in particular, even more intensely human and worth while than it now is.

Section Four

THE FOREMAN'S CO-OPERATIVE
PERSONNEL RESPONSIBILITIES

CHAPTER XI

MODERN WAGE-PAYMENT PLANS

By H. P. Dutton

One important part of the work of the supervisor, the rate setter, and the employer is to assure intelligent compensation of labor. This does not necessarily mean paying the lowest wage. In fact, low labor costs are more likely to result from paying a high wage for the job. Difference in performance and in quality of output are likely to make the higher paid employees cheaper in the end.

The key to good wage payment is accurate knowledge of what constitutes good performance, or a fair task, rather than any intricate formula for paying for that performance. Indeed, much of the benefit from earlier incentive-plan installations probably resulted from the fact that they centered attention on the need for job study and good rate setting.

What the employee has to sell is, first, his time and, second, the sacrifice he makes in fatigue, risk, boredom, and the like. The employer wants to buy results, rather than time.

The first requirement of any satisfactory wage plan, then, is that it shall pay the market rate for the job. Every foreman or factory executive knows in a general way how the going rate of wages for a particular occupation is determined. It may be by trial and error in hiring, by community wage surveys, or by bargains arrived at with union representatives of the men.

The wage should also, as far as possible, tie payment up with an incentive to give full normal performance in the desired direction. It takes little more to turn out a good day's output than a skimpy one. If there is any incentive to do so, a workman may as well turn out 100 pieces a day as 70, provided it does not cost him too heavily in fatigue.

THE PIECE-RATE PLAN

The simplest way of tying performance up with time is the piece rate, one of the oldest incentive plans. However, straight piece rate may impose on the worker risks of loss for which he is not responsible. There may be a tie-up of the line, a shortage of materials, broken tools, or a call to help out on an emergency job. Therefore, it has become common to guarantee the day rate in many cases. Usually, either the day rate is slightly below the real market rate for the job, or the piece rate permits a worker to earn more (perhaps 20 to 35 per cent more) than the day rate.

In spite of the simplicity and logic of the old piece-rate system, it fell into general disrepute. The trouble was that before good time-study technique was developed, what constituted a fair output for a day's work was almost completely guesswork on the part of management. If you put on a piece rate a man who has been on day rate, he may increase his output, in extreme cases, as much as five times, or even more. There is no way of guessing at how far the increase will go until the change has been tried; the increase will not come all at once but will upset rates for some time.

One might argue that if management could make a profit on work at the old rate, it would make even more at the new. But if (as happened in the early days) men had been earning $6 on day rate and could earn $15 a day when the old output, or a little better, was made the basis of piece rate, then the plain fact was that management, knowing now what constituted a day's work, could go out and hire new men at a piece rate which would yield them $6 or at most $7 per day. Or, if the management had made a promise not to cut the rate, sooner or later a competitor would find out that the work could be done at the new rate and would undercut the first manufacturer's price.

Since there was no means of knowing where the real bottom was to rates, they were cut again and again. Naturally, workers came to an agreement among themselves to limit their output to what they regarded as a reasonable figure.

There is no remedy for this evil save by good time study. Unless management is able to determine a good task time, any promise to maintain a rate is almost sure in the long run to be broken. It is a promise that can be kept only when no competitor finds out that more than market is being paid for the job, or when the profit margin is large enough to permit a continuance of the high rate.

The rate-cutting evil has been one of the major grievances of labor, and labor has accused management of bad faith and of constant "chiseling," because of it. Unquestionably, this feeling of a need by labor for united action in self-protection is one of the conditions which explain the rapid growth of the trade union in recent years.

PREMIUM AND BONUS PLANS

In the attempt to meet this difficulty, a variety of premium and bonus plans were developed, some of which were and still are widely used. Some 55 years ago, Henry R. Towne, of the Yale and Towne Manufacturing Company, proposed a plan to take the existing output on a given job as a standard of performance and to divide with the worker any saving made as compared with this standard or allowed time. Frederick Halsey proposed a refinement of this plan which included the setting of the original standards by time study.

One-half, two-thirds, and three-quarters have been common ratios of saving allowed the worker. Under the Halsey plan, if the allowed time for performance is 1 hour, with a 90-cent base rate, and the man does the piece in 40 minutes, he would save 20 minutes. If a 50-50 bonus is used, he would be paid half this saving, a bonus of 15 cents, and would receive 75 cents for 40 minutes' work. While the "gain-sharing" formula of the Halsey plan still seems the most logical plan where there are large uncertainties in the time standards, the trend is generally to the use of the 100 per cent bonus, *i.e.*, to pay the worker for the standard or the actual time, whichever is greater.

Among other early plans which received wide publicity and a greater or less extent of use were the Taylor differential piece rate, the Gantt bonus plan, the Emerson bonus plan, with its variant, the Wennerlund plan (quite widely used in the automobile industry), and the Rowan premium plan.

Taylor pays one piece rate for performance which takes longer than the allowed time and a higher rate for performance in standard time or less. Gantt's plan guarantees day rate and provides a 20 per cent bonus to the man who reaches standard performance. The Emerson and Wennerlund plans start a small bonus at two-thirds or three-quarters of standard output, which is gradually increased until at standard output a bonus of 20 per cent is paid on time worked.

Under the Rowan plan, a man can never earn more than double the allowed time. A standard time is set, and the man is paid a bonus on time worked equal to the percentage of saving over standard time. For example, if 1 hour was the time allowed for the job, and the man did it in 40 minutes, he would receive a bonus equal to 20/60 on the time worked. If his hourly rate was 90 cents, his earnings for performance in 40 minutes would be 60 cents, plus a bonus of $\frac{1}{3} \times 60$ cents, or 20 cents, a total of 80 cents for the 40 minutes' work. The Rowan plan provides unusual protection against bad rates and is more generous than the Halsey plan for slight increases over standard. It is not so simple, looks a bit tricky to the man, and the incentive to further increases of output falls off rapidly as the output of the worker increases.

The Halsey plan provided the model for another job plan, the Bedaux point plan. Under this plan an hour is divided into 60 points, or B's. A man is credited with the allowed time in minutes, or "points," for the job, and charged with the time taken. If the time taken exceeds the allowed time, he is paid day rate only. If the time taken is less than the allowed time, he is credited with the difference. If over a period he has a net credit of allowed time over taken time, he is paid for these points saved, usually at three-quarters of his hourly rate. Often the remaining one-quarter of the bonus is paid to the foreman.

FUNDAMENTALS OF A GOOD PLAN

Before discussing other plans in current use, it will be in order to examine certain fundamentals of wage

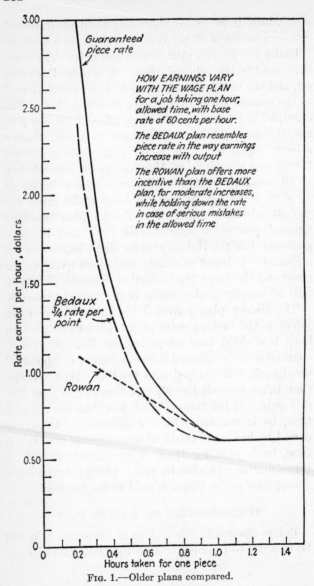

FIG. 1.—Older plans compared.

setting, in addition to those set forth in the beginning of this chapter. It seems logical to consider the real purchasing power of the wage. Many firms have made provision, particularly in periods of rapidly changing prices, for an automatic correction of the wage on the basis of the cost-of-living index. The U. S. Department of Labor collects monthly figures on the cost of living in a large group of industrial communities, based on carefully worked out family budgets. Prices obtained monthly on the articles included in these standard budgets give quite an accurate measure of changes in living costs, which can be compared with some base year to show percentage of increase or decrease.

Of course, it is evident that any rise in wages will be reflected by a change in living costs and that if all employers were to adjust wages to living costs, the rise in costs would defeat the purpose of the plan. However, during periods when rapid fluctuations in prices create real hardship for employees on fixed incomes, the cost-of-living index does provide a basis for adjustment and is currently being used by a num-

TABLE I.—DATA FOR CURVE

Hours per piece	Earnings per hour		
	Guaranteed piece rate	Bedaux	Rowan
1.5	$0.60	$0.60	$0.60
1.0	0.60	0.60	0.60
0.8	0.75	0.63	0.72
0.5	1.20	1.05	0.90
0.3	2.00	1.65	1.02
0.2	3.00	2.40	1.08

ber of firms. But it cannot safely be considered a substitute for market prices in determining wages.

Setting the value of a job is an important and delicate operation. One often finds, even in the same shop, wide differences between the pay received by individuals whose duties are substantially the same. One group of men in one shop of the company may be making $1.20 an hour on day rate, while in another shop the same work on a piece-work basis yields the men $1.75 or $1.85 per hour. Such differences and often stupidities can but produce irritations and disputes.

The techniques of job evaluation, as described in Chap. XII, make possible a substantial harmonizing of rates, so that they at least compare equitably. However, the ultimate test of the fairness of a wage in a free labor market is the market test—could the man get more for the same sort of performance from other employers?

Granted that the time or hourly rate for the job has been correctly settled, the next problem is to connect this rate with performance on the job. The accepted method of doing this today is by time study, but it is worth while to examine briefly what is involved in determining this all-important time standard. A workman, in telling how rates were set in his shop, once said: "A young fellow who had been hired about 6 months came out and told me he was going to set a rate on the job. He flashed a stop watch, watched the job for half a minute, and wrote down some figures. He went back to the office, and the next day I was told that my rate would be so much. How could a kid like that set a good rate that way?" Such rate setting is little better than the guessing of early days and will lead to precisely the same results.

If the rate is "tight," the men have a proper grievance, and the company will be compelled to adjust upward. If it is too loose, management will presently find that earnings are out of line and will cut them. Perhaps management will technically keep its promise not to cut rates unless conditions have changed, by making some inconsequential change in the setup of the job. Such hocus-pocus does not fool workers.

Exactly what is "a fair day's work" is not easy to determine scientifically. Even in the simplest job, employees will turn out a little more when they are anxious about their jobs or have to meet a temporary rush, and a little less when jobs are plentiful and they know the management cannot easily replace them. However, there need not be too wide a disagreement on practical estimates, based on the effort required at various levels of output. The prevailing rate of output will vary somewhat from plant to plant and can be improved by the supervisor through instruction and good leadership.

It is fair to say that willingness to exert oneself is as much a matter of agreement as willingness to work at all. From the standpoint of the community, and eventually of the worker as a member of that community, "featherbedding" and other deliberate restrictions of output are wasteful. But monopoly restrictions are known to have been practiced by managements also, and engineers will do well to remember in setting rates that the general opinion of what constitutes a fair day's work has as much to do with the rate of output as do any "objective" studies of what is physically practicable of performance. Indeed, in today's labor market, it is the wage which is fixed and the problem of securing high output is much more than a problem of demanding it. High output will only be yielded by men who are persuaded that it is to their interest to produce and that by producing, they do not imperil the interests of their fellows.

Merely timing a job without analyzing the method of performance gives little clue as to whether it is correctly performed. However, when thorough motion studies are made, to assure that the job is done right, the setting of the time allowance for the job becomes a comparatively simple and objective process. By the time the new method has been worked out, the matter of pace more or less settles itself. It is still true that when the rate setter puts a time allowance or a piece rate on the job he is making a wage bargain. But most of the guesswork has been taken out of the allowance by this time.

For standardized repetitive jobs involving no special problems of quality or discrimination, there is no better plan of payment than the straight piece rate. The allowed time for the operation is determined, with proper corrections and additions to allow for delays, fatigue, and like elements.

100 PER CENT PREMIUM

One premium plan, the 100 per cent premium, bears many resemblances to piece rate. A standard time is set for the job, and the worker is paid this time, no matter how much shorter the actual time may be. In general effect, this is a guaranteed piece rate. It differs from piece rate in that if the allowed time is 1 hour, a worker whose base rate is $1.50 will receive more for the job than one at a lower base rate. This may permit of recognizing long service, versatility, or other qualifications of which the piece rate does not take account. Also, in case of changes in the market wage level, only the man's rate need be changed, not hundreds of individual piece rates, since the allowed times remain the same. The fact that the same job pays different rates to different men, while it may be used to recognize desirable qualities, may also create a feeling of discrimination on the part of the lower paid men. However, the plan is normally employed where differences in rate are not large.

It may be difficult to set an accurate rate on the job. It may take a learner as long as 6 months to acquire a full normal speed, and it is difficult to estimate the final normal rate of output. This problem is exaggerated during a change in methods, as from day rate to piece rate, or during a general standardization of factory operations. Wherever possible, the setting of rates should be deferred in such a situation. It is better to continue with an old and inaccurate piece-rate system or with a day-rate system until the changes have been completed and the situation stabilized.

Many workers do not like gain-sharing plans of the Halsey and Bedaux types. They argue that if a time has been fairly determined and a worker is good enough to exceed the average earnings on that rate, he should be paid all of what he saves and not three-quarters or some other fraction of it. There is, in fact, some justice to this claim, and in some recent applications of the Bedaux system, the premium has been increased from 75 to 100 per cent, so that it becomes virtually a piece-rate plan. However, there is a justification under certain circumstances for plans of the gain-sharing type, where temporary or transition standards must be set. It can be said for such plans under these circumstances that the worker is guaranteed his day rate and has some incentive to increase his production. Since the rate is admittedly partly guesswork, he shares with the management the gamble involved in his ability to run away with the rate.

POINT SYSTEMS

Still another problem arises where other factors than output are to be considered in setting the rate. For example, it may be desirable to make it worth the workman's while to economize on materials. In punching mica washers, a careless worker may secure only a 30 per cent utilization of the expensive raw material, while a careful one may utilize as much as 65 or 70 per cent. The time factor would enter into this situation to some extent; it would take longer to obtain full utilization of the mica than to put it through without regard to waste.

Or take another case. In many operations, such as installing furnaces in homes, the worker is brought into contact with the customer and meets and has to contend with all sorts of unstandardized conditions. The carefulness with which he does his job may make the difference between a satisfied customer, who will recommend the company to his neighbors, and an irritated, disgruntled one, who will contest the bill. Or take the case of the janitor or move man who tidies up around a production line and who in many indirect ways can give a lift which enables the gang to get out faster work. Numerous other examples will suggest themselves where it is desirable to encourage or recognize some performance not measurable in terms of tangible output. Among these are length and dependability of service, versatility, co-operativeness, and other intangible qualities.

A great variety of point or budget plans of payment have been developed in the attempt to pay for such composite standards. In the mica illustration, a graduated piece rate was worked out with a higher rate per 1,000 washers as the percentage of utilization of the raw material was increased. The percentages were so balanced that it was profitable to the operator to sacrifice speed to a degree sufficient to secure high utilization. Yet incentive was present to maintain output as well.

For supervisors, a common plan of payment is to establish a budget indicating for any given volume the expected costs of operating the department. If a saving is made of these costs, the foreman or supervisor will share in the saving on an agreed basis.

There is always the danger that in emphasizing one feature of performance, such as output, we may inadvertently penalize some other feature, such as quality. Therefore, with foremen's bonuses based on departmental budgets, a rather careful analysis is necessary to avoid putting a premium on driving the men, on neglecting maintenance, and on other practices which temporarily increase production or decrease costs, but which are not good from a long-run point of view. For this reason, it is often better to pay the foreman a straight monthly rate, with the privileges usually associated with it, and to rely on rate increases, promotions, discriminating supervision and recognition of good work for incentive.

A still more difficult problem in wage payment is met when it is not practicable to set any standard of performance for the job. The toolmaker's work, for example, outside of a few cases of volume production, is typically different with every job. Any but the roughest time estimates might take more time for the setting than for the performance. Many other jobs, such as some maintenance work, trucking, and storekeeping, may be so diversified that it is not worth while to attempt to time them. The best plan of payment for such cases is apt to be the straight day rate, adjusted from time to time as quality of work, willingness, etc., merit.

A difficulty with day rate is that the connection between performance and pay is not so immediate and obvious as in the piece rate. All too often a lack of observation or a bias on the part of the supervisor means that the bootlicking employee gets the raise which the good performer misses. And the reward comes only when promotion is being considered, a time that may seem a long way in the future. Day rate, therefore, is psychologically a bad incentive, unless the worker knows what constitutes his expected task and knows that his supervisor keeps himself informed of performance and weighs it fairly in promotions or pay increases.

Notice, however, that most executives, engineers, foremen, research workers, and others, whose work is interesting and stimulating in itself are paid on a time basis. The work provides its own incentive. It is well to remember that the financial incentive is not the only nor always the most important reason why men put their hearts into their work.

MEASURED DAY RATE

There has in recent years been an increase of plans which share the characteristics of day and piece rate, such as "measured day rate" and "engineered performance." In these plans, standards are set by time study or analysis exactly as they would be for piece rate. A record is kept of performance. Or more complex elements in performance, such as quality, saving of materials, and the like, may be included in the record on a point system, just as they would be in bonus records. The operator is paid a flat hourly rate, but this rate is adjusted from time to time to take account of variations in performance. Usually the adjustment would take place a month after starting a job and thereafter at monthly or quarterly intervals.

PROFIT SHARING

A group of plans in which interest has often been very high, although fluctuating, includes the various profit-sharing plans. A distinction must be made between premium plans such as the Halsey, which share with the worker the gain resulting from his *own* effort in exceeding a standard performance, and the so-called "true" profit-sharing plans, in which, usually after payment of a fixed dividend to the stockholders, a share of the *company's* profits for the year is set aside for division among the employees. The assumption in plans of this type is in general that the profit division is in addition to and not a substitute for current market wages. Sometimes the worker's share is divided on a simple per capita basis; more commonly it is distributed as a percentage of wages so that the more highly paid employees receive the larger share of the total.

Experience seems to indicate that profit-sharing plans do result, where wisely administered, in an increase in good will toward the management. There is an incentive to avoid waste and to look out for the interests of the company in ways to which the employees might otherwise be indifferent. On the other hand, it is questionable whether payments of this sort have any very marked effect on production. The effort of any one man is diluted so much by the fact that the profit depends on the efforts of all that there is not a very direct incentive to exertion.

GROUP-PAYMENT PLANS

A good deal of attention has been paid to group piece rate. There is no reason why a standard of performance should not be set for a job requiring several men on exactly the same principles as would be used with a one-man job. A number of new administrative problems are raised, but in principle group piece rate, or group bonus, will follow exactly the same lines as corresponding plans applied individually.

Where a number of people work at the same job, but independently, the group piece rate is not good. For example, take men loading a car. If the work of each individual is not separately tallied, there will be a tendency for the shrewd or lazy man not to pull his full load, and the other members of the gang, resenting his attempt to ride on their efforts, will tend to slow down themselves or to create difficulties. The same trouble may exist where the numbers under a single rate are so large that the members of the gang do not have a chance to know each other well.

On the other hand, where the members of a group perform different operations in a series, as on an assembly line, the slowest individual in the group determines to a considerable extent the pace at which the whole group will work. A shirker cannot let someone else do his work for him. In such circumstances, the group-piece-rate plan has proved excellent. It fosters a feeling of co-operation, since it is to the interests of every member of the group that the learner come up to speed as soon as possible or that an employee who is for a day or two feeling below standard be given a lift. It has been found advisable to include in the group helpers, machine tenders, truckers, and other workers attached to the group in a service capacity.

The group piece rate or bonus also seems to work well with small groups whose tasks are related but unstandardized. For example, a group plan was worked out for four girls employed as packers in a shipping department. When the girls shared in a group plan and one operator was under pressure, those who were not so busy would pitch in to help her to clean up her work, with the result that the shipments were got out materially faster and at lower cost.

Granted a fixed total for the job, stated either as dollar earnings or in time, the earnings under a group-piece-rate plan can be divided among the members of the group in proportion to their basic wage rates, assuming that everybody worked the same amount of time on the job. If an operator is absent, the group may in some cases elect to carry the load and let the absent operator share in spite of his illness or detention. More commonly, the earnings that the absent worker would have made if present are divided among the other workers. In the case of overtime, if all work the full overtime period, time and one-half can be paid for the overtime period and simply added to the amount to be divided among the group. If overtime is not participated in by all members of the group, the extra earnings can be divided among those who did participate.

A question which often arises with group-payment plans is: what shall be done in case the group can get along without some of its members? Often after a gang is organized and has worked for a while, its members will discover (perhaps as a result of temporary absence of one of the group) that they can do the work as fast without one of their number. In such cases the practice has sometimes been to let the group dispense with the unneeded member and to divide the original rate among the remaining members of the group. If changes in method are called for, a new rate could be set, netting the remaining individuals more, but lowering the wage cost for the whole operation.

WHAT A WAGE PLAN SHOULD DO

Often a "tailor-made" plan may work out better than one of the standard plans. However, there are certain tests of a good plan, and if these tests are applied it will be found that for most situations the simpler plans will fill the bill. It is to be hoped that the period has passed when a new wage plan will be looked upon as the cure for all production ills.

Among the characteristics of a good wage plan are:

1. *It should reflect accurately and immediately the performance and effort of the employee.* The incentive value of a plan is watered down at once when the payment depends on some arbitrary or little-understood judgment by the supervisor or when sudden changes in earnings result from a failure to allow for variable set-up times or from irregularities in the job. From this point of view, no plan is so good as the piece-rate plan (usually under today's conditions a guaranteed piece rate) or standard time plan where the conditions are standardized and adaptable to its use.

2. *The plan should be simple.* Probably most workers eventually learn how to compute their earnings even under some of the more elaborate bonus plans. However, simplicity is greatly to be desired. Under the piece-rate plan, the operator is able to translate his work into money as he performs it—two pieces,

20 cents.   Standard time plans can also be set up so as to be understood easily.   Day rate is of course the simplest from the standpoint of records and computation, but the simplicity is gained at the cost of productivity.

3. *The plan should not direct the attention of the worker so exclusively to one type of performance that he is tempted to neglect other elements in the job.*   In simple tasks where close inspection is practicable, the piece rate is entirely adequate; where inspection is costly, or thorough inspection is made impossible by the covering up of operations in subsequent processes, it may be advisable in certain cases to abandon any piece-rate plan and to rely instead on supervision to give proper weight to the various factors in a performance.   The various point plans permit of extending the scope of performance qualities included in the compensation.   However, in a complex working situation it may be inadvisable to attempt a coverage of all desirable qualities, and, instead, it may be better to fall back on day rate and recognition by promotion as the incentives to performance.   Any plan which pays for output, such as a bonus plan, shares this difficulty with piece rate.   To the extent that a bonus has incentive value, it offers a temptation to neglect certain results not subject to bonus.

This chapter has attempted to deal primarily with the different systems of financial-incentive payment. It would be incomplete if it failed to call attention to the power of nonfinancial incentives.   Friendly competition among workers or groups of workers is one of these.   It can make the work fun and increase output while decreasing fatigue.

Another great incentive is recognition.   Every one of us hungers to be told that his work is good.   The sound use of praise is a fine art and one of great importance to any supervisor. One of the most important values of the wage to the man is the implied recognition of merit, of indispensability to the organization. That is why a good job-evaluation plan, administered not mechanically but with discrimination, is so important in the factory. The wage is important for what it will buy, but it is at least as important for what it tells the man himself, his wife, and his associates about how good he is.

Anything which makes the work more interesting, which gives the performer more of a sense of participation and mastery is in itself an incentive to good work. All kinds of wage systems are in use, some of them almost impossibly bad. Almost any system will work, provided that it meets the basic requirement of paying the market wage and provided that the men feel that the management means to be fair and recognizes good work.

CHAPTER XII

JOB EVALUATION

[*Editor's note: This chapter gives a comprehensive treatment of the type of job evaluation which experience indicates is more likely to be encountered by the foreman than the strict "factor-comparison" method described in earlier editions. The Rating Guides on pages 316–322, and some explanatory paragraphs in the introductory portion, are from "Job Analysis," by J. K. Louden and T. G. Newton, in "Reading Course in Executive Technique," edited by Carl Heyel, published by Funk & Wagnalls, to which the reader is referred for detailed treatment. Some simplifying modifications have been made in the Rating Guides as here presented. (The foregoing material is reproduced by permission.) In addition, in the introductory portion of this chapter, some of the text by Samuel L. H. Burk has been preserved from the previous edition.*]

Job evaluation is the systematic determination of the proper wage and salary rates to apply to specific jobs, so that as far as possible comparable rates will be paid for all work of comparable difficulty, hazard, responsibility, educational and experience requirements, and similar appropriate factors.

A program of job evaluation involves first the analysis of all work currently being done, and then the grouping of all jobs into a relatively small number of classes or titles, and further grouping of these titles (or *kinds* of jobs) into a relatively small number of grades, with a specific rate of pay attached to each grade.

Note that job evaluation means the evaluation of *jobs*, and not of the men or women working at these jobs.[1] One of the most frequent sources of misunderstanding arising during a job-evaluation installation is that those affected by the program confuse job evaluation with man evaluation.

Some kind of wage- or salary-rate determination has been going on ever since some prehistoric man first hired someone else to work for him. All organizations that employed any kind of "help," other than slave labor, had to have some way of determining what to pay in wages. At just what point in the history of employer-employee relations, system began to replace rule of thumb, it is difficult to state accurately. We do know that there are still many business organizations that use the old haphazard methods.

As early as 1909–1910, E. O. Griffenhagen prepared job-classification plans for employees of the city of Chicago. Later he took part in the application of these methods to wage and salary problems of the Commonwealth Edison Company. The results of

---

[1] Different writers make different distinctions as to definition of "job," "position," "occupation," "class of position," etc. As used here, "job" represents a recognized collection of duties. Thus there may be only one job of welder in the plant, although 10 men may hold that title. Even though certain fringe duties may differ, it is in practical experience always possible, after analysis of just what everyone does, to consider the work of several persons as essentially so similar, that one "job" can cover all of them. The editor recognizes that in common usage the word "job" also covers a specific incumbency—as when we say that a plant provides 12,000 jobs for a community. However, he is confident that context always makes that meaning clear.

this work were published in 1912, and since that time many others have contributed to the field.

Recent developments include a number of significant advances. More exact techniques have been achieved. The parts played by the foremen and employees have been expanded. Although salaried clerical positions were the first to be covered, interest soon concentrated on hourly rated jobs; lately, however, programs covering salaried employees of all types have been initiated. Labor-market-survey groups have been formed in several communities to co-operate in securing market-rate data. Industrial groups have sponsored industry-wide job evaluation and market-survey plans, such as those engaged in by the National Electrical Manufacturers Association and the National Metal Trades Association.

ADVANTAGES TO EMPLOYEES

A job-evaluation program resulting in accurate descriptions of duties and responsibilities and in fair rates of pay will give every employee a better understanding of his responsibilities, how his job relates to others, and how his rate of pay compares with that of others, with reasons therefor. The job analysis which must precede job evaluation usually results in instructional aids, and the official job descriptions prepared help him realize what is involved in moving up the ladder to other jobs in which he may be interested. Finally, representatives of the employees, in their collective bargaining with management, are in a position to come to intelligent agreement as to rates of pay if all concerned are agreed as to the content of the various jobs, and how they rank in terms of the factors already mentioned.

ADVANTAGES TO MANAGEMENT

Management has an advantage in *selection*, by virtue of the fact that it knows exactly what the various jobs call for, and so can draw up detailed specifications as to the type of employee it wants for every job. Management gains in *training*, because, obviously, if it knows exactly what the job duties, responsibilities, etc., are, it is in good shape to set up a scientific training program. A job-evaluation program also aids management in straightening out its *organization*, and in establishing and publicizing practical lines of *promotion*. Sound *forecasting* and *budgeting of expenses*, in so far as manpower is concerned, can only be accomplished if management has a clear-cut codification of all jobs in the organization, and is satisfied that specific rates of pay are not out of line. And finally, management secures the same advantages as do labor representatives in *collective bargaining*, since it is to everyone's advantage to be in agreement as to the ranking and content of jobs before negotiating about rates of pay.

THE FOREMAN'S PART IN A JOB-EVALUATION PROGRAM

The supervisory force has definite responsibilities in connection with a job-evaluation program. These may be grouped under three headings: *direct* responsibilities, *co-operative* responsibilities, and *educational* responsibilities. Specific duties of the foreman and the limits of his responsibility in connection with each duty vary from firm to firm. In general, however, it may be said that the same general pattern is applied, with major or minor differences to meet specific situations.

In larger installations, the foreman is not directly responsible for preparation of job descriptions or specifications. He is, however, called upon to give full and understanding approval or criticism to specifications prepared as a result of job analyses made by a specialist. Aside from the men on the jobs, no one knows more about the jobs under his jurisdiction than does the foreman. This knowledge must be brought to bear in seeing that the job descriptions give true and accurate pictures of the jobs they cover. It is also the supervisor's direct responsibility to agree or disagree with rates assigned by job evaluation to jobs under him. In disagreements on which he is overruled by higher authority, he must see to it that he is fully conversant with the reasons, so that he will be able to uphold the management's point of view to the men. Moreover, as there is nothing permanent about job content except change, the foreman must inform appropriate authorities when changes in jobs have taken place, so that proper action may be taken.

During the job-analysis phase of the program, the foreman must aid in giving and securing facts and opinions about jobs. When the job-evaluation stage is reached, the foreman may be asked either to serve on an evaluation committee or to counsel with committee members on their work. At all times he must maintain a judicial, analytical attitude toward all questions submitted to him and volunteer any information that appears to be pertinent to the success of the program.

As representative of management, the foreman must be prepared to educate his subordinates in matters involving the basic principles of job evaluation, the company salary and wage policies, the company's specific method of wage determination, and the part that employees should play in the entire program, and to answer workers' questions as to reasons for established job differentials.

MAJOR TYPES OF JOB EVALUATION

Job-evaluation methods differ among different companies. All methods, however, may be broadly classified into four major types: the ranking system, the grading or classification system, the point system, and the factor-comparison system.

1. The Ranking System

This is one of the simplest systems to use. It takes less time to develop and install than any other system, but is not nearly as thorough. The jobs to be evaluated are properly identified and are listed in order from their lowest to highest value to the company.

The ranking is done by a committee or by assembled department heads. They may use job analysis or descriptions. Job factors such as skill, education, and working conditions may be developed and used as a guide by those doing the ranking. Usually the procedure is to start with the jobs in one department and then advance to those in other departments in turn. When all have been completed, the rankings of all jobs are combined and compared. Differences are ironed out by the committee. When the jobs are finally arranged in order, they are divided into groups, and rates of pay are assigned to each group. This is usually done after making a survey of rates paid for similar work in the community and after taking into consideration what it is desirable for the company to pay.

This system is simple. It tends to preserve jobs in

the same relationship which custom has established in the organization. However, since it does not call for detailed analysis and formal evaluation, it is not recommended.

2. The Grading or Classification Plan

In this plan, instead of ranking all jobs in the order from their lowest to highest value to the company, a series of grades is established, usually on an arbitrary basis—anywhere from 15 to 30. Usually each grade will be given a rate of pay before the evaluation of the job begins. Every job is placed in a grade by a committee or through conferences of department heads. Otherwise, the procedure is about the same as that in the ranking system, and the advantages and disadvantages are similar as well. In this plan it is difficult to define a grade unless money is used. When this is done, there is a definite tendency to put jobs into grades upon the basis of the current rates of pay of the employees holding them, so that little more is done than to maintain the status quo whether right or wrong.

3. The Point System

The first step under this system is to develop a set of job factors which will be used in evaluating all jobs. These will differ according to companies. A typical set might be: *education, experience, initiative, physical demand, mental demand, responsibility,* and *working conditions.* These factors must be clearly defined so as to be understandable to those who will use them in the evaluations.

A maximum number of points to be allowed for each factor is then established. Each can be given the same number—or some factors, by being given a greater number of points, can be weighted. Degrees are established for each factor and points allocated to them.

On the basis of job analyses and descriptions, each job is evaluated by determining the number of points it should receive for each of the job factors. This evaluation is usually done by an analyst and checked by the department heads affected.

A series of job grades is established on the basis of points. For example, grade 1 may be 0–100 points, grade 2, 101–200 points, etc. Each grade is then assigned a rate of pay in a manner similar to that followed in the other systems.

Various systems of point values have been developed. For example, the National Electrical Manufacturers Association (NEMA) has developed a widely used system, with points totaling a maximum of 500, with varying amounts assigned to such factors as skill, effort, responsibility, etc. This chapter offers a somewhat more detailed suggested point system.

4. The Factor-comparison System

The factor-comparison system combines the good features of the other systems. Factors are used, as in the point system. However, some eight or ten "benchmark" or key jobs are selected, and for these key jobs, each factor is ranked, and assigned points. These then serve as check points for all other jobs to be evaluated. The method is thus a combination of ranking and point rating. The main distinction is the care with which the ultimate point rating is done— instead of blindly assigning points obtained from some source such as NEMA to all jobs, letting them then rank themselves as a result, all jobs are carefully compared, factor by factor, to the benchmarks.

After points have been assigned to all jobs, a series

of grades and pay per grade is established, as indicated in 3, above.

FACTORS TO BE USED AS A BASIS FOR EVALUATION

The system described in this chapter is the one the foreman is most likely to encounter. It is primarily a point-rating system although it combines some elements of factor comparison. Details as to arriving at total points for each job will be given later. At this point (Table I) we list the specific factors into which

TABLE I.—FACTORS FOR COMPARING JOBS

Factors	Maximum Points
I—Skill, in terms of:	
1. Job training and experience.........	450
2. Mental development...............	125
3. Initiative and versatility*..........	150
4. Dexterity.........................	100
II—Responsibility, for:	
1. Material or product...............	50
2. Equipment......................	50
3. Safety of others...................	50
4. Activities of others...............	100
III—Effort demanded:	
1. Physical exertion	100
2. Mental concentration.............	50
IV—Working Conditions, in terms of:	
1. Hazard..........................	50
2. Surroundings.....................	50
	1,325

* Sometimes the term "Complexity" is used here.

all jobs are to be broken down and compared. Various degrees of each factor will be encountered, and the later instructions furnish guides for arriving at the proper degree—*i.e.*, the number of points up to the maximum indicated which are actually to be assigned.

In the Table I listing (and later pages of this chapter further break down the factors by degrees), the reader will notice that for job training and experience, the point values go as high as 450 (although in actual practice, a job would not be likely to reach that value for that factor, since it would have to score maximum on three subfactors as explained later). For mental development, the points go up to 125, and so on. That merely means that obviously every factor is not of equal weighting. These points as given represent the combined experience of engineers and analysts, who have had a long background in job evaluation, and set forth what in their minds is the relative importance to attach to experience as against mental development, responsibility for materials, etc. In a given plant, there may be very good reasons for different weightings. (The NEMA rating plan goes up to 500, although the relative importance assigned to the four major factors is not radically different from our division of 1,325 points. Of course, since NEMA uses fewer points, when the time comes to translate points into money, each NEMA point will be worth more.)

Even if a different order of weighting is decided upon, the descriptive paragraphs in the following pages on factor values provide ways to get specific as to degrees of these hard-to-measure concepts.

BASIC STEPS IN THE PROGRAM

Thirteen basic steps are to be followed in developing the program. These are:

1. Fix responsibility for the program; set up a small committee to decide upon final recommendations.

2. Select key or benchmark jobs.

3. Secure detailed data on these jobs.

4. Prepare the formal job description of each one of the benchmark jobs.

5. Rank each one of these key jobs, factor by factor, and agree on point values to be assigned to each factor on each benchmark job, and hence total point values for all benchmark jobs.

6. Set up a Rank List of the benchmark jobs, to serve as a guide in assigning point values.

7. Secure detailed data on all other jobs in the plant which are included in the job-evaluation program.

8. Prepare formal job descriptions of each of these jobs.

9. Compare each factor of all jobs with the benchmarks in the Rank List, to arrive at agreed-upon point values for all factors of all jobs, and hence total point values for all jobs.

10. Determine the average relationship existing in the plant between point values and money values currently being paid.

11. Compare certain selected jobs with the same or demonstratively equivalent jobs in other plants in the community and/or the industry, to see if an adjustment is required in the line of average relationship to use in the plant.

12. Agree upon the number of labor grades into which the total point spread between the lowest- and highest-evaluated job is to be divided, and the spread of points within each grade. Determine the rate to be paid for each labor grade.

13. By means of the evaluation points which have been assigned to each job in the plant, allocate each job to a specific labor grade.

ANALYSIS OF KEY JOBS

The list of key jobs should range from the most complex job in the plant to the simplest. (Typical key jobs are given in Fig. 2.) The number of jobs in this range will depend upon the variety of jobs and work performed in the plant. However, the number used as key jobs should be relatively few, chosen in such a way that everyone will recognize some as being more or less difficult than others.

The whole program will depend upon the completeness with which information on the jobs is secured in the first place. Detailed data—"job descriptions" are required. While, as will be shown presently, the information is later boiled down on a standardized form, for the sake of completeness it is usually best to secure the original descriptive data on a separate questionnaire form. This should call for such information as:

Job title, alternate titles, and identification by department

A listing of principal duties, secondary duties, and working procedure

Special equipment and machines used

Special knowledge required, such as elementary shop mathematics, advanced shop mathematics, ability to read simple or complicated blueprints, and the like

Knowledge of special instruments required

Previous experience required, length of time with such experience it should require to break in on the job, and the like

How closely the person on this job would normally be supervised and, conversely, whether the person on the job would supervise others

Types of mistakes that could be made on the job and their seriousness

Description of working conditions, as to hazards, unpleasant surroundings, and the like

Special physical requirements of the job, as lifting heavy weights and the like

It can be seen that, depending upon the plant and upon the knowledge and experience of the analysis, questionnaires and check lists of widely varying degrees of comprehensiveness can be drawn up, as required to assure complete information. Depending upon the class of personnel, amount of information on jobs already in the company's files, and the like, the information can be secured directly from the workers, or by interviews and observation of analysts, from the foreman, or in any of a number of ways. Usually union co-operation is secured, and full agreement reached as to what constitutes the make-up of the jobs before any attempt at evaluation is begun.

The procedure for securing the foregoing type of data will, of course, be the same for all of the jobs in the plant, as well as for the benchmark jobs. The point is that the benchmark jobs are done first, and then, later, all of the other jobs are described and compared, factor by factor, with the benchmark jobs.

The detailed data on the jobs will have to be boiled down into succinct yet complete formal job descriptions, bearing in each case the official title for that work. A standardized form should be developed for this, such as is illustrated in Fig. 1.

It will be noted that on the reverse of the form (Fig. 1*a*) descriptive information is given in terms of the four major factors, broken down into the 12 subsidiary factors already mentioned, and that space is provided for entering the evaluation points for each of these.

Special care is taken to arrive at the evaluation points on the key jobs, since they will be the benchmarks for all other jobs. Therefore, all of the key jobs are first listed separately for each factor, in order from highest to lowest in terms of the requirements under that factor. For example, with respect to training and experience, it may be agreed that toolmaker has the highest requirement, welder next, and

OFFICIAL JOB DESCRIPTION

PLANT ....

.... DEPT.   Machine Shop

DATE ....

SHEET........OF........

JOB NO. ....

JOB NAME....... Bench Mechanic

FUNCTIONS AND GENERAL SCOPE OF JOB:
(USE EXTRA SHEET IF NECESSARY)

Operate small sensitive drills, buffing wheel, semi-automatic horizontal drill press, small
pneumatic hammer, portable air grinder and the like to remove burrs from machined parts, to
drill small oil holes, to remove scale, to chip oil grooves and the like. Work routine in nature
where supervision is readily available.

Work Performed:

Receive instructions from tracer card, blue print and foreman.
Remove burrs from drilled holes with counter sink or hand scrapers.
Operate portable air grinder to remove burrs from machined parts weighing up to 125 lbs.
Operate sensitive drill to drill oil holes in such items as brackets and bearing boxes.
Remove scale from heat treated bolts and rollers with emery cloth and/or buffing wheel.
Operate single and multiple spindle drill press to drill brake rim bolts, cap screws and
   the like.
Operate small, pneumatic hammer to chip oil grooves in bronze bushings and connecting
   rod brasses.
Hand tap oil holes for alemite fittings on brackets, pillow boxes and the like.
Perform such other similar tasks as may be required.

Equipment Used:

Portable air grinder, sensitive drill, buffing wheel, single and multiple spindle drill press, small pneumatic hammer, files and the like.

REQUIRED
INDIVIDUAL QUALIFICATIONS

MALE ☒ FEMALE ☐

HEIGHT: N.P. WEIGHT: LIGHT ☒ MEDIUM ☒ HEAVY ☒

AGE 18 YRS. TO 55 YRS.

ENGLISH: SPEAK ☒ READ ☒ WRITE ☒

EDUCATION: MUST HAVE Grade School

EXPERIENCE: None

JOB DATA

METHOD OF PAYMENT: HOURLY ☒ SALARY ☐
DAY ☐ BONUS ☐

HOURS OF WORK: 8 PER DAY
PER NIGHT PER TURN

SUPERVISED BY (JOB NAME):

JOBS USUALLY ADVANCED TO 1.
2. 3.

JOBS USUALLY ADVANCED FROM 1.
2. 3.

FIG. 1.—Sample job description.

RATING—SUPPORTING DATA

FACTORS		JOB NAME	Bench Mechanic	JOB No.		PT. VAL.
SKILL	EXPERIENCE TRAINING AND	Experience required to operate such small power driven bench and portable machines as sensitive drill, buffing wheel, air grinder, and pneumatic hammer to drill, grind, file and chip a variety of small parts.				45
	MENTAL DEVELOPMENT	Require to read simple blue prints.				20
	INITIATIVE AND RESPONSIBILITY	Work routine in nature where supervision is readily available.				20
	DEXTERITY	Operates several small power driven machines, such as single and multiple spindle drill press, bench drills, sensitive drill, buffing wheel, air grinder, punch press and the like where accuracy is not important.				35
RESPONSIBILITY	MATERIAL OR PRODUCT	By improperly reading blue print, could drill wrong hole, causing up to $5.00 damage. Ordinary care will prevent.				6
	EQUIP- MENT	By carelessness, could drop portable grinder, bending shaft, costing $10.00 to repair. Not likely. Ordinary care will prevent.				6
	SAFETY OF OTHERS	By carelessly operating small pneumatic hammer, chips could hit others, causing minor cuts and bruises. Should warn others near by.				9

ACTIVITY OF OTHERS		None.	0
EFFORT	PHYSICAL	Most of time exerts light physical effort doing such things as drilling holes and grinding burrs. Occasionally moderate physical effort required to lift and position parts.	40
	MENTAL	Must observe work being done.	25
JOB CONDITIONS	HAZARD	Could suffer minor cuts and bruises when handling sharp parts or tools. Ordinary care will prevent.	14
	SURROUNDINGS	Works in ordinary machine shop surroundings.	10
DESCRIBED BY:		ASSIGNED TO GROUP No.	230 TOTAL
RATED BY:		AT .... PLANT	

FIG. 1a.—Reverse side of Fig. 1.

so on, until sweeper is listed as having the least requirement under this factor.

Once jobs are ranked for a particular factor, the next step is to assign point values to each job for that factor. This is done by consulting the Rating Guides given on pages 316 to 322. The benchmark jobs are compared factor by factor, to secure a reasonable and defensible relationship before the values are "frozen" to form benchmark guides for all other jobs in the plant.

RANK LIST

After all benchmark jobs have been assigned point values, a summary, or "Rank List," is prepared to furnish a ready reference guide when the factors of all other jobs are being evaluated.

Figure 2 shows such a Rank List as prepared in one plant. Of course, the list and the individual factor points and total points will be different for each plant, depending upon the jobs chosen as benchmarks, and upon the way in which the analysts and the job-evaluation committee size up each benchmark job, factor by factor.

RATING OF ALL JOBS

After the benchmark jobs have been analyzed, assigned evaluation points, and set forth in official descriptions, data should be secured on all jobs.

The same sort of succinct Official Job Description as illustrated in Fig. 1 should then be prepared on all jobs. On the reverse side of the Official Statement, point values for each of the 12 factors should be assigned by comparing the job with the Rank List (Fig. 2) and by comparing each factor of each job with

Job name	Total points	Skill				Responsibility				Effort		Job condition	
		Training and experience	Mental abilities	Initiative, versatility	Manual dexterity	Material or product	Equipment	Safety of others	Leadership	Physical	Mental	Hazard	Surroundings
Toolmaker	570	115	75	80	85	35	15	11	43	30	50	14	17
Millwright	489	90	75	70	70	15	24	25	0	25	25	35	30
Blacksmith	473	110	75	80	85	9	6	11	28	25	23	11	5
Die setter	376	85	50	55	60	9	21	4	35	12	25	12	8
Inspector	371	75	40	45	50	31	12	4	20	30	45	11	5
Locomotive-crane operator	367	65	20	40	65	15	24	40	0	45	30	11	12
Crane operator	319	35	15	30	65	15	21	45	0	12	50	6	25
Tester	239	25	12	18	60	15	9	16	0	25	25	16	18
Straightener	232	40	15	30	65	9	3	4	0	30	20	11	5
Crane hook-up	229	20	15	15	30	6	3	25	0	55	20	24	10
Oiler (maintenance)	169	20	12	12	25	3	12	4	0	12	20	24	25
Sweeper	110	10	10	10	25	3	3	4	0	25	5	7	5

Reviewed by:

Fig. 2.—Sample Rank List of 12 key jobs.

the same factor of the benchmark jobs, and by reviewing the applicable Rating Guide.

It may happen, in some cases, that an individual worker, whom the foreman has obtained as, say, a welder, is not actually occupied in that particular work for a great percentage of his time, so that job data secured on his individual work may show a high proportion of relatively unskilled duties. However, to perform his welding work, a welder would be required.

When the analyst comes upon such a special situation, correction is called for in terms of the number of welders to be assigned to that particular department, as against other assignments of lesser job titles, not by the creation of a new job title. This is a problem of organization analysis.

RATING GUIDES

Rating guides for the four major factors, broken down into 12 factors in all, are given on pages 317–322. They represent the judgment of experienced raters. The important thing to keep in mind in using them is that they are significant not so much as absolute value points, but as guides to enable an individual plant to rank its own jobs in a consistent fashion. That is why it is so important to give great care to the selection of the original key jobs to be used as benchmarks, and to reach agreement as to the point values to be assigned to the various factors of these key jobs. Thereafter, constant reference to the Rank List prepared for that plant will assure all other jobs being placed in proper relationship to the benchmark jobs and to each other— even though various analysts will be doing the actual rating.

RATING GUIDE I-1

SKILL—In Terms of Job Training and Experience

The analyst should look to the training requirement of the typical individual under usual conditions. The training period should represent the total experience gained on previous jobs and the breaking-in period on the job. The total should reflect the cumulative weeks, months, or years required, assuming continuous progress under adequate instruction. The estimate of value for the length of training period should equal the total point value for A + B + C.

Training and experience required in:	Point values based on time required to reach minimum requirements							
	1 week or less	1–3 months	4–6 months	7–12 months	13–18 months	2 years	3 years	4 years
A. Use of equipment and tools... Hand tools, drills, power saws, multiple control-processing equipment, lathes, mills, automatic screw machines, etc.	5	10	15	25	35	65	100	150
B. Methods.................. Routine and sequence of working procedure; variety, detail, complexity.	5	10	15	25	35	65	100	150
C. Use of materials............. Properties of metals, raw-material formulas, stores, stock, paints, lubricants.	5	10	15	25	35	65	100	150

RATING GUIDE I-2
SKILL—In Terms of Mental Development

Job Requirement	*Rating*
1. Carry out verbal orders.....................................	0–10
2. Carry out written instructions. Fill out simple written report...	10–15
3. Do simple arithmetic.......................................	15–20
4. Read simple blueprints. Issue instructions to small group, such as helpers...	20–25
5. Make calculations involving fractions, decimals, or percentages..	25–30
6. Read complex blueprints, follow out details..................	30–40
7. Elementary technical training, practical trade knowledge.......	40–50
8. Thorough working knowledge of technical principles............	50–75
9. High technical training equivalent to academic degree..........	75–125

RATING GUIDE I-3
SKILL—In Terms of Initiative and Versatility

Job Requirement	*Rating*
1. Routine work, fully prescribed.	0–10
2. Routine and sequence occasionally varied by worker. May select material or equipment within prescribed limits.	10–20
3. May adjust equipment, other than replace tools. May classify product by simple test as to quality, weight, etc.	20–30
4. Plan and perform a sequence of operations where standard methods are available. Usually determined solely by precedent and experience. Variety limited to one trade.	30–50
5. Plan complex routine and sequence with only general methods available. 50% of work nonrepetitive in one or more types of work.	50–90
6. Think clearly, accurately, and independently to plan complex nonrepetitive tasks to be performed by self or other skilled men.	90–150

RATING GUIDE I-4
SKILL—In Terms of Dexterity

Job Requirement	*Rating*
1. Easy tolerance limits; exactness not a factor.	0–15
2. Average tolerance limits; where tool or equipment controls. Obtain easy fit.	15–40
3. Difficult tolerance limits; operator controls set-up, tools control accuracy from 0.0032 to 0.0005 in.	40–70
4. Tolerance extremely exact; fitting lapping; reliance entirely on operator precision.	70–100

RATING GUIDE II-1
RESPONSIBILITY—For Material or Product

This factor appraises the degree of care required to prevent damage to raw material, partially finished, or finished product. It is measured by money loss, total or salvage cost, which may result before normal detection and correction in any one lot or run. Consider probability and expectation of such loss under normal operating conditions, together with money loss.

Probability	Rating based on average cost of loss				
	$0–$25	$26–$100	$101–$300	$301–$1,000	Over $1,000
1. Unlikely. Little attention required.	3	9	12	18	28
2. Easy to avoid. Ordinary attention only.	6	12	15	21	31
3. Possible, with periodic close attention only. (Shut down automatic equipment in case of trouble.)	9	15	18	24	34
4. Possible, with close attention required most of time.	15	21	24	30	40
5. Difficult to avoid, extreme care required.	25	31	34	40	50

RESPONSIBILITY—For Equipment

This factor appraises the degree of care required to prevent damage to machinery and equipment, or to prevent loss of productivity on subsequent operations. It is measured by probability of damage or loss and estimated cost of damage for any one mishap.

Probability	Rating based on average cost of loss				
	$0–$25	$26–$100	$101–$300	$301–$1,000	Over $1,000
1. Unlikely. Little attention required.	3	9	12	18	28
2. Easy to avoid. Ordinary attention only	6	12	15	21	31
3. Possible, but unlikely. Periodic attention only	9	15	18	24	34
4. Possible. Close skilled attention required most of time	15	21	24	30	40
5. Difficult to avoid. Extreme care required	25	31	34	40	50

RATING GUIDE II-3
RESPONSIBILITY—For Safety of Others

The value for this factor is based on the degree of care which must be exercised to avoid or prevent injuries to fellow employees. It considers the probability of accident and the degree of injury caused by some direct act or negligence. The responsibility exists only for those employees immediately exposed to such action or negligence. Total Point Value = Degree of Probability (Points) + Degree of Injury (Points).

A. Probability   *Rating*

1. Little possibility of causing injury. Working with manual tools ... 2
2. Some care required (warning others). Operate power-driven tools, welding ... 6
3. Considerable care required. Working overhead, manually; processing material not in a fixed position ... 10
4. Great care required. Moving or transporting materials with power-driven equipment. Hazards inherent to the job. Others may act to prevent injury ... 15
5. Entirely responsible for safety of others who cannot have warning independently 25

B. Degree of Injury   *Rating*

1. Slight cuts or bruises; temporary pain or discomfort .. 2
2. Lost time; accident under one week ... 10
3. Lost time; accident over one week ... 15
4. Permanent disability; loss of members or sight ... 25

RESPONSIBILITY—For Activity of Others

This factor appraises the requirement of the job for assisting, guiding, or planning the activities of a group of other workmen. Look for the type of labor supervised, and consider whether the "assisting, guiding, or planning" is called for. Then, add to the rating for that subfactor, points relating to the number of employees supervised.

A. Type of labor directly supervised	Rating	*B.* Number	Rating
1. No one supervised.....................	0	None	0
2. Manual, simple duties. Jobs learned in one month or less......................	0–15	1 or 2	5
3. Routine machine or manual operations, requiring some knowledge of methods or material. Usually on same occupation...	15–30	3 to 10	15
4. Variety of work on same or various occupations. Requires mental application and a degree of skill.........................	30–50	10 to 25	20
5. Jobs requiring a high degree of knowledge of materials, methods, precision and responsibilities........................	50–75	Over 25	25

RATING GUIDE III-1

EFFORT—In Terms of Physical Effort Demanded

This factor is a measure of the muscular effort or strength required by the job. To be considered is the degree of effort, measured in weight of material handled (or pounds of force applied) without mechanical aid, and the endurance required. This latter element relates to continuity of effort. Do not consider job surroundings, since they relate to another factor.

Endurance, per cent of time during which force must be sustained	Rating based on strength required (pounds of force applied without mechanical aid)			
	Very light (up to 5 lb.), Rating	Light (5 to 30 lb.), Rating	Medium (30 to 100 lb.), Rating	Heavy (100 to 200 lb.), Rating
10	5	10	15	25
20	6	15	25	50
30	7	20	35	75
40	8	25	45	100
50	9	30	55	
60	10	35	75	
70	11	40	85	
80	12	45	100	
90	13	50		
100	14	55		

EFFORT—Mental Concentration Demanded

Mental effort involves the degree and continuity of direct thought, mental alertness, or concentration which the job requires. Consider the characteristics of the operation and the per cent of time mental effort must be exercised.

Type of operation	Rating based on continuity of effort in per cent of time				
	0–10	11–30	31–50	51–70	Over 70
1. Little attention required; no co-ordination with other operations or operators; automatic tasks........	2	5	10	10	10
2. Co-ordinate manual actions with other operators or operations; flow of work intermittent; repetitive in nature..........................	3–4	8–11	15–20	20–30	20–30
3. Routine decisions. Selects, inspects, and marks or assorts. Careful attention to results............	5	14	25	35	45
4. Attention required to vary speed (few variations); or to maintain co-ordination with others; response fairly obvious and immediate......	6–7	17–20	20–35	40–45	50
5. Concentration required to interpret detailed instructions; plan, analyze.	8	23	40	50	50
6. Exacting attention to involved or complex problems; infrequent repetition, seldom precedent...........	9–10	27–30	45–50	50	50

RATING GUIDE IV-1

WORKING CONDITIONS—In Terms of Hazard

This factor measures the probability and extent of injury or health impairment to which the employee himself may be exposed on the job. Consider those hazards of accident or health which are inherent in the job, even though all usual precautions have been taken for safeguarding the employee. Add A and B to arrive at rating.

A. Probability	*Rating*
1. Accidents or health hazards negligible..................	2
2. Occasional injury or accident, usually controlled by safeguards................	6
3. Considerable care required to avoid injury, some exposure to minor health disturbance.................	10
4. Alertness necessary; working near known hazard; exposure to major health disturbance.....................	15
5. Hazard or major health disturbance a well-recognized characteristic of job........	25

B. Possibility of degree of injury	*Rating*
1. Minor; slight cuts or bruises.	2
2. Severe; lost-time accidents under one week..........	10
3. Maiming; lost-time accidents over one week.......	15
4. Permanent disability; loss of members or sight..........	25

RATING GUIDE IV-2

WORKING CONDITIONS—In Terms of Surroundings

This factor appraises the surroundings or physical conditions under which the job must be done and the extent to which those conditions make the job disagreeable. Consider only those elements which actually affect the physical or mental well-being of the employee and cannot be eliminated by normal means (wearing appropriate dress).

Degree of Exposure	*Rating*
1. No disagreeableness...	0
2. Slight. Inside partially heated. Some dirt or grease, or infrequent exposure to disagreeable element......................	5–10
3. Moderate. Smoky or dusty. Very dirty or greasy. Exposure to other elements not continuous if present....................	15–20
4. Considerable. Continuous exposure to several disagreeable elements or intense exposure to one, such as fumes, heat, noise, smoke, steam, at frequent intervals..........................	25
5. Extreme. Intensive exposure to several disagreeable elements..	40

TRANSLATION OF POINT VALUES TO MONEY

Since the basic purpose of a job-evaluation program is to secure internal consistency between the worth of jobs and the wage rates paid for them, the next step is to establish a relationship between point values and money.

The underlying principle followed is that while in the current situation (*i.e.*, before evaluation) there must obviously be numerous jobs out of line (else why have an evaluation program?) there nevertheless does exist some reasonable *average* relationship. The tool-maker, for example, is already being paid more than the sweeper. Moreover, competition for labor has had a tendency to establish certain average minimums and maximums in any area.

Accordingly, the steps in reasoning to be followed are these:

1. Determine the average relationship between point values and money paid, as it exists now, and chart this as a "line of average relationship."

2. Rates paid that are higher than this average relationship would warrant (*i.e.*, that fall above the line plotted) would have to be brought down, and rates below would have to be brought up, in order to bring all into proper proportion with each other.

3. However, the average relationship might be low, by area or industry standards. Therefore, rates paid for key jobs will have to be compared with rates paid elsewhere. These comparisons will then determine whether the whole line drawn as per 2, above, should be raised (or lowered).

The above points will now be taken up one by one:

1. Determination of Average Relationship

This is done by taking the benchmark jobs and a number of additional jobs, making perhaps 25 in all, and spotting them on a chart, as shown in Fig. 3, to form a so-called "scatter diagram." The jobs selected should be the ones on which there is the least question as to the reasonableness of the point values assigned.

Since, as already stated, there are bound to be existing inconsistencies, these points will not fall on a continuous line. The next step is to draw through them a "line of best fit" to get the line of average relationship.

Note that this line does not necessarily have to be straight—as a matter of fact, it may well curve upward at the high-point end.

2. Bringing Rates in Line

If there were no question about the general level or rates in the plant, the line thus drawn would furnish the final guide for translating points into money. Then, theoretically, all jobs currently being paid more would have to be brought down, and those less would have to be raised. (To keep the promise that no one would have a cut in wages as a result of the study, the rates on the jobs to be lowered would be "pegged"—*i.e.*, those presently on jobs would get the old rate, but newcomers would be brought in at the now scientifically established rate.) However, in actual practice, it is customary to group all jobs into relatively few labor grades, rather than to pay the exact translation of points into money. (This will be explained under the next major subhead, after discussion of the area and industry comparisons below.)

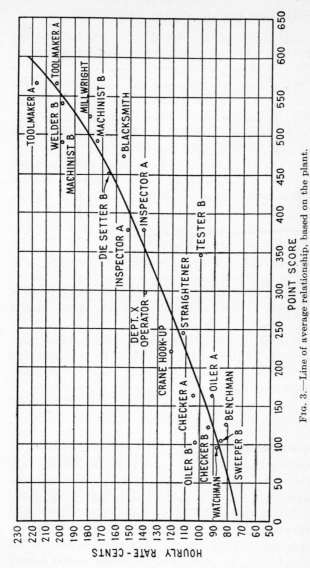

FIG. 3.—Line of average relationship, based on the plant.

3. Area and Industry Comparisons

The wage scale developed as a basis for payment should be in keeping with the community pattern, as well as with wages paid in the industry.

Wage data are obtained for representative jobs common to the plant and the community by visiting or corresponding with selected companies in the area. Great care must be taken to make certain that comparisons are obtained for jobs which are similar. Since the job descriptions are at hand, this determination can be made with reasonable accuracy.

Forward-thinking companies, as well as unions, want their scale to represent at least a median or average of the rate scales in use in the community, so that they can attract a relatively high grade of worker provided other personnel policies are competitive.

The same thinking is in back of making an industry survey. Thus, management will know its relationship not only to the community but also to its product competitors.

With the above information at hand, a decision can be made as to whether the whole plant-relationship curve should be shifted slightly upwards or downwards, and the company is then in a position to establish labor grades and determine upon the final classification and pay for all jobs.

ESTABLISHMENT OF LABOR GRADES AND PAY

Using the adjusted curve as in Fig. 4, the next step is to decide upon the number of classifications or labor grades to be used for pay purposes, and the spread of evaluation points for each grade. Very often, equal divisions are made—a definite number of points for each grade. Thus the NEMA plan (which, as we stated, has a mathematical maximum of 500 points)

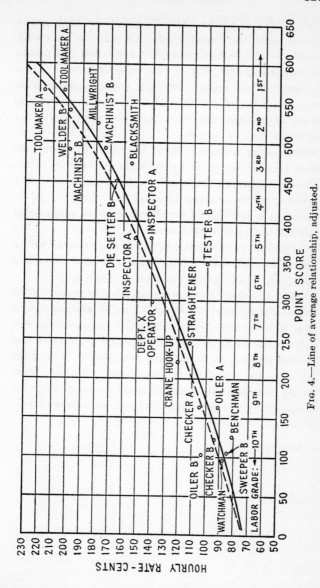

FIG. 4.—Line of average relationship, adjusted.

uses 12 labor grades, with 21 points in each grade, except that the lowest grade, No. 12, has up to 139 points.   The highest grade, No. 1, has 360–381 points.

In our example, Fig. 4, 10 grades are used.   There is no absolute reason for each grade containing an equal number of points.   The number of grades and form of division can be worked out individually for each plant.

Ordinarily, a single rate can be chosen to be paid for each classification in the wage scale.   However, often-times a beginner's rate will be applied where there is a training period of some duration and where the job in question is not one of a natural series of progression through skill and experience.

The money differential between wage classes will of course depend on the number of grades established and the number of points assigned to each grade.

The foregoing procedure means that no matter what the actual number of points for a job amounts to, if that number falls within the point range established for, say, grade 8, the job will be rated as grade 8, and receive the pay established for that grade.   This must be done for practical purposes, for otherwise there would be practically as many labor grades as there are distinct kinds of jobs, all falling along a smooth line.

CHAPTER XIII

MERIT RATING OF EMPLOYEES

By R. S. Driver

Merit rating, sometimes called performance or service rating, produces a description of an employee's performance or ability. The essential features of this technique are:

1. To observe the performance of an employee
2. To record these observations in a systematic manner on a specific form
3. To interpret such performance records in terms of basic qualities of temperament, character, or ability
4. To use this information in the administration of personnel procedures, such as training, promotion, employee guidance, salary change, discipline, etc.

"Ratings" determined as above are obviously opinions. It is true that they are organized opinions rather than snap judgments or guesses. However, it must be clearly remembered that they cannot be so accurate as, for example, measuring distance with a ruler.

Few of the larger, more progressive companies are without some merit-rating plan, and in all these plans the foreman is largely responsible for the success or failure of the program. Some companies have allotted many hours of supervisory and foreman-training meetings to the discussion of this subject.

Other companies assume that their foremen possess a working knowledge of rating techniques. Regardless of the local situation, the foreman who is interested in his company and his men must develop his ability to appraise the performance of others.

IMPORTANCE OF RATING TO MANAGEMENT

The policy of progressive American industry is to pay a fair day's wage for a fair day's work. Promotion to better paying jobs may be based entirely, or in part, on merit, that is, successful performance on lower paying jobs. Job evaluation (Chap. XII), supplemented by merit rating, offers the best available solution to these two difficult problems. For this reason, top managements of many companies are interested in merit rating and other personnel techniques, since these techniques tend to promote employee satisfaction by assuring fair treatment. Many union contracts and statements of company policy consider merit as a factor in promotion as well as in layoff, salary change, etc. Merit rating also may be used as an inventory of the skills and abilities of the employees.

Companies faced with rapid expansion have saved valuable time through systematic upgrading, in which the results of rating have played a considerable part. On the other hand, industries lacking information about their employees have overlooked valuable men in their own organization, with consequent loss of morale and production.

IMPORTANCE OF MERIT RATING TO FOREMAN

The foreman can use the results of a merit-rating program as a proper basis for recommended increases in salary based on changes in employee efficiency.

Whether or not to grant increases has always been a perplexing problem, and the experienced foreman has discovered that merit rating assists him in carefully considering all the pertinent factors. Transfer and promotional procedures are handicapped if information concerning performance is not available.

Merit rating may help quell the ever-present complaint of favoritism. Employees who know that they are independently rated by a number of foremen or that the ratings of their own foremen are reviewed by their superiors are more apt to be convinced that they are receiving fair treatment.

The importance of records concerning performance on the job has been accentuated in recent years by increasing unionization and labor legislation. No longer can the unsupported word of the "boss" be taken as sufficient cause for layoff or disciplinary action. Therefore facts about employee performance, obtained and recorded in a systematized manner, can be of unlimited value. On the other hand, the foreman who acts impulsively and without careful study may find his statements challenged and be unable to bring forward supporting evidence.

IMPORTANCE OF RATING TO EMPLOYEES

Morale and production have often suffered because management has failed to recognize the basic desire of employees for recognition. In any large company, the use of ratings is essential to record just recognition, and without it an employee may feel that he is "lost" in some large department.

MODERN DEVELOPMENTS

Although some form of rating had been practiced for years in American industry, the First World War awakened real interest in this technique. Since that time, psychologists and personnel men have spent many hours in the development of satisfactory rating scales; investigators in governmental, industrial, and academic institutions have helped to develop effective rating methods. Considerable research and developmental work in the subject also has been done in connection with organized foreman training.

The use of merit rating has so expanded that today more companies are employing the technique than ever before. Many of these efforts undoubtedly leave much to be desired. However, that any rating program has failed in one company does not imply that the technique is worthless. Most unsuccessful rating plans fail solely because of the lack of sufficient planning, effort, and interest necessary to produce a workmanlike job.

THE FOREMAN'S RESPONSIBILITY IN RATING

The foreman is directly and solely responsible for the following:

1. Continuously observing the performance of the employees he is required to rate.

2. Carefully and accurately recording the results of such observation on forms distributed to him at stated periods.

3. Discussing the rating results with each employee if the policy of the company permits. (In some companies, however, such discussions are conducted by a member of a functional department, such as Personnel.)

The foreman has additional responsibilities which might well be mentioned at this point. He usually will be required to co-operate with a functional department, where the administration of the rating program will be centered. Each foreman must assist that department by *promptly* recording his ratings and returning the forms when they are distributed to him.

Of even greater importance is the necessity for reporting the performance of each employee *exactly as the foreman observes it.* There exists a quite natural tendency to be lenient or, as it is more often said, "to give a man a break." It would be unfortunate to discourage such a tendency if every employee were given an exactly equal "break." However, the only way in which this can be assured is for each foreman to record his honest and unbiased opinion. Unless rating is done in this manner, differences between the good, average, and poor employees will not be correctly recorded.

The foreman should not *guess.* It is far better to return a rating form without recording all the requested opinions than to mix opinions based on real observation with guesses based on little or second-hand knowledge. The department responsible for the co-ordination and use of this material will be unable to differentiate the guesses from the more carefully considered opinions.

The Foreman's Responsibility to His Men

Every foreman should understand the policy of the company with respect to rating. This means that he should understand how the ratings are to be used and what effect they will have on each of his subordinates. He should be willing and able to explain this policy to his men, showing them why it is a fair policy and how they will benefit from the rating program.

The foreman also should thoroughly understand the *method* of rating, so that he can explain it to any interested employee. He must appreciate the faults as well as the virtues of the rating method and be able to justify the method used in his company. Constructive suggestions which result from such discussions should be forwarded to the responsible functional department.

DEFINITION OF TERMS

In the opening paragraph, merit rating was defined and the use of the terms "service," or "performance," rating was noted. Probably the only other terms that cause confusion are "ranking," "grading," and "rating," when used to indicate a particular method of merit rating.

Ranking consists of listing any group in order, from high to low, and assigning a rank to each particular individual. For example, if employees were to be ranked according to length of service, the employee with longest service would be assigned rank 1, the one with next longest service would be 2, etc. Such a procedure makes no allowances for the differences between each individual but merely arranges them in order.

Grading, or *classifying*, is a procedure by which employees are assigned to a class. Assigning individuals to groups denoted by the letters *A*, *B*, *C*, etc., or by the adjectives excellent, fair, good, etc., is a grading procedure.

Rating usually refers to the assigning of an employee to a definite position along a continuous scale ranging from low to high. This procedure is apparently more precise than the others since it allows for the indication of smaller differences.

TYPES OF SCALES

These methods of merit rating, ranking, grading, and rating are used either singly or in combinations

in many different types of rating scales.   Five different types, by no means all inclusive, are listed below.

The *graphic scale* is the most widely used and is
illustrated in Fig. 1.   In this scale, the employee is
rated on a number of traits or qualities which are
briefly defined in the left-hand column.   A check
mark is placed to the right of each question at that
point on the line where the descriptive phrases
most nearly describe the actual performance.   Early
graphic scales provided for the connection, by a continuous line, of the resulting check marks, thus producing a "graphic profile" of the individual.   Such
a profile may be very misleading, however, since the
units of each trait are probably not equal and should
not be compared directly.

Check lists as illustrated in Fig. 2 are often used.
The rater checks the statements which are applicable
to the employee.   The score is usually the sum of
weighted points assigned to these checked statements.
Such a method has been widely used for rating
municipal-government employees.   Figure 2 illustrates
this method.

Ranking is most simply handled if the name of each
employee is placed on a card, and the foreman arranges
the cards in order of merit.   The resultant ranks
usually are transferred to a permanent record.   A
combination of a graphic scale and a ranking procedure is illustrated in Fig. 3.   On this sheet the
employees' names are listed in the left-hand column,
and each employee is rated by placing a check on the
line opposite his name at some point on the scale.
When all employees have been rated, comparison of
individual positions may result in some readjustment,
and the results can be transcribed into a rank
order.

EMPLOYEE RATING SCALE

NAME OF EMPLOYEE _____   DATE _____

DEPARTMENT _____   RATER _____

INSTRUCTIONS: Place a cross (x) at that point on the line to the right of each of the nine questions which indicates the most accurate answer. The four descriptive phrases opposite each question are designed to assist in the location of the crosses but do not indicate columns. Thus the cross may be placed at any point along the line. The reverse side of this sheet may be used to note any additional information which is important in considering this individual.

1. DOES THIS EMPLOYEE GRASP NEW IDEAS RAPIDLY?	Understands after repeated trials under supervision.	Understands after a detailed explanation of problem and method.	Readily understands if problem and method are outlined to him.	Requires little or no help in order to understand.
2. DOES THIS EMPLOYEE WORK HARD?	Wastes time walking about building, talking to others, etc.	He should be prodded occasionally.	Works steadily.	Habitually drives himself hard.
3. DOES THIS EMPLOYEE WORK SUCCESSFULLY WITH OTHERS?	Annoys others.	Does not fit easily into group.	Acceptable to associates.	Promotes good feeling.
4. DOES THIS EMPLOYEE PRODUCE CORRECT ROUTINE WORK?	I feel that errors impair the value of his work.	I feel I should inspect his work in important matters.	I rely on his work if he assures me it is correct.	I would be surprised if I found errors in his work.

5. HOW DOES THIS EMPLOYEE MAKE DECISIONS WHEN FACED WITH NON-ROUTINE PROBLEMS?	Jumps at conclusions. Fails to consider facts and foresee results of his decisions.	Fails to foresee results of his decisions although he considered the facts.	Considers facts and most of his decisions are acceptable.	Makes sound decisions based on thorough analysis.
6. HOW DOES THIS EMPLOYEE'S MANNER AND APPEARANCE IMPRESS THOSE WHO CASUALLY DEAL WITH HIM?	May irritate others.	Acceptable if certain defects were corrected.	Has an agreeable manner and appearance.	Highly favorable comments are made about him.
7. TO WHAT EXTENT DOES THIS EMPLOYEE CONTRIBUTE PRODUCTIVE IDEAS?	Has never suggested changing the established routine.	Makes occasional suggestions of minor importance.	Has suggested worthwhile changes.	Constantly produces productive ideas.
8. WILL THIS EMPLOYEE ACT IN OTHER THAN ROUTINE MATTERS WHEN NOT GIVEN DEFINITE INSTRUCTIONS?	Will not act unless told to do so.	Will act voluntarily in matters involving minor deviations from routine.	Will act voluntarily in most matters.	Needs restraint in some situations.
9. AT WHAT RATE DOES THIS EMPLOYEE PRODUCE WORK?	He does not finish the work in the time allowed.	I do not feel sure he will complete the work in the time allowed.	I am confident he will complete the work in the time allowed.	He surprises me by completing work before I expect it.

FIG. 1.—Graphic rating scale.

THE PROBST SERVICE REPORT

LABOR FORM

FOR APPRAISING THE SERVICE VALUE OF
UNSKILLED AND SEMI-SKILLED LABOR

FOR THE SIX-MONTH PERIOD ENDING _____

(LABOR FORM)

The facts and judgments recorded on this sheet are evaluated by a scientifically-constructed process and formula, and produce a rating which takes into account all the checked items.

RATING

NAME

TITLE

ORGANIZATION UNIT

DIRECTIONS: On this form you are to report the service value of the employee mentioned above. The report should be for the six-month period shown hereon, unless otherwise indicated.

In addition to the blanks to be filled in below, you should check (with an X) all those items in the left-hand column that you can find which will properly fit or describe this employee. Do not guess; if you are not reasonably sure that the employee possesses the trait or quality indicated by a certain item, do not check that item at all. It is not necessary to check any given number of items. You may be able to check 25 or more for one employee and have difficulty in finding more than a dozen or so to describe properly some other employee. Do not make your X's small; keep them inside the little squares.

This sheet should be checked, wherever possible, by three foremen or other supervisory officers. Each should select one of the three check columns in which to make his X marks. The foreman or supervisor who is lowest in rank or authority should be the first to check the sheet; then the next higher (or equal) in rank should check; and the one in highest authority should check last. (See direction booklet.)

Foremen may add on the other side of this sheet additional items of their own to further describe this employee.

How many days was this employee absent during this period— (Do not include absence for injury in line of duty or absence on regular vacation)

Check Columns 1 2 3	
☐☐☐	Lazy
☐☐☐	Slow moving
☐☐☐	Quick and active
☐☐☐	Too old for the work
☐☐☐	Minor physical defects
☐☐☐	Serious physical defects
☐☐☐	Indifferent; not interested
☐☐☐	Talks too much
☐☐☐	Too blunt or outspoken
☐☐☐	Too much self-importance
☐☐☐	Good team worker
☐☐☐	Not a good team worker
☐☐☐	Resents criticism or suggestions
☐☐☐	Antagonizes when dealing with others
☐☐☐	Might often be more considerate
☐☐☐	Usually pleasant and cheerful
☐☐☐	Always tries to please
☐☐☐	Cranky, or often grumbles or complains
☐☐☐	Often seems dissatisfied
☐☐☐	Is often injured
☐☐☐	Sometimes goes on a "tear"
☐☐☐	Might often use better judgment
☐☐☐	Generally uses good judgment
☐☐☐	Often finds much better ways of doing the work
☐☐☐	Does not do his share of work
☐☐☐	Generally looks for the easy work
☐☐☐	Must generally be told what to do
☐☐☐	Often needs prodding

Active but not strong
Active and strong
Turns out unusually large amount of work
Steady worker most of the time
Keeps busy at work
Does not accept responsibility
Accepts responsibility
Does not always obey orders willingly
Visits too much with others
Needs considerable supervision
Works well without supervision
Often assigned as crew leader or subforeman
Loses temper easily
Careless with tools or equipment
Not skillful with tools or equipment
Too easy-going
Learns new work slowly
Learns new work easily
Understands instructions readily
A willing worker at all times
Takes unusual interest in the work
Might be more orderly
Very orderly and systematic
Often forgetful
Neglects safety measures, or takes chances
Makes many mistakes, or careless in work
Usually accurate
Hardly ever makes a mistake
Slow to understand instructions
Is very skillful in his work
Not generally reliable or dependable ⎫
Usually reliable and dependable ⎬ Check one item only, if any.
Always reliable and dependable ⎭

(a) For sickness, with pay............. _____ days
(b) For sickness, without pay.......... _____ days
(c) For personal reasons, with or without pay _____ days
(d) How many times absent without leave _____ times
(e) (If there was any other absence, or any suspension; or loss of vacation, bonus, merits; or any other penalty, explain briefly here.)

Check only one item in each of the following boxes. Consider not only the punctuality of the employee in reporting for work, but also his promptness in answering calls, and doing specially assigned work.

Check Columns

1	2	3	
☐	☐	☐	Nearly always late
☐	☐	☐	Usually late
☐	☐	☐	Often late (about half the time)
☐	☐	☐	Usually punctual
☐	☐	☐	Never or hardly ever. late
☐	☐	☐	Nearly always quits ahead of time
☐	☐	☐	Usually quits ahead of time
☐	☐	☐	Often quits ahead of time
☐	☐	☐	Watches clock too much near quitting time
☐	☐	☐	Seldom quits ahead of time
☐	☐	☐	Never quits ahead of time

FIG. 2.—Check-list form for appraising unskilled and semiskilled labor. (*Reproduced by permission of Probst Rating System, St. Paul, Minn.*)

EMPLOYEE RATING SCALE

RATER _____ DEPARTMENT _____ DATE _____

INSTRUCTIONS TO SUPERVISORS: Place a cross (X) on the line to the right of each employee's name at that point which you believe gives the most accurate answer to the following question. Remember the phrases do not indicate columns. (For complete instructions see the attached sheet.)

Does this employee grasp new ideas rapidly? Consider whether or not it is necessary for you to give him detailed explanations of new methods and problems.

NAME	Understands after repeated trials under supervision.	Understands after a detailed explanation of problem and method.	Readily understands if problem and method are outlined to him.	Requires little or no help in order to understand.

Fig. 3.—Combination of graphic scale and ranking procedure.

PERSONNEL REPORT—CONFIDENTIAL

Name of Employee_____Date_____

Position_____Department_____

Prepared by_____Division_____

Directions: This report calls for answers to a number of questions concerning the above employee. Your answers should be given IN YOUR OWN WORDS, and should represent YOUR OWN OPINION. When an answer calls for an explanation, state it briefly. If there is not enough space to complete your explanations, use the other side of this report, referring to the question by number.

1. List the good points of this employee as you see them:_____

_____

_____

2. List the faults or limitations of this employee as you see them:_____

_____

_____

3. Can you suggest any point on which this employee should improve in order to increase his (or her) value to the company? YES_____. NO_____ (check). If your answer is "YES," please explain:_____

_____

_____

4. Is this employee in line for promotion to more important duties? YES_____. NO_____ (check). If your answer is "YES," please indicate the type of work for which he (or she) is qualified:_____

5. Considering actual ability shown on the job (disregarding present age, health or scarcity of applicants at the time of hiring), would you hire this employee over again if you were to make the decision? YES_____. NO_____ (check). If your answer is "NO," please explain:_____

_____

_____

6. How do you rate this employee?   (Check ONE):

As OUTSTANDING_____(Definitely superior; represents the "best type" of employee in his (or her) line of work.)

(_____Plus)

As SATISFACTORY (_____) (A good average employee, well fitted for the work.)

(_____Minus)

As a PROBLEM_____(A "poor type" of employee in his (or her) line of work, due to:) Check one or more.

_____Does not learn   _____Lack of interest   _____Health

_____In wrong line of   _____Wrong attitude   _____Personal financial
work   difficulties

_____Limited ability   _____Age   _____Poor personality

Fig. 4.—Classification, or grading, form. (*Reproduced by permission of Guy W. Wadsworth, Jr., Southern California Gas Company, Los Angeles, Calif.*)

COMPARISON OF EMPLOYEES

Department_____ Comparer_____ Date_____

Instructions: Compare these employees on the basis of the question below. In each pair of names cross out the name of the individual who, in your opinion, represents the inferior of the two employees.

Question: Does this employee work successfully with others?

Doe	Roe	Green	White
Brown	Jones	Smith	Thomas
Hughes	Doe	Brown	Roe
Green	White	Jones	Smith
Thomas	Hughes	Doe	Roe
Green	White	Jones	Thomas
Hughes	Doe	Roe	Green
Brown	Smith	Hughes	Doe
Roe	Green	White	Brown
Doe	Roe	Green	White
Brown	Jones	Smith	Thomas
Roe	Green	White	Brown
Jones	Smith	Thomas	Hughes
White	Brown	Jones	Smith
Thomas	Hughes	Doe	Roe
Smith	Thomas	Hughes	White
Jones	Doe	Brown	Hughes
Smith	Thomas	Green	Jones

Fig. 5.—Paired-comparisons method.

A *classification*, or *grading*, *form* is illustrated in Fig. 4. The foreman checks the appropriate square, classifying the employee as a problem workman, outstanding employee, etc. Statements to support these classifications are frequently required. Many personnel men feel that such a classification is all that can be obtained from merit rating, and advocate this method because of its simplicity.

The *paired-comparisons* method is lengthy, especially if the group is large, but it has been used successfully in industry. The U. S. Employment Service, particularly, has made use of it. As illustrated in Fig. 5, each employee is compared with every other employee. One of each pair of names should be crossed out. Each man's score can be obtained by counting the number of times his name remains on the sheet. Many persons who have conducted extensive research with merit rating feel that this method is the one most apt to produce correct results. Because of the labor involved (for example, with 20 employees 180 comparisons are required, while with 30 employees there are 420 comparisons), it has not had wide acceptance.

No rating scale, however, can be depended upon to produce correct results unless the rater is capable of using such a tool. No scale in existence today can take the place of clear thinking and consistent observation of performance. A well-constructed scale will serve to organize the facts about each employee but cannot be expected to do more than this.

RATING PROCEDURES

There is little or no uniformity in the selection of qualities to be rated. The number of traits rated also varies from company to company. Traits such as quantity, quality, accuracy, speed, industry, etc., appear on many rating forms. Other forms include character traits such as honesty, loyalty, etc., which, while undoubtedly important, are difficult to rate since they generally cannot be observed in the performance of the employee.

The classification method and ratings used as a basis for layoff generally produce a rating of the overall performance of the individual. Information of this nature may be all that is necessary for the solution of these problems. In every company the choice of traits to be rated should be determined by the information required for successful personnel administration. The choice of traits is definitely limited, however, by the fact that it is practically impossible to recognize many important traits in the daily performance of the employee on the job.

Step-by-step Procedure for Rating

The foreman has the main responsibility for correct rating. The following procedure should help him properly to execute this duty.

Step 1: *Get the Facts*

Rating should be based on the observation of performance over the period of time which elapses between successive ratings. This may be 3 or 6 months, 1 year, or longer. Untrained raters tend to rate on the basis of general impression or a few outstanding incidents. The foreman who rates on such a flimsy basis will find that his opinion fluctuates rapidly. Later, when faced with the necessity for substantiating his ratings, he will be unwilling or unable to do so. As a result, both his men and management lose confidence in him.

The major error in rating, as it is practiced today, is not so much the result of prejudice or leniency as it is the failure to obtain the facts about employee performance. Any man who has supervised the work of others should be frank to admit that often he cannot be sure that his judgment of employee ability is correct. In the absence of any other technique, persistent and careful observation is the only solution to the problem of obtaining the correct facts.

Step 2: *Study the Rating Scale*

Before recording ratings, the scale and method should be reviewed. Definitions of terms should be studied, and, in cases of doubt, the meanings should be discussed with responsible individuals in the appropriate functional department. In one company, for example, the word "average" was used on the rating scale. It was assumed that all foremen were aware of the meaning of this word. Later analysis showed quite clearly that various foremen held three distinct ideas as to the meaning of this word.

Descriptive adjectives and adverbs ("usually," "outstanding," etc.) are particularly misleading. When using scales on which these words appear, one cannot take too much care to ensure that all raters have the same understanding of the meaning of these words. The rater must also be careful to adhere to standard procedure for recording the ratings and to check against careless errors. Rating scales look deceptively easy to fill out, but accurate rating, in reality, is a careful, thorough, and sometimes tedious process.

Step 3: *Develop a Standard for Comparison of Individuals*

In all rating scales, with the possible exception of the paired-comparison and check-list types, some standards by which to judge employee performance are required. Rating scales of the type shown in Figs. 1 and 3 attempt to solve the problem by using phrases describing performance. Even when such aid is available, the foreman should compare the employees with each other to ensure more accurate rating.

Comparison is usually accomplished in one of three ways. First, and probably least accurate, is the use of the employees of the entire company as a standard of comparison. The individual employee is then said to be better than average, average, poorer than average, etc. Such a procedure is questionable, because few if any foremen can possibly observe a sufficient sample of the performance of this large and diversified group. As a result, the standard of comparison is merely an impression, and most foremen tend to say that as a whole the men in the company are pretty good, but they believe that their department is better than average. Obviously, since average is a mid-point, above which are only 50 per cent of the employees, this is faulty reasoning.

A second procedure is to base comparison on the rater's previous experience with men. The foreman who speaks of an "average welder" or "outstanding machinist" is probably using this procedure. It is true that such opinions can sometimes be formed with reasonable accuracy and consistency, as a result of long experience. The difficulty, however, is that such a procedure is based on memory, which is notoriously unreliable, and there is considerable difference in the standards of various raters.

A third procedure, and probably the one least open to error, is to use the immediate group to be rated as the standard for comparison. Thus, each man is rated according to how well his performance matches those of the other employees in his group. However, the procedure is complicated if the group to be rated is small (fewer than 10 people) or if the work of each employee differs from that of the others. But these complications can be met and solved by the intelligent rater who rates each employee on the basis of his performance in his job. Such ratings tend to be clear cut and objective. No additional variables, such as the "average" man, have been introduced to complicate the interpretation of the results.

Step 4: *Rate the Entire Group at One Time*

Employees under the immediate supervision of the foremen can best be rated all at the same time, rather than having the ratings staggered over several months. If this is done, it is important to complete the rating of every individual on each trait—"accuracy," for example—before proceeding to a second trait.

Every rater is limited in his ability to consider a large number of variables at one time. However, when the rater considers one quality at a time, he can more easily keep the definition of this trait or quality in mind and consequently give greater attention to the employees under consideration. This procedure will reduce the "intertrait," or "halo," effect, which distorts the results in many cases.

Step 5: *Make a Tentative Rating on the Sheet*

Rating should be entered on the sheet, the descriptive phrases given on the form being used as guides. Each employee should be rated only on those qualities which can be observed. When all ratings have been recorded, they should be studied to be sure that each employee's rating lines up properly with the descriptive material on the scale. The relative position of each individual within the group with which he is compared should also be checked.

Step 6: *Review the Ratings*

Ratings should never be returned to the functional department until the rater has reviewed them at least twice. It is suggested that after the ratings have been completed they be reviewed after several days have elapsed. If many changes have to be made, an additional waiting period is clearly indicated. Above all, time should be taken to do a thorough, thoughtful job.

Step 7: *Discuss the Ratings with Employees*

Foremen who discuss ratings with their employees face a difficult task. Employees are not willing to accept vague generalities. Further, excessive leniency is no solution, since the foreman may commit himself by polite statements and later be in a weak position if discipline or other action is necessary.

The chief value of foreman-employee discussion is that the employee may improve his performance as a result of comments, encouragement, and suggestions by the foreman. The foreman should realize, however, that his opinions may not always be correct. He should be willing at all times to be convinced that he is in error. Occasionally it may even be necessary to develop procedures to provide the facts needed to settle some disputed point. Such foreman-employee relationship requires intelligence, honesty, and tact.

Discussions which are not successfully handled can be serious sources of poor morale.

Step 8: Return Completed Scales to Proper Functional Department

The final step in this rating procedure is sometimes unduly delayed. Rating should be considered a serious duty and one which should be accomplished with all speed that is consistent with accurate results.

Common Errors in Rating

Excessive leniency and failure to base ratings on observation of actual performance have already been mentioned as common sources of errors in rating. The "halo effect" has also been widely publicized as being responsible for error. This fancy title has been given to the effect the rating of one quality has upon the later rating of a second quality. The employee who has one or two outstanding desirable characteristics is apt to be rated more favorably on all other qualities. For example, the pleasant, likable employee may be given higher rating for quantity and quality of production than he actually deserves. The opposite may often be true, especially in the case of unco-operative employees, who tend to be rated as less efficient than they actually may be.

Daily experience has taught us that every employee does some things well and other things poorly. The smartest clerk may be lazy. The affable salesman may be dull. Ratings of traits should portray such intertrait differences among employees. If they do not, the chances are good that the "halo effect" is present.

The ratings of most employees should reveal a spread on various traits possibly varying from high for one trait to low for another. Likewise, ratings for a group of employees, if one trait at a time is considered, should also reveal a similar spread. Unless the group is unusually small, has been carefully selected, or is subject to definite restrictive forces, there will be individual members who possess two or three times as much of one trait as the poorer members of the group.

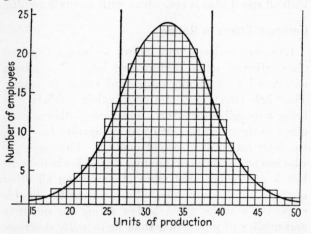

Fig. 6.—Graph of normal distribution. Each of the 354 squares represents one employee. Note that the production of approximately two-thirds of the men is closely grouped around the middle of the curve.

As a matter of fact, the plotted measurements of human abilities, unless drastically modified by the factors just mentioned, generally take the shape of the "normal curve" shown in Fig. 6.

This curve reveals that approximately two-thirds of the group are bunched closely together and may be casually referred to as "average." One-sixth of the group possess unusual ability, and one-sixth are relatively less efficient. While there is no assurance that the ratings for one trait in any department should assume a similar form, still it is well to check the results obtained against such a curve. The foreman who finds, after completing such a check, that all his employees are rated as unusually efficient may well question the accuracy of his results. It is doubtful that with present methods of selection and control, any group can be so uniformly excellent even on one trait.

USE OF RATINGS

Ratings completed and then filed away are of little value. The foreman as well as the proper functional department should frequently refer to them. Many companies post the rating results to personal-history cards in order to ensure such use. In general, it is considered best to use the rating in conjunction with all other available information concerning the employee.

How to Interpret Ratings

Ratings are systematized opinions based on observation. As opinions, the inherent error is probably large in most cases. Interpretations based on ratings must be made with due appreciation of this error Persons used to dealing with the slide rule and the micrometer often attempt to read a rating sheet too closely. In making all interpretations, foremen should use the rating sheet to indicate *general trends* and *probabilities* rather than mathematical certainties. The assignment of relative weights, or scores, to various traits to produce a total score may often be misleading. In some instances, such scores may be desirable, but more often a qualitative rather than quantitative interpretation of the rating scale proves to be of greater value.

In many companies the duties of the jobs are analyzed and graded in accordance with job-evaluation methods described in Chap. XII. The requirements of the job resulting from such analysis may be compared with the ratings of the performance of the individual on that job. Differences between required and actual performance can be noted and used as a basis for employee guidance and routine personnel procedure.

SUMMARY

Merit rating is a necessary and valuable technique. Careful rating and intelligent interpretation of the results will provide information which can generally be obtained in no other way. Unfortunately, possibly because of its apparent simplicity, this technique is misused more frequently than perhaps any other technique for personnel administration. The responsibility of the foreman has been clearly indicated, and adherence to the basic principles previously set forth in this chapter will do much to raise the standard of rating in American industry.

CHAPTER XIV

THE TOOLS OF INDUSTRIAL PSYCHOLOGY

By Charles A. Drake

During the past 40 years, great progress has been made in the development of psychology as a science. Because of this progress we understand human nature much better than ever before. This understanding has come about through tracing human behavior to its causes and through studying how certain causes result in certain patterns of behavior. Modern science holds that for every effect there must be a cause, and for every cause a resulting effect. The aim of science is to discover these cause-and-effect relationships. Applied science then tries to develop methods for producing the desired effects. This is just as true of applied psychology as it is of applied chemistry or applied physics.

INDUSTRIAL PSYCHOLOGY AND THE FOREMAN'S WORK

There are at least five activities of the foreman in which a knowledge of applied psychology can be helpful. These are (1) selection of employees, (2) induction, or placing of employees on the job, (3) training of employees, (4) maintaining the morale or enthusiasm of employees, and (5) supervising employees at work. Proper handling of each is essential to successful foremanship.

353

We must remember that the foreman also deals with other foremen, with his superiors, with various technical specialists, and with persons not directly connected with the company. Obviously, he needs a broad understanding of human nature. Part of this knowledge he will already have if he is a good student of people, as he should be. Part of it he can learn from the experience of others.

Much of this knowledge about other people and how they act belongs to what is called "intuitive," or "common-sense," psychology. Some scientific psychologists claim that this intuitive psychology should not be called psychology at all. It is just applied common sense. Nevertheless, such knowledge and understanding can be very helpful.

ACTIVITIES OF SCIENTIFIC PSYCHOLOGY

Scientific psychology devotes itself to experiments to determine cause-and-effect relationships. It holds that anything that exists at all exists in some amount and that anything that exists in some amount can be measured by suitable instruments. Part of its effort is, therefore, devoted to developing instruments that may be used for measurement. Another part of its effort is devoted to interpretations and explanations of the measurements. Consequently, much of the work of scientific psychology has consisted of making tests of various human abilities, while still more attention has been given to the explanation of what these measurements mean and how they can be used in controlling human behavior.

A further line of activity of scientific psychology is that which deals with mental abnormalities, such as feeble-mindedness and emotional disturbances. The feeble-minded have very definite limitations on their abilities. The idiots, or lowest grade, are not able to talk intelligibly, to clothe, feed, or take care of themselves without aid from others, and so they are not found in industry. The imbeciles are the next higher grade of the feeble-minded. They are able to talk more intelligibly, to look after themselves better, and to do simple jobs, but they are seldom found in industry. The morons, or next higher grade, are able to talk more clearly than the imbeciles. They can perform simple jobs but have difficulty in understanding directions and in learning tasks that are at all complicated. Some of them are employable on simple, unskilled jobs, but it is dangerous for them to be around machinery. They often get into difficulties because they cannot understand many cause-and-effect relationships, nor do they comprehend personal and property rights. Properly placed and supervised, however, they can be useful employees.

The feeble-minded of all grades are primarily defective in intelligence. They are handicapped by their lack of ability to understand. On the other hand, individuals with emotional disturbances are handicapped by lack of ability to control their behavior. The feeble-minded are born that way. They develop up to a certain point, at which their mental growth then stops. Their lack of ability, while often apparent, can be measured only by their performance on suitable mental tests. Such tests have been developed extensively during the past 40 years, but they can still be used satisfactorily only by a trained psychologist.

Individuals with emotional disturbances, unlike the feeble-minded, are not born that way but have become that way. They are usually normal, and sometimes superior, in intellect, and the breakdown of their emotional control may be either gradual or sudden. Sometimes this breakdown also impairs their reasoning and other distinctly intellectual abilities. There are comparatively few tests for measuring emotional disturbances. Discovery of such disturbances still depends very largely upon careful observation of the person's behavior over a period of time. In its most extreme form, such behavior is called insanity. This is a legal rather than a psychological term and implies that the person is not responsible for his acts. There are, however, many emotional disturbances less extreme than insanity. These are found among many persons who have regular employment. The difference is one of degree, that is, of the extent to which these persons can control their own behavior and can be held responsible for their actions.

With suitable understanding and control, many of these slightly abnormal persons can be satisfactory, and even valuable, employees. It is necessary only to know their limitations, to know what to use and what to avoid in dealing with them. Such knowledge is part of the subject matter of scientific psychology and should be acquired by the competent and progressive foreman.

APPLICATIONS OF PSYCHOLOGICAL FACTS

Progress has been made in recent years in developing certain other activities very helpful to the foreman. These are not direct applications of scientific psychology, but they do require some psychological knowledge. One such activity is job evaluation. Another is the rating of employees on their performance, which almost always includes an appraisal of their mental traits, enthusiasm, willingness, and other characteristics of behavior.

Many personnel departments are now using tests to assist in selecting employees and in identifying the particular abilities required on certain jobs. It has been found that industrial abilities are highly specialized and that these abilities can be measured by suitable tests. The latter give positive assurance that a man sent to an inspection job has the ability required on that job and that a man assigned to a foot press has the hand-and-foot co-ordination and the "visual-perceptual" ability needed to do the work.

Still another activity very helpful to the foreman, in which a knowledge of psychology is valuable, is the exit interview. Such an interview should be given to every worker who leaves, whether by resignation or discharge. Often it is conducted by both the foreman and the personnel department. When properly handled, it gives valuable information which may be used by the foreman to exercise better control over his group and to increase the quantity and quality of production.

Finally, the more the foreman knows about psychological techniques, the more effectively he can co-operate with other members of management, and the easier he can make his own job.

Where tests and other measuring instruments are employed in the selection of personnel, the foreman has a direct responsibility in interpreting and applying the data. The information supplied him may indicate an employee's present level of skill and his capacity for further growth. It is then up to the foreman to place the individual on the appropriate job, supervise his training on the job, and follow up the training to make sure that he is progressing as he should.

The foreman also has a direct obligation to assist the personnel department through furnishing information and advice about the men supplied to him, so that selection methods may be improved.

Finally, it is an obligation of the foreman to explain to his subordinates how and why the selection methods are used, what the tests are for, and what they reveal about a man's abilities and disabilities. Employees, in general, are not afraid of tests, but they are eager to know more about them. All men have an interest in their own abilities. The foreman can do much to increase their morale and effort by satisfying this natural curiosity.

DEFINITIONS OF TERMS

Many words are loosely used in everyday speech, and the meanings are sometimes quite different from the meanings when the words are used in a technical field. If we define our terms in the technical sense, the meanings are limited to what is stated in the definition. Let us, therefore, define some of the terms we must use in applied psychology.

Ability. Ability is a general term implying the power to perform as a result of developing an aptitude. That is, it is an aptitude expressing itself in performance. An aptitude is looked upon as innate and constant, but an ability may be developed, depending upon training and experience, up to the maximum permitted by its underlying aptitude.

Aptitude. An aptitude is a potential, or undeveloped, ability. A person may be said to have an aptitude for highjumping. With practice and training, he may develop this aptitude to his "physiological limit," that is, to the utmost extent of the capacity with which he is endowed by nature. An aptitude is inborn, or hereditary, something that is part of a man's native constitution. We commonly speak of mathematical aptitude, mechanical aptitude, sales aptitude, etc. Aptitudes are never measured directly but are inferred from measures of ability. That is, we measure a man's ability on a properly designed test and from it make a judgment about the quality and extent of his inherent aptitude.

Correlation. Correlation expresses a relationship between two or more series of things, such as between the scores made by different men on an aptitude test and the average hourly wages of those same men. This relationship is commonly expressed by a single figure, called a "coefficient of correlation," determined mathematically by analyses of the statistical data.

When the relationship is perfect, that is, when the man who makes the highest aptitude-test score earns the highest average wages, the man who makes the second highest aptitude-test score earns the second highest average wages, etc., this coefficient is +1.00. When the relationship is reversed, that is, when the man who makes the highest aptitude-test score earns the lowest average wages, the man who makes the second highest aptitude-test score earns the second lowest average wages, etc., the coefficient is −1.00. If the relationship is not so clear cut, the coefficient will be somewhere between 1.00 and .00. This is almost invariably the case. A coefficient of plus or minus .90 or more is considered high; plus or minus .50 to plus or minus .80, moderate; plus or minus .40 or less, low or negligible. A zero coefficient means that there is no relationship whatsoever between the two things measured; the one does not tell anything about the other.

Criterion. A criterion is a standard against which other things are measured. Thus, average daily-production figures or piece-rate earnings for a group of men may be used as a criterion against which to measure the usefulness of a rating scale or a test. A criterion is often unreliable because of the large number of different influences that may affect it, such as defective parts or machinery, poor supervision, restriction of output, etc.

Sometimes rankings or ratings of employees by the foreman are used as criteria. Such measures depend largely upon personal judgments and may be made unreliable by prejudice, bias, or "halo effect."

Critical Score. This is the score on a test above which people are acceptable for employment and below which they are to be rejected. It is usually established after making a study of the test scores in relation to success on the job. The point chosen is usually one above which a majority of persons succeed, and below which a majority of persons fail on the job. When applicants are plentiful, the critical score is usually placed high. When applicants are scarce, the score must usually be moved downward in order to get enough persons to fill the available jobs. The critical score is also sometimes called the "criterion score."

Dexterity. Dexterity refers to a person's ability to make smooth, co-ordinated movements of different parts of his body, also to join successive movements rapidly and effectively. In its first meaning we have the example of dual dexterity, in which the two hands perform simultaneous operations. In the second meaning we refer to the smooth flow of successive movements, such as select, grasp, transport, position, and release. Therefore, high dexterity implies the ability to join these movements without hesitation, fumbling, or the addition of unnecessary and ineffective elements in the "operation cycle."

Halo Effect. Halo effect is a term used to explain the tendency to overvalue a man's ability in one line of effort because of his outstanding performance in something else. Thus, a very heavy hitter or a successful pitcher on a department baseball team may be rated as a higher producer than his actual output warrants.

Incentive. When applied to industry, an incentive is anything that causes men to get work done, such as money, praise, status, security, fear, etc. Most effective is a combination of money with one or more of the other incentives.

Morale. Morale pertains to the mental state of the work force. We say that the morale is low when employees are dissatisfied, sullen, non-co-operative, suspicious, resentful, or discouraged. Morale is high when employees are enthusiastic, energetic, co-operative, and cheerful. Morale is usually a direct reflection of the quality of the leadership, particularly the leadership of the foreman.

Perception. Perception is the next response after sensation. The first response to a round, colored object is a sensation of color and roundness. Following this comes the second response, which gives meaning to the color, as red or blue, and identifies the object, as an apple or a ball. The quality of perception is not wholly dependent on the quality of the sensory response. Therefore, defective vision usually leads to slow and imperfect perceptions, but perfect vision does not guarantee perfect perceptions. In fact, many persons who have perfect vision have very poor perceptions.

Physiological Limit. This is the inborn, or innate, maximum limit to which, under the most favorable conditions of training and incentives, a person can develop his ability. The physiological limit for one broad jumper may be 24 ft., while for another it may be 18 ft. The physiological limit operates just as definitely to limit industrial production as it operates in athletics. Usually the physiological limit is not nearly attained in industry.

Skill. Skill is a combination of dexterities and perceptions which expresses itself in superior performance. A skilled man does a job better, faster, and with greater ease than an unskilled man. High skill depends upon a high physiological limit, superior dexterity and perceptions, adequate incentives, and competent training.

Test. A test is a standardized device used under standard conditions to get a definite measurement. Thus, a chemical test may determine the amount of a metal in a compound; a physiological test may determine the strength of a set of muscles; or a dexterity test may measure the effectiveness of certain muscular co-ordinations.

THE DEVELOPMENT OF TESTING

The widespread use of tests for personnel purposes began during the First World War, when hundreds of thousands of men were given the famous Army Alpha and Beta intelligence tests. Alpha was for men who could read and write English, and was performed with pencil and paper. Beta was designed for those who were illiterate or who could not read and write English.

On these tests Army officers and men who had been in professional or executive positions in civil life usually made high scores, while men who had been unskilled laborers generally made quite low scores. It was therefore inferred that individuals making the high scores possessed higher intelligence than the others and that these were the ones who should be selected and trained for technical and administrative positions.

Trade tests were also developed for use in the Army. Some of these were made up of lists of questions about a trade. If a man could answer these questions at the highest level, it was inferred that he had good trade knowledge and probably also had considerable skill. If he could answer only a few of the questions, it was inferred that his knowledge and skill were probably low.

At about the same time, other tests were being developed for selecting clerical workers and for measuring mechanical and other aptitudes. Some of these were pencil-and-paper tests. Others, the mechanical tests for example, required a man to assemble various objects from the loose parts, such as a door lock, a bicycle bell, or a mousetrap. Success in assembling these objects within the time limit was taken to indicate mechanical insight and aptitude.

More recently, the U. S. Employment Service has developed many tests of trade knowledge for use in the public employment offices. This service has also originated an extensive classification of jobs and has found it possible to make classifications of "job families," that is, groups of jobs which require similar skills.

THE MEASUREMENT OF APTITUDES

Since the First World War, much progress has been made in developing instruments for measuring indus-

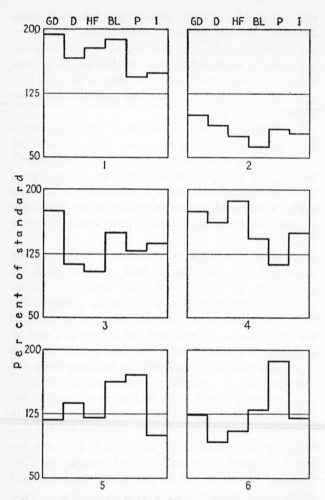

Fig. 1.—Profiles of individual abilities. *GD*, general hand dexterity; *D*, dual hand dexterity; *HF*, hand-and-foot co-ordination; *BL*, bilateral hand co-ordination; *P*, visual perception (inspection ability); *I*, intelligence.

trial aptitudes. The aim in this has been to select the right man for the right job. This means not merely the individual who can do the job best at the moment, but the one who will develop to a high level of performance at the work, who will increase his skill and earnings, and who will not soon become dissatisfied or discouraged and quit.

For certain types of work, performance tests, rather than pencil-and-paper tests, have been found most useful. Such tests give a man an opportunity to demonstrate under standardized conditions just what level of dexterity he possesses. They also indicate his capacity for further development, since a high level of aptitude indicates future skill on the job.

General hand dexterity was once thought to be closely related to many other dexterities, such as those involved in the co-ordination of eyes and hands or hands and feet. We now know that a high level of general hand dexterity does not guarantee the possession of a high level of any of the other specialized dexterities, each of which can be—and must be— measured separately.

This may be clearly seen in the "ability profiles" of six men presented in Fig. 1. Each numbered square presents the scores made by one of the six men on six different tests. (The same six tests were used for all the men.) These tests measured *general hand dexterity*, *dual hand dexterity* (the ability to co-ordinate the two hands in doing the same thing, such as assembling two identical mechanical parts at the same time), *hand-and-foot co-ordination*, *bilateral hand co-ordination* (in which the two hands do somewhat different motions simultaneously), *inspection ability*, or visual perception, and *intelligence*.

The profiles show that these measured abilities are not closely related to each other. Thus, in employee No. 1 we have a man who is high in all of the measured abilities, a case which is very rare. Equally rare is No. 2, who is low in all the abilities. Number 3 is high in general hand dexterity but low in dual dexterity and hand-and-foot co-ordination. Number 4, who is equal to No. 3 in general hand dexterity, is superior in dual dexterity and very superior in hand-and-foot co-ordination. Number 5 is only average in general hand dexterity, in dual dexterity, and in hand-and-foot co-ordination. He is high in bilateral dexterity and inspection ability but fairly low in intelligence. Number 6 is also only average in general hand dexterity, is low in dual dexterity and hand-and-foot co-ordination, average in bilateral dexterity and intelligence, but very high in inspection ability.

In selecting men for specialized jobs, we should prefer No. 1, who is high in all abilities, with the thought that he might be the kind of man we could train to be a foreman or supervisor. We should be willing to place No. 2 only on relatively unskilled jobs not calling for special dexterities and not making heavy demands upon inspection ability or intelligence. We should be careful not to place No. 3 on a dual-operation job or on a foot press or a foot-operated fixture. Number 4 would probably make a superior dual operator and an exceptionally fine operator on a foot press or a foot-operated fixture. Number 5 would probably make a superior operator on a two-hand packaging job on which he was also required to inspect the product as he packed it. Number 6 would probably make a very good inspector, although he would be only an average performer in other respects. If we fail to place him on an inspection job, we should lose the benefit we might gain from his very superior inspection ability.

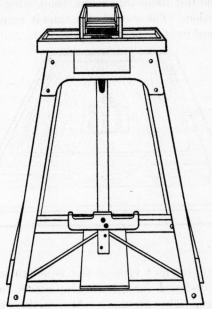

Fig. 2.—Test for hand-and-foot co-ordination.

In a typical test of hand dexterity, special trays or boards are used, in which panels are arranged for the insertion of oddly shaped blocks, and pegs and marbles, according to instructions. The person to be tested is given instructions and some practice in performing this standard job. He is then timed on the whole job from start to finish. The length of time taken is his score.

Another kind of test for measuring hand-and-foot co-ordination is shown in Fig. 2. The person tested is required to perform a hand operation alternating with a foot operation. He is given a period of practice in placing the items in a movable die, controlled by a foot lever. A movement of the foot lever then drops the test items into a box, completing the cycle of operation. The score is the time it takes to pass a standard number of items through the test.

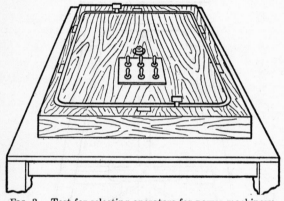

Fig. 3.—Test for selecting operators for power machinery.

A quite different type of test is shown in Fig. 3. This is designed for selecting operators for power machinery. The person tested watches two flags, one of which is moving faster than the other around the outer edge of the apparatus. At certain times these flags will be on two of the white areas along their path. He must anticipate when this will happen and pull the correct one of the six switches to keep the light in the center from flashing. If he fails to pull the switch, pulls the wrong switch, or pulls the right switch too late, the light will flash, and this will count against him. His score is good when he keeps the lights from flashing yet does not pull the switches unnecessarily.

Each of the foregoing tests was designed from an analysis of what the operator is required to do on a

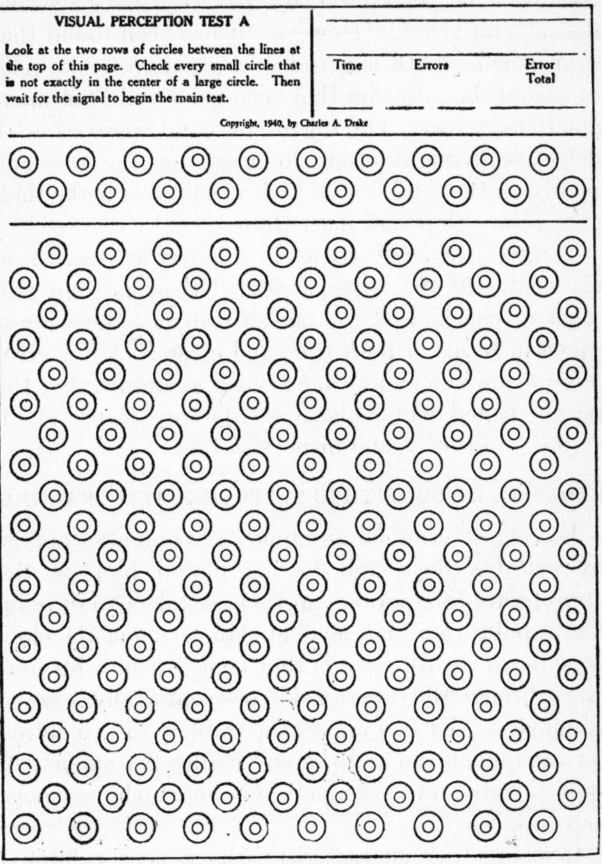

VISUAL PERCEPTION TEST A

Look at the two rows of circles between the lines at the top of this page. Check every small circle that is not exactly in the center of a large circle. Then wait for the signal to begin the main test.

Time	Errors	Error Total

Copyright, 1940, by Charles A. Drake

FIG. 4.—Visual-perception test.

particular job. They have been extremely successful in selecting operators who can learn the jobs quickly and can attain a high level of skill.

The test shown in Fig. 4 has been widely used to

select inspectors for factory work. It is called a visual-perception test because it measures an ability classified as perception by the psychologists and depends on vision. However, it has been found that even persons with superior eyesight may make poor scores on this test and that such persons do not make good inspectors. On the other hand, persons with defective eyesight often do poorly on the test and poorly on the job because their eye defects make their perceptions slow and inaccurate.

Some of the small circles in this test are exactly in the center of the large circles. Others are not and must be checked by the person tested. The score is taken in terms of both time and errors. A low error score made in a short time is good assurance that the person tested will make a satisfactory inspector on certain kinds of visual-inspection jobs.

BENEFITS OF SCIENTIFIC SELECTION AND TRAINING

Having determined an applicant's potential ability by suitable tests and having placed him on the appropriate job, action can then be taken to develop him rapidly to a high level of skill. One of the chief benefits to the foreman is that he can reduce his unit costs through the superior skill of scientifically selected employees. He can reduce the training time required for each employee and thereby reduce the amount of spoiled work and uneconomical use of machines, tools, and supplies.

Certain other characteristics have been exhibited by employees selected by scientific methods. It is known that their stability is higher; that is, the turnover among them is less. These employees have higher morale, because they know that they have been selected from among many others for their superior ability. Finally, the tests make it possible to predict what production each worker should attain under favorable conditions on the job. It then becomes the business of the good foreman to make sure that each employee so selected reaches this high level as soon and as economically as possible.

TESTS VERSUS RATING SCALES

In appraising a man's worth, we may classify him merely as skilled or unskilled. We may say that he is loyal or disloyal, or we may rate him as having or not having many other traits. We may set up a scale that expresses the degree in which he possesses each trait, from highest value to lowest—that is, he is very highly skilled, highly skilled, moderately skilled, low in skill, or unskilled—and develop techniques for comparing various employees against one another, as outlined in the chapter on merit rating.

Rating scales are frequently used when we have no tests for most of the traits. In general, rating scales are not so good as proved tests, but they are better than unsystematic and ungraded judgments about the traits. Often the rating scales afford a beginning in measurement from which objective and reliable tests are afterward developed.

PSEUDO PSYCHOLOGY VERSUS SCIENTIFIC PSYCHOLOGY

From time to time during the past century, men have thought that they had discovered methods of analyzing personality traits through physical signs, such as bumps on the head, shape of the face, color and texture of hair and skin, or through the handwriting. So there arose the pseudo sciences of phrenology, physiognomy, graphology, and others. All of them, when subjected to careful scientific study, have been found to be false and misleading. Only the study of actual behavior in a number of different situations permits one to draw inferences about personality. It is not how a man looks that counts, but what he does and how he acts.

Many persons show peculiarities of behavior that cause them to be termed abnormal. The study of such behavior belongs to the field of abnormal psychology, which is one of the most interesting and worth-while phases of psychological knowledge. Such persons can be understood and classified only from a study of their actual behavior. Severe cases require the attention of a psychiatrist, who is a physician specializing in mental disorders. Some knowledge of the field, however, is indispensable for anyone who must deal with people, since many of these persons are found employed in business and industry. Their conditions are not severe enough to require medical attention, but they do need understanding and special consideration from their superiors and associates. The subject is too broad and too complicated for treatment here, but the foreman who is aggressively increasing his own supervisory skill will inform himself more fully on this subject.

Some persons profess to be able to distinguish criminals, radicals, and other types merely by looking at them or as a result of a very brief interview. This is sheer nonsense. So also is the claim made by others in supervisory positions that they can select a person who will make a good inspector or machinist or shipping clerk by such methods. Nevertheless, they have continued to use such slipshod methods in employment for months, and sometimes years, to the detriment of their organizations.

The wise supervisor will also be on his guard against the belief that the best applicant for a job is one who has performed the same, or a similar, job in some other organization. Sometimes foremen and personnel interviewers do not trust their own judgment in selecting employees and therefore hope to make a better choice by selecting only persons who have done the job before. Usually they know little or nothing of how well the person has done the job. In fact, the experience may be a real handicap, because the worker may have been very inefficient, even though he shows a record of employment over months, and even years, on the job. A suitable test either for experienced or inexperienced applicants affords the best assurance that the individual possesses the ability required on the job.

Section Five

BACKGROUND INFORMATION FOR THE FOREMAN

CHAPTER XV

THE BACKGROUND
OF SCIENTIFIC MANAGEMENT

By Lewis K. Urquhart

As the beginnings of the movement known as "scientific management" recede into the past, its significance looms ever larger. Perhaps no influence since Darwin's theory of evolution has so profoundly affected the destiny of the human race. No other factor in industrial development has led more surely to low production costs and high standards of living.

What were the beginnings of scientific management? How much should the foremen in America's factories know about its history? Enough, certainly, so that mention of yesterday's great names in management will bring at least a flicker of recognition. Enough, indeed, so that the younger men in management today will have some of the background they need for better understanding of the doctrine they accept more or less on faith and practice more or less imperfectly.

This short chapter is therefore aimed at telling the foreman quickly how it all started. Should our outline whet any foreman's appetite for more, there is plenty of good reading on the history of scientific management in America.

A MILLION DOLLARS A DAY!

The public first read of scientific management in the newspaper headlines of late 1911. It was the

pleasant custom in those days to let the public foot
the bill for railroad wage increases, and the Eastern
railroads of the country were hoping to present another
itemized account. They had raised wages that spring
and had therefore asked the Interstate Commerce
Commission for a general advance in freight rates.
They were opposed by the shippers affected.

The hearings that ensued were full-dress affairs.
Fifteen to twenty lawyers represented the shippers.
There were 50 or so for the railroads. Large sums of
money were involved; great principles were at stake;
far-reaching precedents were in the making. The
fight made good copy for the newspapers, which had
no major wars to excite them. The shippers, the
average citizen gathered, were advancing a novel
theory. If, they argued, the railroads were run more
efficiently, they could save more than they needed to
offset higher operating costs.

Chief attacker was Louis D. Brandeis, later an
associate justice of the Supreme Court. Brandeis
sprang the big surprise of the hearings when he produced 11 witnesses, all successful engineers, who
testified that through something called scientific
management it was possible to raise wages and at the
same time reduce costs.

And he fired the big gun when he called an engineer
named Harrington Emerson to the stand to testify
that scientific management could save the railroads
$1,000,000 a day! Emerson just about stopped the
show with that one. A million dollars a day! It
staggered imagination. America had not yet learned
to babble of billions.

Scientific management! The magic words made
the headlines. They were on every tongue. Within
a few months *The American Magazine* was running a

series of articles by a man named Taylor. And soon
the so-called "Taylor system" was being investigated
by a Senate committee. Organized labor had almost
immediately turned on the pressure that has never
since been shut off.

THE FATHER OF SCIENTIFIC MANAGEMENT

Frederick Winslow Taylor was not at the Eastern
Rate Case Hearings. But his name kept cropping up.
Witnesses referred again and again to his work and to
his system.

For Taylor was the father of scientific management.
No one but the man himself has ever disputed his
right to the title. He had started from scratch
35 years before in a Pennsylvania steel yard, and out
of his original researches there, plus half a lifetime of
work, he had painstakingly evolved a set of principles
that were to place the art of management on a solid
foundation of fact, that were to revolutionize the conduct of industrial production.

America of 1878 was slowly pulling itself out of a
postwar depression when young Fred Taylor—he was
twenty-two—applied for a job at the Midvale Steel
Company. There was still widespread unemployment. Wage earners knew why: there was not
enough work to go around. They had seen piece
rates cut—and then cut again. They distrusted the
"bosses." Morale was low. Management's idea of
a day's work was whatever a rough, tough foreman
could drive his men to do. The wage earners, being
human, naturally figured on turning out as little as
they could and still hang onto their jobs.

Taylor was taken on at Midvale as a laborer. He
had served his apprenticeship as patternmaker and
machinist. But work was dull. So the young man

of well-to-do family—he had had to give up thoughts of Harvard on account of his eyes—began in the yard. He was soon assigned to the machine shop. Later he became a timekeeper when someone found out he could do clerical work. Finally he got a job on a lathe.

Advancement came swiftly. He got to be gang boss in the lathe department, foreman, master mechanic in charge of all maintenance, chief draftsman, chief engineer—all in the space of 6 years. And during his 12 years at Midvale, while he was moving so rapidly up the ladder, he developed a system of shop management that was utterly different from any other. No one had ever seen its like. He developed it with such success that before he was through the entire shop had accepted it.

There was opposition, of course. There always is to anything new. Even the men at Midvale who let Taylor go ahead and make his experiments were not always completely in sympathy with what he was doing. His biographer, Copley, tells the story, for example, of Taylor's meeting his former chief, Charles J. Harrah, Jr., some years after leaving Midvale. Taylor politely asked Harrah how things were with him. He replied that he was doing fine. He was making a lot of money. And when he had made a few millions he was going to build the finest insane asylum the world had ever seen—and Taylor was going to have an entire floor!

Harrah was kidding, to be sure. But the record is clear that many people in industry would not have opposed commitment proceedings.

A FAIR DAY'S WORK

"Soldiering," Taylor soon found, was the accepted practice among the workers at Midvale, just as it was throughout industry at that time. There were, he learned, two kinds of soldiering—the natural kind and the systematic kind.

Natural soldiering is the result of a perfectly understandable instinct to take it easy. Any good foreman can put a stop to it. But systematic soldiering, as Taylor found it, was something else again. It arose from the belief, however mistaken it may have been, that there was only so much work to be done; if a worker did any more than he had to, he would deprive another of a job.

As a laborer and mechanic Taylor had done his fair share of soldiering. When he got to be a foreman, however, and was able to look at things from the other side of the fence, he knew perfectly well that the men were not doing anything like a full day's work. So he began a long, bitter battle to force them to do more. To do so, he became just another rough, tough foreman. There was no other kind in those days.

It was a fight. Midvale was on straight piece rates. But piece rates, although designed to stop soldiering, did nothing of the kind, mainly because employers cut rates as soon as the men began to earn more than they were supposed to. There is no evidence that the Midvale management had resorted to rate cutting, but the men in the machine shop knew it was general practice in industry and could therefore happen there. Naturally, they were angry when a young upstart of a foreman tried to force them to increase their production.

Taylor won out in the end. At least, after 2 or 3 years of wrangling and fighting he succeeded in doubling production. But it was a hollow sort of victory because he was sure he was not going at it in the right way, and he was equally sure that the doubled production still did not amount to a *full* day's work.

Many years later, while being "investigated," he put it this way:

When I got to be foreman of the shop and finally won out and we had an agreement among the men that there would be so much work done—not a full day's work, but a pretty good day's work—we all came to an understanding and had no further fighting.   Then I tried to analyze it, and I said: "What has been the matter with all this thing?" I said: "The main trouble with this thing is that you have been quarreling because there have been no standards for a day's work.   You do not know what a proper day's work is. Those fellows know ten times more than you do, but personally we do not know anything about what a day's work is. We make a bluff at it, and the other side makes a guess at it, and then we fight.   The great thing is that we do not know what is a proper day's work."

So the earnest young foreman, who had no theories he wanted to try out but merely wanted to get the output that every foreman was hired to get, set out to determine by research and experiment—which is to say, on a factual basis—what his men ought to be able to do with the equipment they had and the materials they were provided with.

His chief at that time was William Sellers, one of America's great engineers and a firm believer in the research method.   Sellers readily consented to Taylor's making some experiments, experiments that Taylor thought would take 6 months.   He was still working on them a quarter of a century later.

Taylor first withdrew a machine from production, drafted a skilled worker, and appropriated a pile of scrap.   He knew that he must hold all the variables constant except the variable he happened to be studying at the moment and that he must control variations of that variable.

He therefore studied every sort of variation in the operation of that particular machine—variations in belting, shafting, tools, speeds, feeds, materials, methods, motions, etc. He was trying to discover the combination of conditions that would permit best use of existing facilities. And in the long run he *did* discover what is now so evident—but which nobody before him had ever perceived—that there is a right combination of conditions for every operation, which, when correctly set up and maintained, will make it possible for a worker not only to increase his output, sometimes as much as several hundred per cent, but also to increase it without additional fatigue.

There were many by-products of these initial studies. Taylor's "Notes on Belting" is still an authoritative work. Most important perhaps, from the standpoint of immediate value, was his discovery that "a heavy stream of water poured directly on the chip at the point where it is being removed from the steel forging by the tool would permit an increase in cutting speed, and therefore in the amount of work done, of from 30 to 40 per cent." The quotation is from Taylor's "On the Art of Cutting Metals," not published until 1906 but based on experiments that began in those far-off Midvale days. The same studies led to his development of high-speed tool steel around the turn of the century, a discovery that made it possible to increase machine-shop feeds and speeds, and therefore production, from two to four or more times.

PIONEERS AND PROGRESS

Unit time study, one of Taylor's momentous discoveries, was slowly applied in the years that followed to industries other than metalworking and became the basis for all planning and scheduling. Those early years saw the slow, groping development of better methods of inventory control, functional control, scientific cost accounting, production control, and methods of maintaining quality. A little later came micromotion study (study of repetitive operations by means of slow-motion pictures), now so widely accepted and applied as a tool of modern industrial management.

Such were the first small beginnings of the scientific-management movement as we know it today. Thus was the system worked out in principle in those 12 crowded years at Midvale and later refined under more complicated conditions at Bethlehem Steel, where Taylor had the mathematical genius Carl G. Barth and the practical economist and great engineer Henry L. Gantt to help him. Barth and his famous slide rules were to solve many a perplexing problem. Gantt is remembered chiefly for the charts that are used today in a thousand forms and still bear his name; his task-and-bonus plan also was an outstanding contribution to the science of management.

Other pioneers there were in plenty—Dwight V. Merrick, a specialist in time study; Frank B. Gilbreth, who made the first micromotion studies and whose name back end to, with the last two letters transposed, is the "therblig," or elementary motion, of modern work simplification; Sanford E. Thompson, inventor of the decimal-dial stop watch. The roll of management "greats" is far too long to be called here. Suffice it for the foreman of today to know these few at least by name. Each of them made significant contributions. And if industry today is a little hazy about what they did, it is none the less indebted to them and their work. Although more recent developments have modified the early techniques, the "founding fathers" built on such a solid foundation that the principles of management as they laid them down remain unchanged and are in general use throughout industry today.

EARLY LITERATURE AND A DEFINITION

Why did Taylor not sit down back in the eighties and tell the world about the system that was going to revolutionize industry? Partly because he had no inclination to write, no time to write. He was a doer. When he forced himself to write, he wrote well. But he wrote little, and, until *The American Magazine* signed him up in 1912, his papers were prepared for technical audiences.

Then, too, Taylor did not have a system in those early days. Scientific management did not spring full grown from his brain. It was slowly evolved and gradually built into a system. Indeed, his principles were stated for the first time in "A Piece-rate System," read before the American Society of Mechanical Engineers in 1895 and published in the transactions of that society. He stated them again in new form in "Shop Management" (1903) and once more, in 1911, in "The Principles of Scientific Management," as follows:

Scientific management, in its essence, consists of a certain philosophy, which results in a combination of four great underlying principles of management:

First. The development of a true science.

Second. The scientific selection of workmen.

Third. Their scientific education and development.

Fourth. Intimate friendly cooperation between the management and the men.

And in the hearings before the special committee of the House of Representatives (1912) he defined scientific management in these words:

Scientific management is not any efficiency device, not a device of any kind for securing efficiency; nor is it any bunch or group of efficiency devices. It is not a new system of figuring costs; it is not a new scheme of paying men; it is not a piece-work system; it is not a bonus system; it is not a premium system; it is no scheme for paying men; it is not holding a stopwatch on a man and writing things down about him; it is not time study; it is not motion study nor an analysis of the movement of men; it is not the printing and ruling and unloading of a ton or two of blanks on a set of men and saying, "Here's your system; go use it." It is not divided foremanship or functional foremanship; it is not any of the devices which the average man calls to mind when scientific management is spoken of. The average man thinks of one or more of these things when he hears the words "scientific management" mentioned, but scientific management is not any of these devices. I am not sneering at cost-keeping systems, at time study, at functional foremanship, nor at any new and improved scheme of paying men, nor at any efficiency devices, if they are really devices that make for efficiency. I believe in them; but what I am emphasizing is that these devices in whole or in part are not scientific management; they are useful adjuncts to scientific management, so they are also useful adjuncts of other systems of management.

Now, in its essence, scientific management involves a complete mental revolution on the part of the workingman engaged in any particular establishment or industry—a complete mental revolution on the part of those men as to their duties toward their work, toward their fellow-men, and toward their employers. And it involves the equally complete mental revolution on the part of those on the management's side—the foreman, the superintendent, the owner of the business, the board of directors—a complete mental revolution on their part as to their duties toward their fellow workers in the management, toward their workmen, and toward all of their daily problems. And without this complete mental revolution on both sides scientific management does not exist.

The substitution of this new outlook—this new viewpoint—is of the very essence of scientific management, and scientific management exists nowhere until after this has become the central idea of both sides; until this new idea of cooperation and peace has been substituted for the old idea of discord and war.

There, in substance, is scientific management as Taylor saw it 45 years ago. It was his final statement of principles. He died in 1915. Great social and industrial changes have taken place since his death. Yet, to get the fundamentals of scientific management as it applies to industry today, it is necessary only to recast Taylor's principles in new perspective. This has been done many times, perhaps never better than by the American History Committee for the 1938 International Management Congress, as follows:

As a historical and practical development, scientific management is the utilization of policies and methods derived from analysis of all of the facts which bear upon a managerial situation. It involves *research* for the factual determination of policies and methods, *standardization* of the requisite procedures, *control* of the procedures involved in the use of standards, and *co-operation* of all individuals associated with the activity.

MASS PRODUCTION

It is important to note here that scientific management is not to be confused with the modern phenomenon of mass production. One thinks instinctively of the big mass-production industries as being scientifically managed. And probably they are.

But, although scientific management and mass production are often found in the same shop, they are never identical. Mass production must be based on mass markets, usually consumer markets. It is characterized by a big volume of orders, by highly standardized products. The automotive industry supplies the most familiar example. Here we find high output and low cost made possible through a steady flow of materials. We find single-purpose machines. We find workers whose jobs are routinized, who perform single, highly repetitive tasks.

This is not to say that the mass-production automobile plant is not necessarily scientifically managed. Far from it. Some outstanding examples of scientific management are to be found in the automotive industry. Witness the speed and completeness of its conversion to war production. But it *is* to say that scientific management was developed in small (or, at least, in not-so-big) plants where products are not standardized—where hundreds, maybe thousands, of items are made. Not on specially designed, single-purpose machines, but on machines that can be used on any number of jobs. Not by highly routinized workers who do nothing all day long but tighten bolt *A*, but by highly skilled machinists and machine operators who know how to adapt their machines to any job that comes along. Therefore, let there be no mistake about it, we may have job-shop production *and* scientific management.

RATIONALIZATION

Nor are scientific management and "rationalization" one and the same. We heard much of rationalization after the First World War. We may be hearing of it again. So it is important to know that it is not identical with scientific management. Any confusion that may exist is attributed to the sole fact that rationalization, especially as practiced in pre-Hitler Germany during the early twenties, tended to make complete use of the techniques of scientific management.

Rationalization means the merging of all the plants in a given industry, with a view to increasing efficiency and lowering costs. It involves governmental regulation of production to balance consumption. It runs necessarily into price control, standardization of methods and materials, stabilization of wages, and a great many other things that we in American care to encounter only in times of great stress, such as a war for the survival of our way of life.

OPPOSITION OF LABOR

Scientific management first came to public notice during the Eastern Rate Case hearings already referred to. Organized labor immediately took up the opposition.

In a way, it was natural that labor should oppose the introduction of scientific management. Industry had strongly opposed the labor movement. What little standing organized labor had at the time had been gained only after a long, bitter struggle. And here was something new. Since it was advocated by management, it must be to management's advantage—and to labor's disadvantage.

Scientific management seemed to labor like the end of craft distinctions and therefore the end of the power labor derived from its possession of craft knowledge and skills. Labor was equally sure that, if what they said about scientific management and the resulting savings was true, its wider acceptance would mean layoff and discharge of thousands of wage earners.

Also, labor reasoned, this thing called time study obviously meant speed-up. Speed-up meant wearout. And worn-out workers were naturally headed for the scrap heap—and eventually over the hill.

Ultimately, through larger experience and wider observation of the facts, organized labor's opposition to scientific management largely disappeared. Where it exists, it may usually be traced to inexperienced leadership or to the few leaders who adhere more or less closely to the "party line."

Opposition has in many notable instances given way to co-operation. Today it is not infrequent to see labor leaders on the platform at the meetings of management societies and manufacturers' associations—and to find management executives heeding their words of counsel. We even see the big unions in the clothing industries helping employers out of difficulties by paying for and making available the services of managerial experts.

SOME RECENT DEVELOPMENTS

The Second World War gave great impetus to the application of scientific methods, particularly those employing mathematical techniques, to problems of strategy and tactics. Since the war, these methods have been carried over into business management. Associated with these developments—and, indeed, helping to make them possible—have been the fantastic forward strides made in electronic computers, or "electronic brains," which were first designed for engineering computations, and since the war adapted to business uses and made available as standard commercial equipment. Since the war, also, stimulated by the new controls and automatic "thinking" made possible by the computers, intensive and increasing attention has been given to making all operations in a factory as completely automatic as possible, eliminating not only obvious movements between processes, but also elements of human choices and judgments hitherto thought of as requiring operator attendance or guidance.

The above developments have led to the currency of certain new terms in the literature of management. While it would, of course, be beyond the scope of this chapter to go into the concepts in detail, we deem it proper at least to allude to them briefly here, so that the foreman will have a notion of what is involved should he run into them.

Operations research is one of the terms widely used. It denotes not a basically new and revolutionary concept, but rather a renewed emphasis on applying the scientific method to management decision-making. This consists essentially in analyzing operations *as a whole*, and bringing to bear the orderly, co-ordinated, intensive analysis of all of the physical sciences involved—mathematics, chemistry, physics, biology, and the like. This *grouped approach* has helped companies solve such diverse business problems as improving inventory and reordering policies, planning minimum-cost production schedules, estimating the amount of clerical help for a new operation, directing the salesmen to the right accounts at the right time, setting up the best advertising budget, and the like. The basic objective is to clarify the relations between several courses of action, determine their outcomes, and indicate which measures up best in terms of the goal desired. Of course, the final decision is still up to management itself, which must make the choice between the alternatives.

Linear programming is another term the foreman

may have seen or heard rather frequently in late years. It is a tool of analysis which should really be considered as simply one of the many new, effective devices used in operations research. In some of the analysis work in linear programming, certain new mathematical techniques developed especially for it are used. Simply stated, the objectives of linear programming are to state a problem in mathematical terms, and then come up with the one right answer when the problem has several possible answers. The emphasis is on "programming," *i.e.*, planning courses of action, as distinguished from the later execution of the plans.

In general, in connection with both operations research and linear programming, the foreman will find that specialists will be carrying on any work of that sort in his company—but he may very well be a participant in the fact-gathering stage, and conceivably may be consulted on matters pertaining to his department when final interpretations are made. Perhaps the most important thing for him to remember is that while in the past many heads of businesses have been somewhat leery of attempts to help solve their problems with mathematical formulas, results achieved during the Second World War, and in peacetime applications since, have definitely given a new status to the mathematician, and at the same time have brought all pure science into closer contact with day-to-day industrial needs.

Automation is probably a word that the average foreman has heard much more frequently, and much "closer to home," than the other two. In general usage, the term has been applied to the objective of making as many operations in a plant as automatic as possible—a process which, of course, has been going on ever since Arkwright patented his water-powered spinning frame in 1769. However, engineers specializing in automation do not consider the simple combination of mechanized conveyors and automatic equipment as true automation. They call for the complete "rethinking" of the whole production process—in the case of metalworking, for example, right back to the milled stock itself. Automatic loading from one machine to another is considered a step in the right direction, but they contend that "true" automation requires the elimination of this in-process inventory, and the design of one integrated unit that will perform *all* operations. They contend that loose parts should not be processed. Thus, if raw stock is used in a product, perhaps it should be made from strip feed, permitting continuous punching out of parts as one of a series of sequential operations. The numbers and configurations of pieces going into a product must be completely restudied, every step questioned, and every process in manufacture challenged.

MANAGEMENT SOCIETIES

Much of the progress in scientific management must be attributed to the work of the various societies that have provided the forums where men can discuss their theories, describe their practices, and swap their ideas. It would be impossible here to evaluate the contributions to the movement made by these associations. There is room merely to list the more important ones.

Taylor read his papers, it will be remembered, before the American Society of Mechanical Engineers. The A.S.M.E. was not a management society, of course. Its members were not, in point of fact, any too receptive to Taylor's ideas. It was not until 1921 that A.S.M.E. organized its Management Division, which since its formation has regularly made invaluable contributions to the movement.

The first *management* association was launched in 1912. It was called The Society to Promote the Science of Management. When Taylor died, the association was renamed in his honor. It continued as the Taylor Society until 1934, when it was combined with the Society of Industrial Engineers, which had been formed in 1917 to supplement the work of the Taylor Society, with special emphasis on production methods. The resulting combination has since functioned as the Society for the Advancement of Management. The Efficiency Society, also started in 1912, did not last long.

In 1919 came the National Office Management Association and the National Association of Cost Accountants. And in 1922 the American Management Association was formed, its scope being gradually enlarged until it now embraces all phases of management.

The International Management Congress was initiated in 1923 by President Thomas G. Masaryk of Czechoslovakia. The first congress was held the following year in Prague, and thereafter congresses were convened at 2- or 3-year intervals—in Brussels (1925), Rome (1927), Paris (1929), Amsterdam (1932), and London (1935). The highly successful Seventh International Management Congress was held in 1938 in Washington. Thereafter came a break caused by the Second World War, but the Eighth International Management Congress convened again in 1947, in Stockholm, to pick up the threads of international co-operation, followed by one in Brussels (1951) and São Paulo, Brazil (1954), with the next one scheduled for Paris in 1957. To further the scientific application of predetermined time standards, the MTA Association for Standards and Research was formed in 1950. And to make more widespread the techniques of operations research, the Operations Research Association was formed in 1952.

Among the many successful but somewhat localized management groups may be cited the Industrial Management Society of Chicago, which each year attracts many hundreds of plant-operating men to its annual motion-study clinic.

The formation of the American Marketing Society (1931) reminds us that, although we are here mainly interested in tracing the history of scientific management as it is related to industrial production, the science of management has been applied with equal success to other fields of business, to sales, for instance. In scientific sales management the same principles are involved as in the scientific management of industrial production. They are evidenced in improved design of product, better cost methods, in budgeting sales, defining territories, setting quotas, and establishing fair methods of remuneration. And, more recently the Society for the Advancement of Management has stimulated the application of the techniques to agriculture.

Evidence of the spread of scientific management to other countries is found, of course, in the institution of the International Management Congress. In passing it may be noted that Taylor's "Principles" (1911) was translated within 2 years into French, Spanish, Russian, Dutch, Swedish, Lettish, Italian, German, and Japanese—and later into Chinese.

CHAPTER XVI

FORMS OF INDUSTRIAL ORGANIZATION

By Robert Wray Porter

Results in the industrial world are accomplished by organization. A company employs the processes of organization to combine the constructive forces of men, materials, machinery, and money, so that they may work together, in an orderly way, to turn out finished goods at a profit. What are these processes? How do they work?

If a farmer decided to put in a fence post, he would go into the wood lot, cut down a tree, trim it, cart it to the selected spot, dig a hole, insert the post, "true it up," and nail on the fence. This would require manual effort but very little organization and practically no planning, system, or control. If the job was satisfactory to the farmer when he was finished, that would end the matter. Only the simplest forms of order and system are needed when an individual does a job for himself.

If the farmer decided to have his hired man do the same job, he would issue instructions as to time, place, and kind and then check the job when it was finished. This would require a certain amount of planning, instruction, supervision, and inspection on the part of the farmer. When a person employs another person, the man who is boss must issue orders and check results. This requires a simple form of organization.

WHY THE NEED FOR ORGANIZATION?

If a farmer employed 100 men cutting down trees, another 100 draining a swamp, and still another 100 putting in fence posts, in order not to go out of his mind he would need organization, which means interlocking systems of planning, estimating, hiring, instructing, supervising, paying, etc. Furthermore, the farmer would require check systems to hold down waste motion, disorder, delays, interference, extravagant use of materials, and lost time due to loafing. Through co-ordinated systems an employer plans, directs, and controls the money, men, and materials used on a job. These systems are designed to prevent wastes, delays, and inefficiency.

To get the work done, the farmer would have a number of gang bosses, who would take their orders from him. Most likely the bosses would hire their men, instruct them, give them their tools, direct them, and keep their time records. Here we have an example of *straight-line organization*, where each boss runs his section of the job, whatever its nature might be, just as though he were a farmer with a single hired man.

Suppose that this were a very big operation, so big that the system of organization required "staff" people, who did specialized work. One man would specialize in hiring, another would buy the tools, another would distribute them to the men, another would work out the time schedules, and another would check the costs of the work accomplished. In this case, the responsibilities of the staff specialists would cut across the divisional lines and affect the activities of each of the men working under all the bosses. However, the staff men would have no direct authority over the workmen. This type of organization is known as the "line staff."

Suppose that the workmen instead of having one boss had a number of bosses. One boss would decide what the workmen should do, another boss would work out the exact ways they should do it, and still another would supervise them to see that the work was done according to instructions. Here we have a *functional* type of organization, where the workmen are supervised by separate bosses responsible for their different functions.

These illustrations show that there are a number of ways to manage a group of people in order to get things done. There is no one best way; each has certain advantages that recommend it for certain situations.

It is definitely to the foreman's advantage to have some knowledge of organization principles in general and of his own company's organization in particular. Such knowledge will help him to understand how the staff departments in his company work and will enable him to take advantage of the help they can give him in operating his own department. It will also help him to issue instructions and to delegate authority more effectively.

TYPES OF ORGANIZATION

No one of the three types of organizations that have been mentioned is used wholly and exclusively by any one company; each is used to fit the peculiar requirements of a given situation. But their basic purposes are identical, namely, to hold disorder to a minimum, so that the constructive powers of men, materials, and money may work together smoothly to turn out maximum production in minimum time and under working conditions that are satisfactory to workers. Just wages, fair dividends, and plant improvements are possible only when the details of the business are well ordered and controlled by system.

Line Organization

Briefly, the line type of organization provides a line of authority, proceeding directly from the highest officer to the lowest employee and stepped down through intermediate supervisors at successive levels of responsibility. The line of authority and responsibility extends directly in from the point where an order originates to the point where the task is completed.

Line-staff Organization

Line-staff organization is used more generally by industrial companies because industrial work is highly specialized. In such an organization, the responsibility of a line division is to supervise personnel in carrying out orders. The responsibility of a staff division is to provide other divisions with specialized services, or specifications, which they need in carrying out their line orders.

An Engineering Division is a line division when engaged in doing engineering work; it is a staff division, also, because its work (as represented by its designs, specifications, and procedures), determines the work of the Manufacturing Division. In this respect the Engineering Division functions as a staff unit for the Manufacturing Division. A division doing such double duty is known as a line-staff division.

Although the staff Engineering Division has no authority over the manufacturing personnel, the manufacturing personnel must work according to the designs, specifications, and procedures of the Engineering Division. Other divisions may also do double duty as line-staff types.

Functional Organization

The functional type of organization is used where functions of a similar character are centralized under a separate authority and where such authority crosses divisional lines. Thus, the Engineering Division could operate as a functional-type division in charge of inspection. In this case it would be responsible for inspection functions throughout a plant, with sectional inspectors working *directly under its supervision*. These inspectors would see that all parts and products in process were being made strictly in accordance with engineering specifications. The Engineering Division under these circumstances would perform quality inspection throughout the plant, regardless of what divisions produced the work. Other basic functions, such as planning, preparation, scheduling, and production, are sometimes handled in a similar manner.

PLAN—DO—CHECK

Basically, all work is accomplished by three fundamental functions, namely, *plan—do—check*, formally known as planning, production, and inspection. This is a cycle that underlies every operation of an industrial company. Every work order must be planned as to the details of time, effort, material, and cost, just as an architect plans the design and specifications of a house, covering time schedules, labor and material needed, and cost. Likewise, every work order must be put into production, just as a builder builds the house called for by the architect's plans. Similarly, every work order must be inspected, or checked, just as the owner, mortgage company, or the building inspector inspects the house after construction.

Certain departments are distinctively planning departments, like the Sales-planning Department; other departments are "doing" departments, like the Production Department; others are checking departments, like the Auditing Department. Every divisional unit of a company performs a distinctive function of either planning, production, or inspection.

When each divisional work unit is competently organized within itself and efficiently worked into the other units in accordance with the plan-do-check system, all parts mesh together and form a smoothly operating machine. When the divisional units are not competently organized within themselves or efficiently worked into the others because the proper system of line, line-staff, or functional-type organization is not used, then the machine "knocks" and allows disorder, waste, delay, and extravagance to creep in.

DISSECTING AN ORGANIZATION CHART

The various forms of organization generally employed are easy to understand if one has the interest to take an organization chart apart to "see what makes it tick." An admirable chart for such analysis is that of the Manufacturing Division of a large-scale manufacturing company, as originally published by *American Machinist*. This company is known throughout the world for its management techniques. It manufactures a wide variety of office and business machines. At the time this chart appeared, the Manufacturing Division handled some 225,000 different operations, performed on a job-lot basis. (Although, of course, no business organization remains static, the charts as published constitute useful examples of underlying principles.)

Figure 1 shows that the manufacturing operations are placed under the jurisdiction of a Vice-President of

Manufacture, who has a staff of seven members, each in charge of various divisions, such as Purchasing, Product Engineering, Manufacturing Engineering, Personnel, Factory Comptrollership, Factory Super-

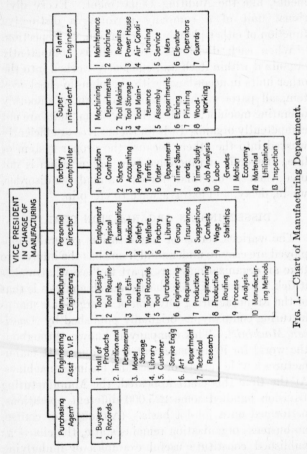

Fig. 1.—Chart of Manufacturing Department.

intendence, and Plant Engineering. Each of these divisions has exact authorities and responsibilities, covering the itemized activities shown in the lower boxes of the chart. Each operates as a line-type unit within itself. All units, except the Factory Superintendent, also operate as staff-type units for the benefit of the other units. The Factory Comptroller, in addition to operating as a line and staff unit, also operates as a functional unit.

The Purchasing Division buys all materials for the other divisions, with the exception of tools for the Manufacturing Engineer, who purchases them directly. Thus it performs a staff purchasing function for each of the other divisions. If this were a strictly line-type-organization setup, each division would do its own purchasing. It is easy to imagine the disorder such a practice would introduce and how it would result in higher costs, a lack of uniform standards, irregularity of deliveries, etc.

The Product Engineering Division is responsible for technical research, invention and development, and customers'-service engineering. It operates as a centralized Engineering Division, providing engineering designs, specifications, and procedures for the use and benefit of the other divisional units. Consequently, it functions as both a line and staff division. This is also true as regards the Manufacturing Engineer's Division, which operates as a line and staff unit, responsible for tooling, production engineering, process analysis, and manufacturing methods throughout the plant.

Personnel direction is responsible for all employment, safety, employee-welfare, insurance, and similar employee benefits, supervising these services for all employees within the plant. Consequently it performs a line-staff service for the other divisions.

Next on the chart is the Factory Comptroller's Division, whose responsibilities are detailed on Fig. 2.

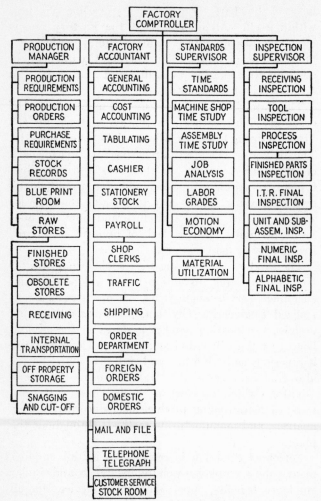

Fig. 2.—Chart of Factory Comptroller's Division.

They cover the preparation of production orders and purchase orders, the control of stores, customers' orders, standards, and product inspection. This is an unusual, but enlightened, piece of organization work, wherein the executive with the title of Factory Comptroller is responsible for all inspection and control functions dealing with the work of product controls, material controls, accounting controls, standards control, and product inspection. These organizational duties constitute line-, staff-, and functional-type duties—*line*, within the department itself; *staff*, since the Comptroller's Division sets up production requirements and schedules for the Manufacturing Division; and *functional*, since it has control of all product-inspection functions. This setup illustrates how all the internal factors affecting the income, cost, and expense of manufacturing are sometimes put under the supervision of one executive. In this manner many of the factors which might introduce disorder are routed under the vigilant eye of one executive. (More normally, perhaps, a Factory Manager would have been put in charge of these functions, and he would likewise have the Superintendent and Plant Engineer reporting to him—eliminating the title of Factory Comptroller as here used.)

Details of the Factory Superintendent's organization are shown in Fig. 3. All shop activities are grouped generally under machining operations, assembling operations, etching, printing, and woodworking. These operations are typically line activities, because they deal with the direct supervision of productive labor. All shop sections in this company are supervised by foremen, whose desks are located in the shop, where they can give constant attention to the work in progress and see that all schedules, procedures, operations, and regulations are carried out according to

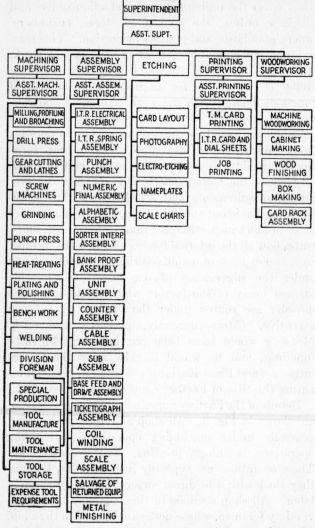

FIG. 3.—Chart of Factory Superintendent's Division.

management's instructions. In this respect foremen operate with line-type authority.

By referring again to Fig. 1, it will be seen that the Plant Engineer has charge of maintenance, machine repairs, powerhouse operations, and air-conditioning equipment, in addition to the supervision of service men, elevator operators, and company guards. These activities are rendered for the benefit of the other divisions of the plant and are classified as line-staff.

From the above description it is obvious that line, line-staff, and functional organizations should be used in such a way that each divisional unit will function efficiently within the scope of its own authorities and at the same time aid and supplement the work of each of the other divisional units.

Sales and Financial Activities

Of course, in addition to the above manufacturing duties, an industrial company also engages in sales and financial activities. The function of the Sales Department is to distribute manufactured goods. It operates largely as a self-contained unit, and its activities are characteristically of a line-type nature. The Sales Department has no authority over either the Manufacturing or Financial Department. Sales requirements which guide the manufacturing schedules as to what, when, and how much of each product is to be made are passed to the Manufacturing Department through the office of the General Management, which co-ordinates all activities of the Sales and Manufacturing Departments.

The Financial Department controls the company funds, operates the books of account, supervises all auditing activities, prepares reports, and maintains records and statistics. In performing these duties the

Financial Department exercises authority over all company procedures dealing with these matters. Its activities are both line, line-staff, and functional in type and are co-ordinated with the Sales and Manufacturing Departments through General Management.

General Administration

Overlying the activities of the Sales, Manufacturing, and Financial Departments are the General Administration Departments, which consist of such offices as the Board of Directors, President, Executive Vice-President, Secretary, Treasurer, and Legal Department. In this group policies are formulated for the direction of all divisional units. Technically, the top group acts as a staff organization for all operating departments, supplying them with fundamental policies, plans, facilities, money, and all the things required to make each department function as a member of the company-family.

Naturally, the top organization does not work out all policies in complete detail for all departments, divisions, sections, and units. However, it does lay down the broad policies, principles, and procedures affecting the security and prospects of the company. Then the heads in charge of the various operating units, in consultation with the administration officers, work out the application of these policies to their own individual tasks and develop the necessary operating techniques for making them a success.

Policy and Performance

It will help in understanding the structural setup of an industrial company to recognize that it is divided into two parts, namely, *policy* and *performance*.

Policy is the head that decides what shall be done, and performance is the body that carries out the policy. The work of top management in an organization deals with executive policy, while the work of the lower part of an organization has to do with performance.

Policy varies in quality and is good or unsound according to the wisdom, experience, and know-how of those in command. Since policy underlies every activity of a company, it can be divided into logical operating parts. Each part has a distinctive job to do. Each is dependent on the others for its successful operation. Just as a chain is only as strong as its weakest link, so is a company only as strong as its weakest policy. The foreman's perspective of his own department will be broadened if he acquires a conception of the type of policy problems with which top management in an average corporation must deal. Following is a list of 37 policies usually found in an industrial company.

1. *Capital Practice.* Securing and handling of funds with which to run the business.

2. *Economic Programs.* Type and character of long-term company activities, so that the business will continue profitably.

3. *Potential Income.* Development of markets, products, and processes to give the company consistent and sound growth.

4. *Public Relations.* Development of sound and enlightened public understanding of a company's intentions, operations, and objectives.

5. *Organization Practice.* Development of efficient, economical, and constructive means for co-ordinating policies, personnel, procedures, and controls, so that everybody may do a better day's

work in less time, with less effort, at less cost, and with greater profit to everyone.

6. *Ownership Relations.* Improvement of intelligent understanding on the part of owners (stockholders) regarding the company's affairs.

7. *Interdepartmental Co-ordination.* Improvement of techniques, so that each company divisional unit may work to a better advantage and aid the work of all departments that it contacts.

8. *Employee Relations.* Improvement of employee understanding, attitude, and morale.

9. *Employee Co-operation.* Improvement of personal relationships so that workmen, foremen, managers, and executives may work as a team.

10. *Consumer Requirements.* Study of what the customer wants and needs, so that the company may hold old customers and win new ones.

11. *Product Utility.* Scope and performance of the company's products, what they can save or do for customers.

12. *Price Setting.* Establishment of catalogue prices that are fair to the customer and company.

13. *Distribution Administration.* Organization setup, procedures, and regulation of budgets for distributing the company's products.

14. *Trade Promotion.* Scope and kind of publicity designed to stimulate increased buying on the part of prospective and old customers.

15. *Competition.* Study of competitors' policies, products, practices, and other factors to protect markets.

16. *Product Development.* Design and development of new products and processes.

17. *Engineering Administration.* Technical organization setup, procedures, and regulation of budgets for engineering.

18. *Plant Improvement*. Acquisition, maintenance, and improvement of plant facilities, tools, and equipment.

19. *Purchase Practices*. Procurement of materials and services.

20. *Employment Practices*. Engagement and training of personnel.

21. *Production Standards*. Establishment and maintenance of quality control.

22. *Order Handling*. Work flow of customer orders from receipt to shipment.

23. *Production Administration*. Manufacturing organization setup, procedures, and regulation of budgets for manufacturing.

24. *Wage Setting*. Establishment and adjustment of wage rates.

25. *Incentives*. Development of proper means for stimulating the best efforts of employees.

26. *Inventories*. Procedures for controlling raw, in-process, and finished stocks.

27. *Management Controls*. Ways and means of regulating and co-ordinating the activities of all departments, divisions, sections, and units.

28. *Budgetary Practice*. Arrangement and allotment of funds for distribution, manufacturing, and financial purposes.

29. *Customer Credit*. Financial terms and conditions of sales.

30. *General Accounting*. Keeping the books of account in sound balance, as regards company assets, liabilities, surplus, reserves, depreciation, etc.

31. *Cost Accounting*. Assembling and reflecting sound costs of manufacture, so as to price the manufactured goods properly, and to reflect operating profits on the profit and loss sheet.

32. *Statistical Controls.* Watching the progress and trend of all factors affecting the company's interests.

33. *Auditing Administration.* Detail checking on all income, asset, and disbursement items and seeing that all moneys received and spent are properly accounted for.

34. *Taxes.* Complying with all city, state, and Federal tax authorities.

35. *Depreciation and Reserves Practices.* Write-down and reserve for wear and tear on plant, tool. equipment, and other assets.

36. *Insurance.* Proper protection against losses arising out of fire, accident, theft, and other industrial hazards.

37. *Regulations.* Conforming with all city, state, and Federal statutes.

It is evident, when one glances back over the above list of policies, that each policy has a separate and distinctive duty to perform. Some one executive is usually responsible for the performance of each policy. To keep the various policies working together as a unit requires a management system of organization. Otherwise, some of the policies will push too far ahead, while others will lag behind, thereby throwing the operation out of balance.

Lines of Authority

When a supervisor is put in charge of a job (policy or performance), he is charged with the responsibility of accomplishing certain results. In order to obtain these results, he is given a corresponding authority to issue orders and command the people who work under his direction. Authority and responsibility should be coequal. When they are not equal, trouble follows.

In organizational matters, authority proceeds downward, from top to bottom, varying in proportion to the responsibilities involved. Lines of authority extend in and through an organization and tie together all its departments and subdepartments. Employees, procedures, and activities are thus held in unison by lines of authority, thereby permitting all factors of policy and performance to work co-ordinately, as a single unit, to achieve company objectives.

ACHIEVING ORGANIZATION-WIDE CO-OPERATION

An industrial company functions because of the effort of widely varying types of people: rich and poor, well educated and illiterate, young and old. Some have highly specialized abilities; others classify as common laborers. The important thing is the spirit of the people who comprise the company. When a management plan of organization is constructive, it is reflected in the spirit of the personnel. When the attitude of the personnel is not healthy, the plan of organization is generally at fault and needs correction.

Developing and maintaining employee co-operation is a management task requiring the human touch. Wise management appreciates the value of voluntary employee co-operation; it also knows that the attitude of the employee is the direct result of the kind of treatment accorded him by management. It should always be borne in mind that the spirit of the people who comprise the company personnel is mightier than any systems of procedure and is more important than any buildings, machines, or money that a company may own. Organization procedures which are properly designed foster good will on the part of the personnel and strengthen the ties of employers and employees.

The "Ten Commandments of Good Organization," issued by the American Management Association, states, "If you are a manager, (supervisor or foreman), no matter how great or small your responsibility, it is your job in the final analysis to create and develop voluntary cooperation among the people you supervise." The A.M.A. "commandments" follow:

1. Definite and clean-cut responsibilities should be assigned to each executive, manager, supervisor and foreman.

2. Responsibility should always be coupled with corresponding authority.

3. No change should be made in the scope or responsibilities of a position without a definite understanding to that effect on the part of all persons concerned.

4. No executive or employee, occupying a single position in the organization, should be subject to definite orders from more than one source.

5. Orders should never be given to subordinates over the head of a responsible executive. Rather than do this, the officer in question should be supplanted.

6. Criticisms of subordinates should be made privately. In no case should a subordinate be criticized in the presence of executives or employees of equal or lower rank.

7. No dispute or difference between executives or employees as to authority or responsibilities should be considered too trivial for prompt and careful adjudication.

8. Promotions, wage changes and disciplinary action should always be approved by the executive immediately superior to the one directly responsible.

9. No executive or employee should be an assistant to, and at the same time, a critic of the person he is assistant to.

10. Any executive whose work is subject to regular inspection should, whenever practicable, be given the assistance and facilities necessary to enable him to maintain an independent check of the quality of his work.

INDUSTRIAL ORGANIZATION: SUMMARY

Good organization is the goal of all ambitious management. It is not difficult to achieve. It merely calls for the conscientious application of a few basic rules, which may be divided as to policy and performance and stated as follows:

POLICY RULES

1. Determine what you want to do, decide the best way to do it, and check all angles to be sure that it may be done successfully according to plan.

2. Formulate definite, clear-cut policies to cover all angles.

3. Provide adequate facilities—men, money, and materials—equal to the requirements of the job, as set forth in the plans.

4. Divide the job into logical divisions of effort and set up proper departments, divisions, sections, and units to care for the requirements of each class of work.

5. Put people in charge who are qualified.

6. Exercise leadership authority in an understanding way.

7. Follow a system of plan-do-check.

8. Apply line-, line-staff-, and functional-type authority where best suited.

9. Be fair in pay and promotion.

10. Keep things simple, clear, and direct.

11. Develop procedures and techniques for doing each work task and strive for order, dispatch, and economy.

12. Provide controls to show exactly what is being done and how well it is being done.

13. Provide a system of co-ordination to keep all operations in balance as to time, cost, and effort.

Performance Rules

1. Set working standards to regulate the time and cost of each operation.

2. Issue definite work instructions as to what is wanted and how it should be done. Make all instructions exact.

3. Supervise each worker intelligently.

4. Maintain accomplishment records of each operation and employee.

CHAPTER XVII

WHAT THE FOREMAN SHOULD KNOW ABOUT ECONOMICS

By James J. Bambrick, Jr.

"The best economist I know is my wife," said Jack Lloyd, foreman of the Hill plant, as he sat at his desk in the small office next to the machine shop. He was talking to Al New, a first class machinist and key man in Jack's group. As he spoke, he idly fingered the cover of a loose-leaf manual on his desk. It bore the title "Economics for the Foreman."

A puzzled look came over Al's face.

"Sounds silly, doesn't it?" Jack asked. "I never thought of it that way either until I started taking this economics course the company gives us new foremen. The instructor says that, when you boil it down, an economist is just a person who tries to make the best use of scarce things. My wife certainly does make good use of the things we have at home and of the pay checks I give her. I guess you would call her a good economist because she economizes."

"Jack, why are you so interested in economics? During the seven years I knew you as a machinist you never spoke about this kind of stuff. Why is the company spending money on you for economics, and what are you going to get out of it?"

"There's more to this foreman's job than what goes on in the shop," Jack replied. "The president of the company wants us to know more than just our jobs.

He wants us to know the whys and wherefores of what we are doing; how our work helps other people in America and in the world.

"You know, Al, I am also getting a lot of personal satisfaction out of this economics course. I was made a foreman to be a leader of men. When you're a leader, you've got to know the answers. We have some men around here who don't believe in our way of life but believe in a lot of 'isms.' You know, because you've argued with them. One thing I'll say about the 'ism' boys is they certainly use economics to try to show our workers that their 'ism' and not our way of life is best. Well, now I think I got some answers for them."

Jack pushed his economics manual towards Al and said, "Here, look this over. It has some of the answers you might want to use in case you argue with them again." [This chapter discusses the important points covered by a manual such as Jack's.]

WHAT IS "ECONOMICS"?

Economics is the study of man's activities in business. It inquires into how he gets his income and how he uses it. It is, therefore, on the one hand a study of wealth, and on the other hand a study of man.

A foreman's interest in the subject rests primarily on how it can help him in his job. Economics helps the foreman to see his job in the light of how it ties in with the work of his firm and with the larger activities of industry and the nation—and even the world. A foreman is also interested in economics because he is a leader of his men and may be asked by them for information regarding economic questions.

The importance of the subject of economics to management lies in the fact that management is merely a part of the larger science of economics. Economics relates all activities to each other in so far as they affect the production, consumption, and valuing of goods and services.

A foreman should have some background in the economics of wages, hours, working conditions, profits, investment, unemployment, and the like. Without such background, the foreman merely carries out orders without any knowledge as to the whys and wherefores and so without the ability to answer the questions of others.

THE "BIG FOUR" ECONOMIC SYSTEMS

The foreman as a citizen and as a leader of men is naturally interested in the four economic and political systems that presently control the world.

Capitalism. This is the term often used to describe our present economic system. It is, however, a misnomer. The real name to be given to our economic system should be "regulated, competitive private enterprise," which, however, is usually referred to as "free enterprise," although, of course, it is not "free" of restraints. Free enterprise allows the individual, within limits, to make, consume, and exchange what he pleases, when he pleases, and how he pleases. He sells his goods and services in the market for money and with this money he buys what, when, where, and how he wants. The things that distinguish our system of free enterprise are personal liberty, private property rights, and free contract.

The United States and Canada are among the last great bulwarks of the capitalistic system.

However, even though the United States is considered a private-enterprise country, it is interesting to note that there is nevertheless considerable government ownership.   More than half of the total area of six states is owned by the Federal government.   Most of the Federally owned land in the United States is in a dozen western states, although in New Hampshire 11.8 per cent of the land area is owned by the Federal government.   Another field in which there is considerable encroachment by government on private enterprise is the production of electric power.   The per cent of government-operated electric power plants in the United States rose from 5.4 in 1930 to 20 in 1954.

Socialism.   The distinguishing feature of socialism is that it usually requires state ownership of all basic industries, such as railways, coal, steel, and the like.

However, socialism would grant to the individual certain basic liberties, such as private ownership of personal property, the right of the individual to engage in certain trades or industries which are not considered basic, and the right of the workman to hire for wages. The fact that under socialism a man may own his home or his car, enter into certain professions or trades, or work for wages makes this economic system much less severe than the next to be considered.

England has experimented extensively with the socialistic system since the close of the Second World War.   The pendulum swung far in that direction under the Labor government, which began a program of extensive nationalization of industry.   However, this trend was halted when the Conservative government was returned to power in 1951 (although with a very slim majority) and a gradual reversal was begun. The coal and steel industries were denationalized in 1953.

Communism.   The general distinguishing feature of communism is that the state owns and operates the entire productive system.

Communism today is synonymous with unlimited control over the individual by the head of the Communist Party. The decisions of the party are totally binding on every single economic, political, social, and cultural activity and point of view. Since no dissent with the decisions of the party congress are tolerated and since the member's time, abilities, and energies are completely at the disposal of the party, the individual exists utterly and solely with the permission of the party or state.

Soviet Russia is the greatest exponent of the Communist system. She is presently trying to impose this system on the people of her "satellite" nations, such as Hungary, Rumania, Czechoslovakia, and Poland.

Fascism, Nazism, Francoism, etc. These are all systems wherein the state dictates the entire economic life of the nation while, at the same time, supposedly leaving industry in the hands of private enterprise.

Spain is currently an example of this philosophy.

PRINCIPAL PHASES OF ECONOMIC ACTIVITY

This chapter will deal with only one of these economic systems, that is, our present system, "free enterprise." Our present system is the one that decides what are the economic problems in our way of life and so is the one of most immediate concern to the foreman.

The system of free enterprise assumes that man's own self-interest will make him produce those things for which there is a demand and that thereby buyer and seller will both be the gainers. This system of free enterprise breaks down into four principal phases, which, in the terms of the economists, are *production*, *consumption*, *value*, and *distribution*.

Production

Production is the creating of economic goods and utilities, a good being anything that is capable of satisfying human wants. This power of satisfying human wants is known as utility. Utility is largely a matter of the relationship that exists between the person and the good that is outside himself. For goods to have their effect they must yield services or render utility, which are different ways of expressing the same thought. The good may be a sack of flour, a loaf of bread, or it may be something intangible, such as the personality of an individual.

Economics, however, is interested only in those goods which in contrast to others are relatively limited. In the country the air is free, but in a factory where a large number of people work together and fumes are given off, the problem of securing air makes it no longer free. It is only then that the air assumes an economic importance.

Thus it is that what is a free good sometimes may at other times not be so. The things that can be said to be free goods are growing scarcer and scarcer. Land, for example, which was once plentiful in the United States, is now scarce.

The production of economic goods consists in one or more of these principal activities: (1) Changing the *form* of things, as growing wheat to make flour to make bread or growing cotton to make thread to make cloth; (2) changing the *place* of things, as transporting the clothing to retail stores; (3) *holding* things until such a time as they will be wanted, as clothing held by retailers until the proper season; and (4) affecting the *ownership* of things, as the activity of brokers to buy a million bushels of wheat.

There are generally considered to be four main factors of production. These are labor, land, capital, and enterprise.

Labor is human effort that helps to make economic goods.

Land is a classification of the free gifts of nature which are used in the making of economic goods.

Capital is the product of man's past efforts that is held for the production of economic goods. (A hammer is, in this sense, capital.)

Enterprise is the activity of a person or group of persons who assume the risk for the success or failure of a business.

Consumption

Consumption is the opposite of production. It is the using up of utilities, the destruction of economic goods in the gratification of desires. Through the medium of money, consumers make their wants known to the producers, and thus production and consumption are interrelated.

Value

Value is that phase of economics that has to do with setting the price to be paid for any goods. It is generally set by balancing the forces of supply and demand. Sometimes, however, especially when there is scarcity of goods during a national emergency, the price is fixed by the government.

Distribution

Distribution is that phase of economics which deals with how the four factors of production—land, labor, capital, and enterprise—share in the total price paid for the product.

It can be seen that the phases of economics are interrelated. The producer produces only what he knows the consumer will buy. The thing that determines the value is the balancing of the producer who has something to sell and the consumer who has something to buy against each other. Distribution is concerned with how the price paid will be shared among those who help to produce the goods. Union leaders are primarily concerned with this phase of economics.

This chapter will deal primarily with production, not only because of lack of space to treat the other factors, but because production is the phase of economics with which the foreman is most vitally interested.

DIVISION OF LABOR

A feature of present-day production is division of industry by specialization. Eli Whitney was one of the first to bring this down to a science.

Division of labor involves the specialization of labor power, both among groups and among individuals, in such a way that the output is greater than would otherwise be possible. In early times, back in the caveman days, there was little or no specialization beyond breaking up the work between the sexes. However, as communities developed, division of work among various groups evolved. Later on division of labor within the groups themselves came to pass.

With our modern system of production and the great use of machinery, there is now a very fine and minute division of labor. This generally takes the following forms:

1. Division of the community into whole industries, callings, or professions, such as cotton manufacturing,

farming, or teaching. This was characteristic of early handicraft days, when the worker made the whole product himself. The shoemaker made the whole shoe. The tailor made the whole suit.

2. The division of these occupations into groups of complete processes, for example, in the cotton industry, spinning, weaving, dyeing, merchandising, etc. This is breaking down the manufacture of a good into the successive stages that it must go through from the raw material to the finished product.

3. Division of these into subprocesses, for example, division of work in the aircraft-engine plant as between machine shop and foundry, assembly, etc., and a further breakdown of the workers in the machine shop into specialized men, such as lathemen, drillers, reamers, millers, boring-mill workers, etc.

4. Territorial division of labor. Location of industry due to physical or climatic conditions such as mineral necessities and transportation facilities.

Advantages of Division of Labor

The advantages of division of labor are increased output, better quality of work in general, saving of time, increased use of machinery, and the more economic use of machinery. Under division of labor a complete set of tools is no longer necessary for each worker. Now expensive and delicate equipment is given only to one skilled man.

With division of labor, the worker is able by constant practice at one operation so to develop his skill that he can do the work with great speed. With division of labor, it is possible to break the work up in such a way as best to suit each job to the particular ability of the worker.

Use of Past Savings

The idea of division of labor led inevitably to mass production. Mass production requires that certain specially made machines or tools be used. These tools may be made long in advance of the time when the actual product is turned out. In the automobile industry, before a new-model car is put out, years of planning and research are carried on. Then perhaps the larger part of a year is spent in retooling and designing special machinery for the manufacture of the car.

When to all of the above is added the time spent to make the machinery and the time necessary to mine the iron and bring it through all its stages, it is readily seen that many months and even years may be needed before the iron mined is ready to do its work for the final consumer, in the form of a finished automobile.

Under our system of deferring the use of materials a great deal of money has to be paid out for wages, machinery, and other necessary equipment while the product goes through the various stages. This money (capital) can be obtained by one means only—from savings. Savings are the result of somebody's foregoing the immediate pleasure of spending for the purpose of using the money in the future. These savings can then be invested in a business to help pay for wages, machinery, and equipment until the final product is ready for sale.

EFFECTIVE USE OF MACHINES AND MEN

What the foreman is primarily interested in is how land, labor, enterprise, and capital may be combined to give greatest production.

Suppose, for example, a foreman has under him a

small, completely outfitted lathe shop. On this he puts to work first one man, then two men, three, four, etc. This is shown on the accompanying chart, Fig. 1.

We assume that all the men he hires are equally skilled and (to keep our figures in round numbers) that

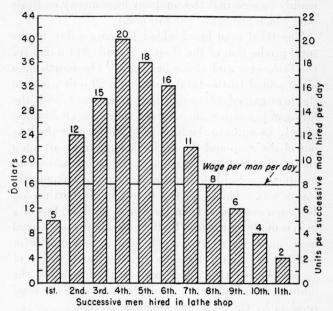

FIG. 1.—Diminishing returns in a lathe shop. (Figures at tops of bars represent units turned out per man per day.)

he pays each man $2 an hour, or $16 a day. The product that the lathe operators can turn out renders the company a profit of $2 per unit *exclusive of labor cost*. The first man the foreman puts to work, since he was the only man on the job and had to start and stop the machinery himself, could turn out only five units of work a day. Since the firm paid him $16, it lost $6 a day by his hiring. The second man hired, because of the efficiency of division of work with the other man, added 12 units. The firm gained $8 a day by hiring the second man. (In Fig. 1, the scale at the left shows the dollar profit of the output exclusive of labor cost, *i.e.*, $2 for each unit turned out. It can readily be seen that the company loses money on those bars which are below the $16 line.)

The third man hired added 15 units a day to the total production of the shop, and made $14 a day for the firm, over and above his wage. The fourth man hired added to the total production 20 units, and so the firm gained $24 a day by hiring him. With the hiring of the fifth man, however, there was an addition of only 18 units to the total product, because the layout of the shop and the available equipment are such that full advantage cannot be taken of additional manpower. Subtracting the man's wage from $36 leaves $20. This is $4 less than for the fourth man. For each man hired from the fourth man on, less of a gain is made by the firm by the hiring of the additional man, until after the seventh man it is a matter of indifference to the foreman (from a profit point of view) whether this eighth man is hired, because the addition of 8 units means only $16 added to the total product by the man, just equaling his pay.

The ninth man in this small lathe shop, if hired, would be able to add only six units. This would bring the firm $12, while his wages for the day would be $16. Therefore, because the firm would lose $4 a day by his hiring, the foreman does not hire a ninth man.

Now we can assume that all these men are equal in skill and ability to turn out work. Had the ninth man been hired as the first one, he would have been able to turn out five units, and had he been hired as the fourth, 20 units. It is not a case here of difference between men, but a case of what any additional man hired will add to the total product because of limitations of space, equipment, and facilities.

This, in simplified form, is the problem with which the foreman must often deal, and it should never be lost sight of in any business planning. The eighth man is the marginal man. The ninth, tenth, and the eleventh men are submarginal additional employees, who do not earn their own pay and who, under ordinary circumstances, cannot be hired or kept. In every shop and for every machine this question exists.

The economist calls this whole process the "law of diminishing returns." He says that after a certain point, increases in machines or men applied to the production of any type of goods will bring about less than a proportionate increase in the amount of the product. In words of the foreman, after a certain point is reached, every additional workman he hires will produce less.

ORGANIZATION OF THE BUSINESS ENTERPRISE

The business enterpriser's job is to combine and direct the other three agencies of production—land, labor, and capital—so as to secure the greatest possible product. His function differs from those of the other three factors in being largely that of risk taking. He assumes responsibility for the conduct of the business, and whether or not he is to make a profit or to lose his money and his business depends on his decisions. To be sure, he can insure himself against certain of these risks, such as fire, cyclone, hail, earthquakes, water damage, workmen's compensation, and the like. But there are thousands of risks which he cannot insure against and which he has to assume himself.

The business enterpriser must have a wide knowledge of business conditions in general and his job in particular, so that he may know the methods of securing necessary capital, tools, and workmen. He must be able to make reasonably accurate forecasts of business conditions, so that he may produce for the future market. He needs a certain shrewdness in bargaining.

In making all decisions, the business enterpriser is presumed to act on purely economic motives, that is, by considering whether or not he will gain or lose. Of course, there are always other considerations. There may be a certain amount of prestige value for his work. His business may also give him a chance to meet socially people with whom he would like to come into contact. And above all, he may value the chance to work and to do a job well.

At this point it will be well to state the difference between business enterprise and capital. The former is the activity itself. The latter means the saved-up funds and other forms of wealth—plant, machines, etc. —needed to carry on the activity. Very often the business enterpriser uses his own capital. If, however, he needs more capital than his own resources can provide, he must borrow from others. Our gigantic corporations borrow almost all their capital. Thus, the business enterpriser may be purely a business enterpriser and nothing else, or he may combine his function with that of the capitalist, who has utilized his savings in creating future goods. And at the same time he is an organizer who works with land, labor, and all the other equipment necessary for the production of goods.

Single Proprietor

The simplest and best known type of business enterprise is the proprietorship, or "one-man" business organization. Of course, this does not imply that the enterpriser will have no employees, but it does mean that he is the sole owner of the business. He is master. Everything belongs to him. He has the final say as to his own time and that of his employees. All the gains in the enterprise are his, and likewise all the losses.

In the eyes of the law there is no distinction between this individual and his business. Therefore, in a case of debt or bankruptcy of the business, the entire personal fortune of the owner may be laid claim to. This is a distinct disadvantage, because in case of bankruptcy the creditors may force the sale of the owner's personal property as well as his business property in satisfaction of any claims.

There are certain distinct advantages to the proprietorship form of business organization: (1) All the profits are the owner's and do not have to be shared with others; (2) there are no split directions for business, all decisions being made by one man; and (3) there is a minimum of legal expenditure in getting started, no corporate papers having to be secured and no corporation fees having to be paid. The limitations of the single enterprise are (1) the capital of the firm is limited to the business enterpriser's own personal money, plus what he may be able to borrow on his credit; (2) there will often be no one but the enterpriser himself to entrust the business to during his absence; and (3) there is the extreme personal liability already mentioned.

The Partnership

The next simplest type of business enterprise is the partnership, which consists of two or more individuals who are joint owners. Several individuals can pool their resources, and so much more capital can be raised for the business. In a partnership there is always an agreement, written or verbal, as to how much each of the partners shall contribute to and take from the business.

Legally, each partner is responsible for and is bound by any act committed by any of the other partners in the firm's name and is responsible for debts of the partnership. For example, suppose a full partnership of three men, A, B, and C, conducts a business worth $1,000,000. One of the partners contracts for several million dollars' worth of goods, and the value of these goods falls to such an extent that the entire capital of the business is wiped out. The firm is thrown into debt and bankruptcy. Legal action may be brought by the creditors against A, B, and C or against any one of them, and the entire amount may be collected from any of them. Though this may seem rather harsh, it protects the public, since it would be almost impossible to deal with the partnership if all the partners had to be consulted every time anything was to be done.

The Corporation

Both the single proprietorship and the partnership were often found to be inadequate with respect to raising sufficient funds for a business, or perpetuating the business after the death of the owner or all partners. It was found necessary to devise a form of business which would raise greater quantities of capital and produce greater efficiency of organization. This was possible through securing the resources of a large number of people. These resources could be secured only with the assurance that there was limited liability and that the persons having a share in a business would not be liable for its debts beyond the amount they risked in buying its stocks. The form of organization developed for this purpose is the corporation.

A corporation is generally defined as an association of individuals, known as stockholders, acting under a charter from the state as a *single person* in the running of the business enterprise. Most state laws require at least three persons as stockholders in order for a corporation to be formed. Stockholders of a corporation are limited in liability. Usually this limited liability is equal to the amount actually invested in the business. This lessens the risks that come from investment and makes it possible for corporations to secure greater capital than is possible under either proprietorship or partnership.

Management of a corporation, while it is nominally supposed to rest with the stockholders themselves, is generally delegated by the stockholders to a board of directors. An important feature of the corporation is that in the event of the death or the retirement of any one of the stockholders, the stock may be transferred or sold, and the corporation still continue its existence. The principal purpose of incorporation is to secure quantities of money in order to form a larger organization than is possible under either partnership or the single enterprise. There are, however, certain limitations as to the size of the business.

Problems of Size

There are certain advantages to large enterprises: (1) economies of large purchases; (2) economies to be made in the use of materials and power; (3) advantages of the efficient division of labor discussed previously in this chapter; (4) utilization of by-products, such as is done by Armour and other large packing houses and by the oil companies; (5) fixed expenses of the business spread over a much larger volume; (6) ability to spend money on advertising, experimentation, and research; and (7) the necessary cash reserve to cope with trade fluctuations.

However, there are also definite advantages to small-scale production: (1) The owner of a small business usually shows more personal interest and supervises the business; (2) there is often greater regard for detail; (3) smaller businessmen usually have better ideas of the likes and dislikes of their customers and clients and are, therefore, better able to fill their needs, especially if the market itself is small and specialized; (4) greater flexibility enables the small business to change with conditions (less and less true of late); and (5) there is more direct contact between employer and employee.

Distinct disadvantages of large-scale production are that in case something goes wrong in the business the errors are tremendous; and in many cases if the business failed it would bring down with it many other firms.

PROTECTION AGAINST RISKS

Risk taking, of course, is part of the normal and regular function of business enterprisers. However, while the worker must assume the risk of unemployment, and the capitalist and the owner of land may not be certain of return on their investment, the enterpriser (often called "entrepreneur") must undertake the risk of paying for all factors in the production of goods for which there is always an uncertain future. The business enterpriser produces for the future, but at any time some unforeseen event, such as fire, earthquake, flood, death, price changes, etc., may devaluate or absolutely destroy the goods he is holding.

Risks can often be greatly reduced and sometimes prevented entirely. Much in this line has been done by fireproofing buildings; industrial accidents have been substantially reduced through modern safety devices; and in the field of health, widespread use of preventive medicine and other measures has greatly minimized the risk.

Insurance

Risks that cannot be eliminated can often be shared with other persons. Insurance companies make risk bearing their business, and insurance distributes risk among people. To secure this co-operative relief, the person insured agrees to pay certain fixed sums, known as premiums. While it is impossible to predict when an individual may die, a factory burn down, floods occur, or other catastrophes take place, it is possible through statistics to know approximately how often they will take place on the average and to calculate premium rates accordingly.

Other Methods of Transferring Risks

Speculation

The speculator tries to estimate the future movement of prices and on the basis of such estimates buys or sells in the hope of making a profit. For example, in a certain year there may be a very good crop of wheat, but at the same time a distinct prospect that the next year will bring with it a short crop. With a large supply on the present market and a demand no more than ordinary, there would be a great tendency for the price to be extremely low and, because of this low price, for wheat to be used extravagantly and even wastefully. The following season, however, the exact reverse would be true. Wheat then being scarce, the price would tend to soar, and there would be a scarcity of the commodity.

The speculator would anticipate the rise in price of wheat and decide to take advantage of the existing low price to buy up this commodity to sell it in the future market. This action has the effect of withholding the wheat from the present and adding it to the future market. The use of wheat is thereby made much more equal throughout the years, and the present waste and future scarcity are thus very much reduced, with the consumer benefiting thereby. The action of speculators also has the effect of stabilizing prices by preventing prices of goods from falling too low when the goods are very abundant. Thus speculation, when based upon the intelligent study of market statistics, may contribute a great deal to business in general.

Hedging

Hedging is a method of eliminating some of the speculative risks of business. It is in reality taking a position on both sides of the market.

Suppose, for example, a miller has stored a supply of wheat at $1 a bushel and desires to sell flour at a price to cover all his costs plus the nominal profit of 5 cents a bushel. However, it takes time to mill wheat, and by the time the miller is ready to deliver it, the price of wheat, and therefore the price of flour, may have gone down. In order to protect himself, therefore, he makes an agreement with a speculator on a produce exchange, agreeing, at the time he purchases wheat, to sell the same amount in the future *at the present price*. After he has milled the wheat and is ready to deliver it as flour, if the price of wheat has declined 15 cents and the flour correspondingly, it will wipe out his profit on milling and cause him a 10-cent loss. At the same time, however, the miller will stand to make 15 cents on his "futures" transaction, because, although he agreed to sell wheat at $1, he is now able to purchase it at 85 cents. What has been an adverse price fluctuation for his milling operation has now been entirely offset by profits on wheat, and he makes a 5-cent profit, as he anticipated.

To take the other side, if the price rose, the miller would stand to make an extra profit on milling but would lose a sum equal in amount on his futures deal. The big thing to the miller is that, whether the price of flour goes up or down, he still has the profit he counted on when he bought the wheat from the farmer—a profit on his own activity (converting), with which he is content since he does not want to be in the business of speculating.

CURRENT ECONOMIC QUESTIONS

As management's representative, the foreman often has occasion to discuss with his subordinates the economic aspects of taxation, wages, and the cost of living. To aid in such discussions, certain factors important in these problems will be considered briefly here.

The High Cost of Government

Since the beginning of the Second World War, business organizations have taken on tremendous burdens of increased taxes. For example, in the year 1940, the total amount of corporation taxes collected was about $1,148,000,000. This figure rose to some $16,000,000,000 for 1945. After the war, the tax rates for corporations were cut and this figure declined to $9,676,000,000. With the Korean War and the subsequent cold war, taxes on corporations again went up. The amount of corporation taxes collected in 1954 amounted to about $21,546,000,000.

No one can say where this trend will end. However, there does exist a point beyond which businessmen find it unprofitable to take the risks attendant upon a new enterprise because the profits that come from risk taking are eaten up by taxes. Thus an increase in tax rates can actually lower the total amount of taxes collected. Where this point exists for American industry has yet to be discovered.

The individual worker, supervisor, and executive have likewise been hit hard since the beginning of the Second World War—both by increased taxes and by a "declining dollar." For example, if a foreman with a wife and two children earned $3,000 in 1939, he would have had to earn $6,063 in 1954 to maintain his 1939 purchasing power. If he was a department head earning $5,000 in 1939, he would have had to earn $10,490 in 1954 to maintain his living standards. And if he was a $50,000-a-year executive in 1939 he would have had to earn $173,892 in 1954 to maintain his 1939 purchasing power. (See Fig. 2.)

The above figures do not take into consideration other forms of taxation, such as, for example, excise taxes. In 1953, these taxes amounted to 50 per cent of the cost of a pack of cigarettes, 25.8 per cent of the cost of gasoline and 51.8 per cent of the price of a fifth of whiskey. In addition to excise taxes, there are other hidden taxes. It has been estimated by the Automobile Manufacturers Association that 29.1 per cent of the retail price of a $2,000 automobile goes for these hidden taxes. (See Fig. 3.)

Taxes, both direct and indirect, amounted to 28.4 per cent of the national income in 1953. Of this 21.5 per

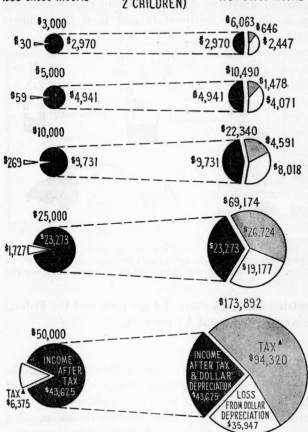

INCOME VS. TAXES AND INFLATION
(MARRIED COUPLE & 2 CHILDREN)

1939 GROSS INCOME

1954 GROSS INCOME

▲ INCLUDES BOTH INCOME & SOCIAL SECURITY TAXES

SOURCES: TREASURY DEPARTMENT; THE CONFERENCE BOARD

Fig. 2.—Income needed to maintain purchasing power, 1939 and 1954. (*Road Maps of Industry, No. 989, Courtesy The Conference Board.*)

cent went for Federal taxes and 6.9 per cent for local and state taxes. This is far different from the 1929 picture, when but 11.5 per cent of national income went for taxes, with state and local governments

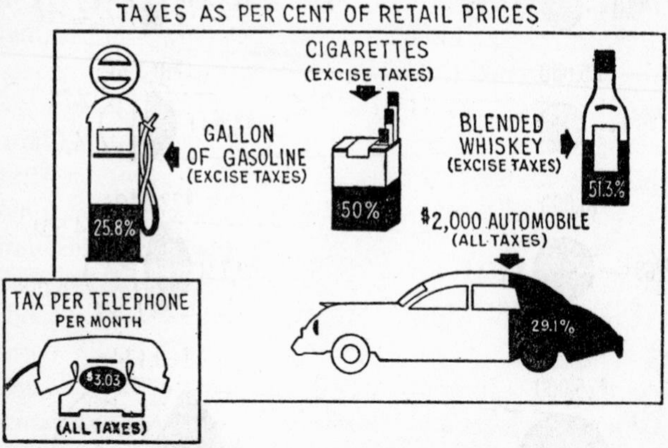

TAXES AS PER CENT OF RETAIL PRICES

Fig. 3.—Who finally pays the cost for government? (In this chart, cigarette taxes do not include local excises, and telephone taxes do not include state and local excise taxes. *Courtesy The Conference Board.*)

getting the lion's share, 7.4 per cent, and the Federal government a scant 4.2 per cent.

Cost of Living

Whenever the term "cost of living" is used, the average person immediately thinks of the prices of the things he regards as the necessities of life, and of the comforts and luxuries that his income permits. A person may have a vague feeling that he is spending more today than a year ago. He may also know that it costs more to live in certain booming factory towns than it does in a more quiet and normal city. However, he rarely knows *how much* more these cost items are, and his concept of cost of living is usually distorted because he tends to put undue weight on certain items.

To give a more precise measure of cost of living, certain cost-of-living indexes (officially called "Consumers' Price Indexes") have been developed. The U. S. Bureau of Labor index and the National Industrial Conference Board index are the two most widely used. They measure the living cost of an average factory wage earner and lower salaried worker. The chief reason for emphasis on these two groups is that in their families there is little margin between income and outgo, and, therefore, variations in prices can work considerable hardships upon them.

Cost-of-living indexes are made up by taking food, clothing, rent, fuel, light, and miscellaneous costs incurred by a factory wage earner's or a lower salaried worker's family and weighting these in accordance with their importance in the family budget. A month in a specific year, or an average for certain specified years, is set at 100, and the cost of living for all other dates is based on that unit. Thus, if January, 1939, is the base, a figure of 182.3 for August, 1954, means that, for the weighted cost items in the budget considered, a man had to spend $1.82 in August, 1954, to enjoy the same standard of living he enjoyed in January, 1939, for $1.

In addition to the indexes mentioned, there have been a number of studies of living costs and expenditures of single persons, both male and female. A good example is the New York State Department of Labor figures on the living costs of single women.

Wages Directly Tied to Production

Wages are paid to the worker in money. But in the eyes of the economist and, for that matter, the housewife, they are not measurable in money. The way the economist and the housewife measure a man's wage is by how much they can buy with it. How much they can buy is largely determined by the amount of money everybody in the world has available for spending compared with the total amount of goods the people of the world have produced.

If everybody in the world were at the same time to secure an increase in wages it would do no one any good. For the increase in a worker's wage would force up the price of the product on which he is working. And the increase in the wages of all other workers would force the price of their products up.

The net result of everybody getting a wage increase would be that they would have more money to spend, but there would be no change in the amount of things they could buy. They would compete with each other to buy these things and thus force the price up. This is inflation. It is largely what happened throughout the world during the postwar period.

General over-all wage increases are justified economically only when there is a general over-all increase in production. Then only can the higher wages secured through a general wage increase buy more goods.

How the Cost of Living Affects Wages

There is a tremendous interest in the cost of living. Keenly aware of its importance, the foreman wants to know how it affects the big increases in hourly and weekly pay secured by workers during the Second World War and during the postwar years. He wants this information not only for his discussions with the men he leads but for talks with his wife, friends, and neighbors on the subject.

The tables on pages 444 and 445 show the large-scale increases received by the average worker in his hourly and weekly earnings. They also show how increases in the cost of living have affected earnings.

"Real" Hourly Earnings

The average American worker in manufacturing plants as shown by Table I (page 444) received 63 cents an hour at the start of the war. In August, 1954, he received $1.79 an hour. This is a 186.9 per cent increase. But the cost-of-living index during this period jumped from 99.1 to 182.3. This represents an increase of 84.0 per cent. Now what is the effect of this increase in the cost of living on his hourly wages? It means that he could buy 64 cents worth of goods with his 63.4 cents hourly pay in August, 1939; but with the $1.79 he received for his hour's work in August, 1954, he could buy only 98 cents worth of goods in "1939 dollars."

The 98 cents is known as the worker's "real" hourly earnings. It represents what the worker can buy with his hour's work in terms of 1939 dollars. The foreman can simply and easily get this figure by dividing the worker's hourly wage for any month by the cost-of-living index for that month.

It is thus seen that during the period of August, 1939, to August, 1954, the average worker bettered the purchasing power of an hour of his work from 64 to 98 cents. In August, 1954, he could get 55.6 per cent more for an hour of his time.

Real Weekly Earnings

A worker is not only interested in his hourly earnings but in his weekly pay. Table II (page 445) shows that the average manufacturing plantworker

Table I.—Comparison of Hourly Earnings with Cost of Living

Date	U.S.B.L.S.* average hourly earnings	Percentage increase over amount of previous period	N.I.C.B.† consumer price index	Percentage increase over amount of previous period	Real hourly earnings	Percentage increase over amount of previous period
August, 1939	$0.624	.....	99.1‡	.....	$0.630	.....
August, 1940	0.660	+ 5.8	100.6	+ 1.5	0.656	+ 4.1
August, 1941	0.736	+11.5	106.7	+ 6.1	0.690	+ 5.2
August, 1942	0.870	+18.2	117.5	+10.1	0.740	+ 7.2
August, 1943	0.965	+10.9	123.1	+ 4.8	0.784	+ 5.9
August, 1944	1.016	+ 5.3	125.9	+ 2.3	0.807	+ 2.9
August, 1945	1.024	+ 0.8	127.8	+ 1.5	0.801	− 0.7
August, 1946	1.112	+ 8.6	135.3§	+ 5.9	0.822	+ 2.6
August, 1947	1.255	+12.9	154.4	+14.1	0.813	− 1.1
August, 1948	1.373	+ 9.4	166.5	+ 7.8	0.825	+ 1.5
August, 1949	1.399	+ 1.9	161.5	− 3.0	0.866	+ 5.0
August, 1950	1.464	+ 4.6	165.2	+ 2.3	0.886	+ 2.3
August, 1951	1.590	+ 8.6	176.6	+ 6.9	0.900	+ 1.6
August, 1952	1.670	+ 5.0	182.6	+ 3.4	0.910	+ 1.1
August, 1953	1.770	+ 6.0	182.5	− 0.1	0.970	+ 6.6
August, 1954	1.790	+ 1.1	182.3	− 0.1	0.980	+ 1.0
Net percentage increase	.....	+186.9	.....	+84.0	.....	+55.6

* U. S. Bureau of Labor Statistics. "Average Hourly Earnings of Production Workers in Manufacturing Industries." (Slight varia-
tions in earlier figures from those given in previous edition of this Handbook are due to U.S.B.L.S. revisions.)
† National Industrial Conference Board. "Consumer Price Index for the United States," January, 1939 = 100.
‡ N.I.C.B. consumer price index for Aug. 15, 1939, is latest figure issued prior to German invasion of Poland.   U. S. Bureau of
Labor Statistics index for same date is an estimate.
§ Estimated.

TABLE II.—COMPARISON OF WEEKLY EARNINGS WITH COST OF LIVING

Date	U.S.B.L.S.* average weekly earnings	Percentage increase over amount of previous period	N.I.C.B.† consumer price index	Percentage increase over amount of previous period	Real weekly earnings	Percentage increase over amount of previous period
August, 1939	$23.77	.....	99.1‡	.....	$23.99	.....
August, 1940	25.41	+ 6.9	100.6	+ 1.5	25.26	+ 5.3
August, 1941	30.25	+19.0	106.7	+ 6.1	28.35	+12.2
August, 1942	37.38	+23.6	117.5	+10.1	31.81	+12.2
August, 1943	43.52	+16.4	123.1	+ 4.8	35.35	+11.1
August, 1944	45.88	+ 5.4	125.9	+ 2.3	36.44	+ 3.1
August, 1945	41.72	− 9.1	127.8	+ 1.5	32.64	−10.4
August, 1946	44.99	+ 7.8	135.3§	+ 5.9	33.25	+ 1.9
August, 1947	50.07	+11.3	154.4	+14.1	32.43	− 2.5
August, 1948	55.06	+10.0	166.5	+ 7.8	33.07	+ 2.0
August, 1949	54.70	− 0.7	161.5	− 3.0	33.87	+ 2.4
August, 1950	60.32	+10.3	165.2	+ 2.3	36.51	+ 7.8
August, 1951	64.08	+ 6.2	176.6	+ 6.9	36.29	− 0.6
August, 1952	67.80	+ 5.8	182.6	+ 3.4	37.13	+ 2.3
August, 1953	71.69	+ 5.7	182.5	− 0.1	39.28	+ 5.8
August, 1954	71.06	− 0.9	182.3	− 0.1	38.98	− 0.8
Net percentage increase	.....	+198.9	.....	+84.0	.....	+62.5

* U. S. Bureau of Labor Statistics, "Average Weekly Earnings of Production Workers in Manufacturing Industries." (Slight variations in earlier figures from those given in previous edition of this Handbook are due to U.S.B.L.S. revisions.)
† National Industrial Conference Board, "Consumer Price Index for the United States," January, 1939 = 100.
‡ N.I.C.B. consumer price index for Aug. 15, 1939, is latest figure issued prior to German Invasion of Poland. U. S. Bureau of Labor Statistics index for same date is an estimate.
§ Estimated.

received $23.77 in August, 1939. During August, 1954, he received $71.06 for his week's work. This is an increase of 198.9 per cent. The cost-of-living index during the same period increased 84 per cent. In terms of what he could buy with 1939 dollars the worker received in August, 1954, only $38.98. This $38.98 was obtained by dividing his August, 1954 pay-envelope earnings of $71.06 by 182.3, the cost-of-living index figure for that month.

The average manufacturing plantworker increased his *real* weekly earnings from $23.99 in August, 1939, to $38.98 in August, 1954. In terms of purchasing power he is 62.5 per cent better off.

Real Wages Are the Only Figures That Count

The foreman must always remember in any discussion of wages that the only figures that count are real hourly and weekly wages. All other figures are illusionary. He can get the real hourly or weekly wage figure for his plant by dividing the pay-envelope wage by the cost-of-living index for the month. This real-wage figure tells him what the wage will do in terms of purchasing power.

HOW THE FOREMAN CAN SECURE FURTHER INFORMATION

In the limited space available in his handbook, it has been possible to give only the highlights of economics. The subject is a very broad one, with many specialized branches. The interested foreman should see his plant librarian, if there is a plant library. If there is not, the Personnel Department of the firm should be ready and eager to help him. The primary source, however, still remains the neighborhood library. Librarians are only too glad to help, since that is their job.

A beginner, who knows little of the subject, should not try to read an economics book of the more advanced type. It will only discourage him, since he will not fully understand it. Somebody has always had the beginner in mind and has made a special effort to take difficult material and boil it down for the more elementary reader.

CHAPTER XVIII

GOVERNMENT, LABOR AND THE FOREMAN

By Bleick von Bleicken

It is impossible for the foreman to handle grievances and other industrial relations problems within his jurisdiction consistently and sure-footedly unless he understands their background. And he must always remember that representatives of organized labor who are vocal about industrial-relations problems, and who so importantly influence the thinking of their rank and file, are usually well drilled in at least one side of the picture.

Unfortunately, it is not unusual to see the foreman bypassed in situations which are logically his concern, but in which he is not allowed to participate. Consequently, the foreman of today has two simple choices:

1. He can continue to neglect and remain ignorant of the background of industrial relations. If this is his choice, he can expect a continued lessening of his status.

2. He can prepare himself for assuming the responsibility that is logically his—to supervise and deal with his workers as a fully accredited member of management. This means that he should acquire at least an informal familiarity with the historical, social, and industrial development of modern industrial-relations concepts.

By the second choice, he will himself help to remove

one of the major causes of a virtually universal complaint by foremen, which runs somewhat along these lines: "Our superiors tell us that we are management men and a part of their team, but they won't allow us to act like it."

This chapter is addressed to the foremen who have made the second choice. Management must depend more and more on competent and informed men and women who know how to convey and interpret management's thinking and objectives to the workers. Conversely, management must rely more and more on the same men and women for a reliable interpretation of the workers' thinking, aims, and desires. It is now well recognized that where such two-way communication is inadequate, unreliable, or nonexistent, outside agencies take over.

Undoubtedly, the most important single influence on industrial relations has been the pattern of state and Federal legislation aimed at protecting the rights of the public, management, and labor—with Federal legislation, of course, having the overriding effect. Thus, the immediate purpose of this chapter is to help the foreman gain a general understanding of what role government, labor, and the foreman have played and may be expected to play in relation to one another.

In view of continual changes in specific pieces of legislation, a discussion of the technicalities of present or possible future labor legislation in one short chapter, even if this were possible, would serve little or no purpose as a foreman's guide. However, it *is* essential that the foreman acquire a broad understanding of the forces which bring about labor legislation, so that he will have the proper perspective with which to form judgments. That understanding is what this chapter is designed to help bring about. We shall accordingly stress general trends rather than specific or isolated legislative measures. Mention of detailed provisions of specific laws will be avoided except as required to illustrate general principles.

One thing to remember is that even though a given labor law may remain on the statute books for a number of years, the nature and degree of enforcement or its interpretation by the courts can and will change from year to year. Even the absence of laws designed to cover a particular social need does not mean that the administration or the courts need be helpless in the face of any pressing situation. On the contrary, quite the opposite may be the case in connection with organized labor, as we shall presently see.

BACKGROUND OF LABOR LEGISLATION

To begin with, one may wonder why the United States government has been so slow in formulating laws and thereby indicating its policies in respect to American labor. Except for certain measures dealing exclusively with railroad personnel, the first Federal law actually dealing directly with labor was the Clayton Act, passed in 1914. The United States was far behind all the other predominantly industrial nations in labor legislation even though its labor problems were very similar. There were two major reasons for this. First, the Constitution of the United States specifically limits the authority and responsibilities of Congress, and the regulation of general working conditions is not included as a field of authority or responsibility. Therefore, this becomes the function of the individual states. Second, until 1914 many Americans regarded as an unwarranted restraint of trade any of labor's efforts to gain recognition and exert pressure collectively.

The Sherman Act, passed in 1890, although not for the purpose of controlling labor, had nevertheless been the legal justification for any restraint the government might be asked to place on the growing pressure of organized labor.

One still learns of occasional opinions voiced in and outside of Congress in favor of placing labor organizations again under the jurisdiction of the Sherman Act. The reasons given are that the power of unions to withhold the supply of hundreds of thousands of workers or millions of production man-hours is, or can be, restraint of trade. However, even if these answers were based on fact, the majority of the public would not permit a return to the concept that human labor is a commodity.

In other words, up to 1914 the public apparently was content with simply restricting labor, and the Sherman Act did this to its satisfaction. By 1914, however, organized labor had gained sufficient strength to influence public opinion and, through it, Congress. The result was the Clayton Act, the first legislative act in behalf of labor other than railroad employees who had always been the direct responsibility of Congress because of the interstate character of their industry.

This act, designed to take organized labor out from under the almost blanket restrictions of the Sherman Act, declared that *"the labor of a human being is not a commodity or article of commerce."* It further declared that *"nothing contained in the antitrust laws shall be construed to forbid the existence and operation of labor organizations or to restrain individual members of such organizations from lawfully carrying out the legitimate objects thereof; nor shall such organizations be held to be illegal combinations or conspiracies in restraint of trade, under the antitrust laws.*" On the face of it, this established and protected the rights of labor. Moreover, Congress had acted within the limits of its constitutional authority. Article 1, Section VIII, authorizes Congress to regulate interstate commerce. The First Amendment guarantees, among other rights, peaceful assembly; and the Fourteenth Amendment forbids any state to deprive persons of life, liberty, or property without due process of law. Depriving a person or persons of the right to join an organization or participate in a lawful collective action through passage of a state law prohibiting such an organization or collective action, can be declared unconstitutional.

However, as we pointed out in the beginning of this chapter, the mere passage of a law is not sufficient. Administration and interpretation of the law are equally important. So it was with the Clayton Act, which permitted individual members of labor organizations "*lawfully*" to carry out the "*legitimate objects thereof.*" But no authority had defined what was and what was not a legitimate object or what constituted "lawfully carrying out." Consequently, definitions or interpretations of lawful acts and legitimate objects were up to the courts.

The courts, in turn, had traditionally considered it desirable to restrict labor, and they were removed from direct contact with the new trend in public opinion. Therefore, the overwhelming majority of Federal court decisions handed down in connection with the Clayton Act labeled attempts of labor to organize, gain recognition, or secure better working conditions as unlawful conspiracies and illegal restraint of trade, and therefore still a violation of the Sherman Act. Thus public opinion, somewhat more favorable toward labor, and the resulting Clayton Act were almost entirely neutralized by the attitude of at least one branch of the government, the judiciary. Nor was public opinion strong or articulate enough to do something about it.

The "Pro-labor" Era

It is generally conceded today that the era beginning with or even prior to the enactment of the Sherman Antitrust Act, in 1890, until 1932 was an era of undue and frequently flagrantly unfair repression of organized labor. The attitude of the Federal government in all three branches toward labor appeared to be at best indifferent and at worst actually unfriendly. All this suddenly changed. The crash of 1929 and the resulting widespread unemployment and dire financial straits of a very large segment of the American public drew attention to the social problems of a modern industrial society. As a result, labor organization, working conditions, wages, job security, and old-age security became definite responsibilities of the Federal government. Clearly, the government's attitude toward labor had changed. It declared a "new deal" and the overwhelming majority of the public applauded. Beginning with 1932, Federal laws favoring labor followed in quick and almost alarming succession. It is interesting to note that while in the preceding half century labor came out second best in almost all contests with employers, this was not due to any Federal laws specifically designed to hobble or repress labor. It was simply that the Sherman Antitrust Act was adapted to a purpose originally neither foreseen nor intended.

The foreman in turn took his stand according to the dictates of circumstances. In most instances, he remained on the side of management, where he logically belonged because of the very nature of his job. However, there were many instances where either he, the rest of management, or labor had forgotten his logical position. Then the foreman either chose or was forced into the position of fighting management.

Slow as public opinion is to exert its pressure, once started it does so with considerable force and momentum. As a result, the servants of the public, our government, and especially Congress, frequently "go overboard" to yield to this pressure. The history of labor legislation of the 1930's bears witness to this. In respect to the actions and the laws passed by the Federal government, this may be called the pro-labor era. Roughly it began with the Norris-LaGuardia Act, passed in March, 1932 (*prior* to the Roosevelt administration). This act restricted issuance of injunctions against labor by Federal courts to a very limited set of circumstances, such as where (1) *unlawful acts have been threatened or will be committed, and have been authorized or ratified by the persons against whom the injunction is to be issued;* (2) *substantial and irreparable property damage will follow;* (3) *greater injury will result to the complainant from denying the injunction than to the defendant from granting it;* (4) *the complainant has no adequate remedy at law;* (5) *public officers are unable or unwilling to furnish adequate protection;* (6) *the complainant has complied with every legal obligation involved in the dispute and has made every reasonable effort to settle the dispute by negotiation or with the aid of available governmental machinery.* Furthermore, the act declared unenforceable in Federal courts any employment contracts in which a worker must agree not to join a union or to resign if he is then a union member. (Such an agreement is generally known as a "yellow-dog contract.")

A year later, in the summer of 1933, when the Roosevelt administration was only a few months old, Congress passed the National Industrial Recovery Act. This law came very close to making unionization compulsory. Among other things, it attempted to regulate wages, working conditions, and labor-management relations, and gave labor an iron-clad guarantee against any interference. Two years later, however, the Supreme Court decided that Congress and the administration had gone too far, declaring the N.I.R.A. unconstitutional in May, 1935.

But the momentum of public opinion and the resulting government action had not spent itself. The year 1935 also saw the enactment of the National Labor Relations Act, better known as the Wagner Act. It, too, is quite one-sided. Section 7 provides almost as strong protection for labor to organize as the N.I.R.A. did, and Section 8 lists a number of unfair labor practices of which only an employer can be guilty. There is no mention in the entire bill of any unfair practices of which labor might be guilty. This was frankly admitted by the sponsors and the supporters of the Wagner Act. Their claim was and still is that employers and the public needed no more government protection against labor than a hunter needs protection against possible attacks from the rabbit. This may have been the case in 1933, when union membership numbered less than three million, and widespread unemployment weakened union influence even more. But by 1935, union membership had increased approximately 33 per cent, with prospects of even faster growth. Moreover, labor's allies predominated in the Federal government and in the vast majority of the state and larger city governments. The Federal legislative mill ground on in favor of labor. Also in 1935, the Social Security Act was passed providing for old-age and survivors' insurance, unemployment insurance, and public assistance for the needy old, needy dependent children, and needy blind.

The next year (1936) saw the Public Contracts Act, better known as the Walsh-Healey Act. This law actually prescribes the working conditions under which materials, supplies, articles, and equipment are manufactured, furnished, assembled, handled, or shipped on United States government contracts exceeding $10,000. This law regulates wages on the basis of the prevailing rates in the particular industry, hours of work being 8 in any one day or 40 in any one week. This law also prohibits employment of boys under 16 and girls under 18. It regulates health and safety conditions, prohibits industrial homework, and regulates employment conditions of learners, apprentices, and the physically handicapped.

Of course, detailed regulations of this kind are possible only because the United States government is in this instance in the same position as any individual who chooses to award a contract under prearranged and mutually agreed upon conditions. A manufacturing or other commercial organization is free to comply with these regulations or to ignore them by not bidding for contracts with the Federal government. Nevertheless, this law is of tremendous significance simply because it reveals the government's basic thinking in the entire area of working conditions. As a contracting party, the government is not limited by the constitutional restrictions and is in a position to bring to bear its authority on every phase of labor-management relations. Therefore, its present and future changes of attitude toward labor can be most accurately gauged by watching the degree and kind of enforcement as well as the possible amendments to this law. For here is one area where the contest between local and state authority on one side and Federal authority on the other can least obstruct our understanding of the government's and (we must assume) the public's thinking.

The next important law in favor of labor came in 1938. Its official title is the Fair Labor Standards Act, but it is more popularly known as the Wage and Hour Law. It prohibits child labor and provides for minimum wages and overtime payment for workers engaged in interstate commerce or in the process or occupation necessary to the production of goods for interstate commerce. The coverage is broad. For example, a manufacturer of buttons not necessarily made to be shipped out of the state but made for shirts which are, would be considered subject to the Fair Labor Standards Act. The act lists a number of exemptions, but space will not permit going into detail here. One exemption, however, we do want to mention. A foreman is not subject to this act provided the following are true: (1) if he manages an establishment or department or subdivision thereof; (2) if he customarily directs the work of other employees; (3) if he is paid a salary not less than $30 per week; and (4) if his hours of work of the same nature as that performed by nonexempt employees do not exceed 20 per cent of the number of hours worked in the work week of nonexempt employees under his direction.

This exemption foreshadowed a definite trend which has become more and more important to the foreman, and has become more and more evident over the 17 years, which, at this writing, have passed since enactment of the law. The next indication of the trend occurred with the Taft-Hartley Act which will be discussed later. As a result of these two pieces of legislation, plus general developments in management thinking and procedures, the foreman has become more and more integrated into the management team and more and more distinct and separate from rank-and-file or hourly rated workers.

A supervisor is classified as an administrative employee when he assists an executive or administrator in nonmanual work, when he is required to exercise discretion and independent judgment, and when he is paid at a rate not less than $200 per month. It should also be mentioned that the work week is defined as seven consecutive 24-hour days. It may begin on any day of the week and at any time of the day, but each week must be considered by itself. That is to say, overtime must be paid for any time worked in excess of 40 hours in any given week even though the previous week an employee may have worked only 1 hour. In other words, there may be no "averaging" of hours of two or more work weeks.

There is one interesting exception which holds true of both the Fair Labor Standards Act and the Public Contracts (Walsh-Healey) Act. Wherever there is a labor-management agreement certified by the National Labor Relations Board which provides for a minimum of 1,000 hours in 26 consecutive weeks, or for 2,080 hours in 52 consecutive weeks with a guaranteed annual wage, employees subject to these acts may work 12 hours a day or 56 hours a week before the payment of overtime rates is required. This should give some hint as to what the Federal government thinks about year-round employment plans, which have assumed ever-increasing importance in the last few years. Indeed, this type of employment, popularly termed "guaranteed annual wage," is fast coming to the front as one of the major bargaining points unions are expected to raise in mass-production industries such as automobiles, steel, etc.

The foregoing, then, constitutes an outline of the part the Federal government played in labor-management relations during the New Deal. Omitted are some minor bills, dealing with isolated aspects of the entire subject, such as the Anti-Strike Breaker Law (Byrnes Act) of 1936, Anti-Racketeering Law (Hobbs Act) of 1934, the Bituminous Coal Conservation Act of 1935, and the various railway labor acts and their amendments. While all these acts were important to the solution of the specific problem for which they were designed, they add little light to the subject discussed here. All of them were part of the pattern described in the foregoing pages, a pattern of a definite bias in favor of labor in Federal legislation.

What effect such a pattern had on organized labor can probably best be shown by the following figures: At the beginning of or shortly prior to the New Deal, organized labor claimed union membership of less than 3 million in all unions, or approximately 8 per cent of all working people in the United States who could conceivably be unionized. Ten years later, organized labor claimed a union membership of nearly 10 million in all unions, or approximately 25 per cent of all working people in the United States subject to possible unionization. Another 12 years later, in 1954, organized labor claimed a total membership of about 17 million members, or more than 33 per cent of all working people subject to possible unionization. In addition, it must be remembered that persons such as parents, spouses, or children are directly exposed to the thinking and the influence of each one of the 17 million union members. Therefore, those coming directly under the influence of labor's thinking in the United States can safely be estimated to number between 50 and 60 million persons. This certainly takes labor out of the "rabbit" class, where friends of labor had represented it during the formulation of the New Deal program, beginning with the N.I.R.A. Labor became a power to be reckoned with in connection with any changes affecting our economic and social welfare. Evidences are multiplying that the public and therefore the government are thinking along those lines.

The New Trend

The first indications of the new trend was the War Labor Disputes Act, better known as the Smith-Connally Anti-Strike Law of 1943. It was passed over the President's veto, therefore requiring a two-thirds majority. It was the first Federal law in over 50 years designed to restrict labor. The law provides for (1) government seizure and operation of industrial establishments under certain conditions of national emergency, (2) strike-notice procedure, and (3) prohibition of political contributions by labor organizations. During government operation of an industry or plant, the law forbids (a) instigation, inducement (forceful or otherwise), encouragement, or conspiracy to strike, slow-down, or lockout, and (b) aid, guidance, direction or provision of funds to aid lockouts, slow-downs, or strikes. However, it is not unlawful for an individual to cease work, refuse to continue to work, or to accept other employment.

The implications of this law are clear. While even in wartime the Congress did not abridge the individual worker's right to make known his dissatisfaction with working conditions by ceasing work, Congress did find it necessary to curtail the powers of *unions* as well as of *employers*. In other words, Congress had also recognized that labor, or our "rabbit," had grown to a size where, uncontrolled, it could do irreparable damage to our war effort. Specifically, the coal miners proved this through the United Mine Workers and their president, John L. Lewis. Undoubtedly he, more than any other single person in the labor movement, has reminded the public and thus Congress that organized labor represents a tremendous power and influence. He further has proved that misuse of such power can be just as disastrous to the American way of life as misuse of economic power in the hands of employers. Together with the public's will, including labor's will to win the war, the Smith-Connally Act provided the necessary restrictions.

However, with the war over, labor prepared to consolidate its gains and go after more. We are all familiar with the results immediately after the war, a period of strife in practically every major industry in America—mining, transportation, steel, lumber, automobiles, communications, etc. Labor certainly had grown in power. Its pressure was sufficient to win important concessions from even the most powerful corporations. Such concessions were often sought at the expense of the average citizen's grocery basket, his comfort and, yes, even his health and safety. The public was more than a little surprised and certainly aroused. A wave of reaction set in, resulting in a predominantly anti-New Deal Congress in 1946. The National Labor Relations Act of 1947, better known as the Taft-Hartley Act, was the result.

We shall discuss one point of this law in detail because it is of immediate interest to the foreman and because it seems that, by virtue of its inherent logic, this point will continue to be an expression of the public's will and therefore the will of Congress. All other provisions will be mentioned only in so far as they highlight the evident shift of public opinion and thus reflect the recent behavior and possible future conduct of Congress and the Federal government.

The Taft-Hartley Act places the foreman definitely on the side of management, and considers him an integral part of management. This must be clearly understood by the foreman, so that he may recognize his full responsibility to management and to the employees under him. What it means is this: Any statement or act of the foreman will be interpreted by public opinion, by labor, and by law as emanating from management. Therefore, the law specifically states that management is not required to recognize any pressure that any foreman or group of foremen may attempt to exert by means of membership in labor organizations or by forming their own foremen's or supervisor's organization. However, this does not mean that a foreman or supervisor is prevented from joining a union or any other organization. It simply means that he may not use such an organization to exert pressure on management.

The supervisor or foreman is specifically defined in Section 2, Paragraph 11, of the National Labor Relations Act: "*The term 'supervisor' means any individual having authority, in the interest of the employer, to hire, transfer, suspend, lay off, recall, promote, discharge,*

assign, reward, or discipline other employees, or respon-
sibility to direct them, or to adjust their grievances, or
effectively to recommend such action, if in connection
with the foregoing the exercise of such authority is not of a
merely routine or clerical nature, but requires the use of
independent judgment." It will be noted that the
above definition is a close parallel to that contained
in the Fair Labor Standards Act.

The result has been a gradual but constant rise in
the foreman's status in management. This may perhaps be overstating the case for the Taft-Hartley Act,
since the trend of management's attitude toward
greater and greater decentralization also has contributed to the increasing importance of the foreman's
job. However, this change in management methods
and thinking is hardly conceivable without the specific
assurance to management that the foreman would not
turn up some day in the ranks of union opposition.

Here again, an occasional grumble may be heard
that the foreman's job in pay and security still leaves
much to be wished for. Some of these grumbles may
even have added that having union protection would
be better. Yet, foremen will do well to ask themselves what working group or element has ever had the
good fortune to be promoted by law into an assured
position with management. Of course, there have
been occasions when management or foremen or both
have failed to keep pace with the trend. This is, however, hardly sufficient reason either to wish for or to
try and reverse the trend.

In order to understand the full significance of the
Taft-Hartley Act, we shall have to recall some of the
events in labor history during the past 15 years. We
have learned that unions grew from a relatively small
and ineffectual particle of our American society to

perhaps the strongest and most influential single bloc
of the American public. As a political power, they
began to assume an important role in American
political and social life. The results have not been
happy. The closed-shop practice began to dictate to
both employer and employee as to who could or could
not hold a job. Secondary boycotts frequently
paralyzed a whole series of plants or even entire industries, many of which had no part in a labor-management disagreement other than supplying or receiving
supplies from a plant which had. Intra- and inter-
union warfare resulting in jurisdictional disputes frequently victimized employers who had worked in
harmony with labor over many years. Strikes were
called in complete disregard of public welfare, safety,
and health. Employers were threatened and defamed,
with management almost powerless to present its case.
The Wagner Act had made it a risky business for an
employer to utter statements in defense of himself
and in criticism of union actions or statements. Thus,
the Taft-Hartley Act can best be described as public
opinion's and government's attempt to equalize the
two major powers—the power of numbers in union
membership on one hand, and the economic power of
business and industry on the other. Government
sought to establish itself as the arbitrator or mediator
of both.

A look at this act may help us determine whether
this observation is correct, and if so, whether it has
succeeded in the purpose for which it was intended—
to achieve a balance of power. Even though certain
aspects will probably be modified by legislation, it will
be helpful to discuss the act as it was originally passed,
as an illustration of how far the pendulum swung.

As we know, according to the Wagner Act, only

employers could be guilty of unfair labor practices. The Taft-Hartley Act, on the other hand, listed a number of unfair or unlawful practices of which unions could be found guilty. Thus, a union could be found guilty of not bargaining in good faith. The secondary boycott was made unlawful. This means that it is unlawful for a union to forbid its members to handle or process material in an organization which is not on strike, simply because the material to be handled or processed has been secured or is in transit from a firm which is on strike.

Another practice forbidden by the Taft-Hartley Act was the jurisdictional strike. This means a work stoppage caused by a dispute between two or more unions over the control of a work area, for example, plumbing as opposed to steamfitting, new electrical work as opposed to maintenance, and the like.

Still another practice forbidden was "featherbedding." This means exacting payment, service, or any other "thing of value" for services or work not performed or to be performed. A typical example is the former practice of the musicians' union of requiring a theatrical producer to hire an orchestra for a play which did not call for music of any kind. Consequently, a group of musicians played cards at full musicians' pay for every day the play ran.

But, beyond making certain practices unlawful, the Taft-Hartley Act placed additional restrictions on unions. An important one was the prohibition of the closed shop. The closed shop, as the reader may know, is one where it is required of management to hire none but union members in good standing, and to discharge an employee who is no longer a union member in good standing. Furthermore, prior to the Taft-Hartley Act, the union was the sole judge of who was or was not in good standing. In contrast, according to the Taft-Hartley Act, any union member with paid-up union dues was stated to be in good standing.

In addition, unions were made accountable for the funds they control. They were also required to be certified by the National Labor Relations Board; a union had to prove that a clear-cut majority of employees in any plant or firm chose that union as their bargaining representative. Finally, unions had to deny officially any connection with the Communist Party.

The Taft-Hartley Act also provided for a "cooling off" period before strikes. It required resort to mediation machinery of individual states. However, perhaps the most important and certainly the most disputed provision of this law was the fact that the government was again empowered to place an injunction on labor's or an employer's causing a general work stoppage wherever or whenever such action was considered necessary to public interest. It should be noted that this was the first time that injunctions were reintroduced as a major tool to restrain the growing power of organized labor.

As for the employer, most of the restrictions listed in the Wagner Act were retained in the Taft-Hartley Act, with a few exceptions. The most notable was that freedom of speech was restored to the employer. He could now tell his side of the story to both the public and his employees, *so long as his statements did not contain any threats or even disapproval of lawful union activities. He could not express preferences for one union at the expense of another, or make expressed or implied promises to his employees for not joining a union or participating in organizations of labor activities.* This last statement should be clearly understood by foremen, since the foreman has been definitely designated as an integral part of management and since he is likely to remain in that position. In other words, management or the foreman has a perfect right to make known and talk about the advantages and benefits the employer offers to all his employees. However, he must refrain from expressing any pro- or antiunion bias, either in reference to all unions, or to one particular union.

It is at this writing some 8 years since the Taft-Hartley Act was passed. Despite criticism on both sides, it has definitely stabilized and clarified relationships between management and labor. To be sure, there are those who favor returning to use of the anti-trust law to control labor and there are those who clamor for the return to the Wagner Act.

Predictions are, of course risky, but this much may be said on the basis of the past 8 years with the Taft-Hartley Act: Only extreme conditions caused by a serious depression or war and/or excesses perpetrated by the extremists on either side could upset the basic balance gradually brought about by the Taft-Hartley Act plus the good sense of the public, management, and labor. Minor adjustments are possible and indeed probable, but in the main, the foreman may assume that the basic principles on which this Act is based will remain protected. Free enterprise must remain free, but so must the right of the individual to protect his job and his security if he prefers by choosing his own spokesman or agent, without fear of reprisal.

State Legislation

The foregoing broadly outlines the history of the Federal government's activities in labor-management relations. Needless to say, the 48 states also played an important part in this over-all development of labor-public-government-employer relationship. In the main, the attitude of state governments followed the same pattern as that of the Federal government. This should not be surprising, for the same public sentiment which influenced the Federal government also influenced the governments of the individual states.

To be sure, public opinion and the resultant individual state legislation did not progress at a uniform pace. Regional interests and regional patterns of population influenced developments. For example, the highly industrialized North Atlantic region is slightly ahead of the national government in liberal, as distinguished from conservative, labor legislation, while the predominantly agricultural Southern and Midwestern states have lagged somewhat behind the national trend. Moreover, individual states, or possibly even geographical regions, differ in their concept and their approach to what may or may not be permissible union influence and control in respect to the individual worker's employment rights. Broadly speaking, here again Southern states and the Midwest and Northwest have displayed a more restrictive attitude toward union influence and control.

This is probably best illustrated by those legislative provisions of individual states which are generally referred to as "right-to-work laws" (see list of states having right-to-work laws, Table IV). Technically speaking, the phrase "right-to-work laws" is not always correct because in many states this right-to-work provision is an additional or changed part of a more comprehensive state labor law enacted, in some cases, years before.

Such state legislative provisions qualify that portion

of the Taft-Hartley Act which permits a union-management contract calling for a "union shop." The union shop provision or clause is simply a modification of the now prohibited "closed-shop" agreement. Under the Federally permitted (Taft-Hartley Act) union-shop agreement, management and the union have the right to agree that, as a condition of employment, the individual worker must become and remain a union member in good standing *after* he is hired and successfully completes his trial period.

Under the now-prohibited closed-shop provisions, it was possible for the employer and the union to agree by formal (union) contract to require union membership from workers *before* they could even be considered for employment. Therefore, the Taft-Hartley Act modifies, but does not eliminate, the possibility for employers and the union to enter an agreement which restricts the individual job seeker's or job holder's right to decide for himself where to seek and hold a job.

Seventeen states have enacted such right-to-work laws or amendments, and other states are considering similar provisions. There are many individuals who contend that this admittedly complex question is a matter for individual states to decide. Most of these favor such laws. Ultimately, however, the question must be decided on its merits as a national policy lest it become a source of continued regional conflict, or even worse, cause an unhealthy partitioning of the country into spheres of unduly varying economic levels and labor markets. (For further study and evaluation, see tables at the end of this chapter.)

PERSPECTIVE FOR THE FOREMAN

What does all this array of evidence and historical data mean to the average foreman? Outstanding is the fact that it has been decided as a result of numerous trials and errors and by the will of the public as expressed by its legislators that the foreman is an integral part of management. Once legally (and, we trust, mentally) part of management, he should evaluate the history of labor-management relations over the past 65 years through the eyes of enlightened management.

To begin with, the foreman must realize that American labor has developed its own pattern of thought and behavior. This is not the pattern of most European labor, which is quite properly labeled "class thinking." To be sure, American labor has frequently been violent, arrogant, and blind, but it has been so in a peculiarly American way. With few exceptions, labor has rejected the European version of class thinking and class strife. There are three major reasons for this.

The first is the deep-seated acceptance of the American Constitution and the structure of the American government. In the beginning of this chapter we mentioned Article 1, Section VIII, of the Constitution, as well as the First and Fourteenth amendments. These, along with other provisions in our Constitution, have left sufficient elbowroom for all elements of American society to protect their basic rights. The structure of the American government provides for the necessary flexibility through Congress on the one hand and for the necessary stability through the Federal courts on the other hand whenever the more sensitive branch of the government tends to swing too far in one direction.

Second, discounting a small minority, American labor accepts the profit system as the American way of doing things. The future holds out so many promises for all that the rank and file of American labor is quite satisfied to be able to acquire and maintain sufficient influence to gain and protect what it believes to be an adequate standard of living and adequate security. It has refrained from forming into a class movement. And it can be expected to continue to do so. The rank and file does not seek political or social power for the sake of power, even though some of its leaders may be tempted by the apparent promise of power which union leadership holds out to them.

The third major reason for labor's adherence to the American way is the increasingly flexible attitude of American management. Management's production know-how, inventiveness, and organizational skill have made possible ever-increasing total returns, which have enabled it to meet the ever-increasing demands of American labor. Moreover, American businessmen know that the living standard of all the American people, of whom labor is an important part, determines the welfare of their own businesses.

Like American labor, American employers have refused to consider themselves a social group or class—in this case, a privileged class. This attitude, too, can be expected to remain. Too many employers stem from and are familiar with the ways of life and thought of working people, to feel otherwise. Consequently, again discounting a small minority, they have merely sought power and influence in order to gain reasonably stable political, social, and economic conditions. Power for the sake of power is no more the desire of the employer than it is the desire of the rank and file of labor.

Broadly speaking, over the past 65 years government has seen to it that the rights and privileges of all individuals as well as groups were preserved. As the need has arisen and the public will has decreed, government has thrown its weight of influence and protection sometimes in favor of labor and sometimes in favor of employers. Despite occasional swings of the pendulum, it has sought to establish a balance of power and has assumed the role of arbitrator when the contest between the two appeared to reach a deadlock. That, too, can be expected to continue as long as we retain the kind of government we have. The foreman, therefore, can have no better guide for anticipating future developments in labor-management relations than what in his opinion is happening to our Constitution and form of government.

But in connection with all of this, what about the foreman's everyday headaches and difficulties? The first answer to that question is that once the broader picture is more fully understood, the foreman will develop a better sense of proportion and a calmer attitude toward his thousand and one daily annoyances. He will be able to judge whether a given problem is a perfectly normal happening in the light of all that has been said in the preceding pages, or whether it is time to sound the alarm and alert management. Remembering the broad picture, he should know now that seeking better pay and greater security is perfectly normal behavior for working men and women, though they are not always attainable in the light of the employer's ability to pay. He should also know that attempting to gain undue power is the thing to be feared and fought. How to fight it is best left to those whom we, as Americans, have designated to do that for us. If we are not satisfied with the way they have fought for us, we can tell them so in our next election.

The Foreman's Responsibilities

Thus, remembering the title of this chapter, the foreman, as a member of management, has two broad responsibilities. They are, first, protecting the rights of management within the framework of the laws of the land, which is the expression of the government's attitude and the public's will; and second, the observance of the laws.

The specific responsibility of protecting management's rights is generally placed in the hands of those who are fully conversant with what exactly are the rights of all concerned in respect to Federal, state, and local laws. However, they need help because often they are confronted with a situation after it has grown into a serious problem over a long period of time. There are many occasions when serious trouble could have been averted if the problem had been met before it became serious. Intelligent observers on the firing line—in other words, intelligent foremen—are the answer.

When dealing with a particular problem, let each foreman ask himself what is involved. Is it a case of the understandable attempts of individuals to gain greater economic benefits and security, or is it a case where an individual or a group is questioning the authority of management in order to increase its own? One of the surest signs that the latter is the case is when labor makes a set of general demands impossible for management to meet, or when it becomes obvious that those involved in a disagreement have no particular interest in solving it. In other words, when the particular issue they have raised is not a *reason* but an *excuse* for the dispute. With a little practice, any reasonably intelligent person can recognize the difference between a real problem and an artificial problem. It is the latter type which raises the danger signal and calls for a general alert.

If the history of the last 65 years has told us anything, it has told us that the temper of the public and of our government, and the resulting laws, are impatient with any attempts on the part of labor or of management to play for dominance over the other. The attitudes of the public and the government are plain: *they want labor and management to resolve their difficulties on the spot and on the job.* That is what is meant by bargaining in good faith. This phrase was written into the Wagner Act to direct and check employers only. But the same phrase appeared in the Taft-Hartley Act in order also to direct and check labor. The foreman, as the outpost of management, is in immediate contact with labor. *No one is in a better position to judge what is and what is not bargaining in good faith, provided he has gained the proper perspective.*

Observance of laws is the foreman's other responsibility. To meet it, he should be reasonably familiar with the basic provisions of Federal laws, plus the basic legal controls and limitations set up by his state and local authorities. The basic Federal provisions have been sketched out in the preceding pages against the background of the broad picture. The foreman knows now that the Federal government imposes detailed requirements of employment conditions only in the event that his firm is either directly or indirectly working on materials or services contracted for by the United States government. In that event, the provisions of the Public Contracts (Walsh-Healey) Act are applicable to the actual working conditions of all nonsupervisory, nonprofessional, and nonadministrative employees in his firm. In all probability that includes the employees under the foreman's supervision. In all other cases, state and local laws direct and control working conditions. These laws include safety and security provisions, health and sanitary controls, employment of minors, and workmen's compensation. The foreman will do well to secure for himself the information necessary to stay within the limits of local requirements on one hand, and to recognize what are or are not justified demands on the part of labor in view of local provisions.

How does he do that? In plants where foremen's meetings are regularly held, he can request that a series of discussions on this subject be placed on the agenda of these meetings. The discussions would be designed to brief him thoroughly on management's will, provisions of the union contract (where applicable), plus basic local, state, and Federal provisions affecting the exercise of his job as foreman.

Where such meetings are not regularly scheduled, he can request a series of meetings for the same purpose. In either case, the foreman should know and, if necessary, make his management aware of the fact that he cannot adequately represent his company in the day-to-day contact with the rank and file unless he is permitted to gain a well-informed and sound management perspective. Without proper information and guidance, he will be insecure and may become either unduly aggressive or unduly cautious. This cannot help but ultimately reflect on the company as a whole.

For immediate references and perhaps as a talking point for a series of briefing sessions, several tables of assembled information have been provided.

Table I shows what arbitration agencies the fore-

TABLE I.—PROVISIONS FOR LABOR ARBITRATION ESTABLISHED
BY THE STATES

State	Special mediation board outside of labor department	Mediator or mediation staff within labor department	Arbitration service for public utilities or general welfare	None
Alabama		✓		
Arizona		✓		
Arkansas		✓		
California		✓		
Colorado		✓		
Connecticut	✓			
Delaware				✓
District of Columbia				✓
Florida	✓			
Georgia	✓	✓		
Idaho	✓	✓		
Illinois		✓		
Indiana	✓	✓		
Iowa		✓		
Kansas			✓	
Kentucky	✓	✓		
Louisiana	✓	✓		
Maine		✓		
Maryland		✓		
Massachusetts		✓	✓	
Michigan	✓	✓		
Minnesota	✓		✓	
Mississippi				✓
Missouri		✓	✓	
Montana	✓	✓		
Nebraska			✓	
Nevada		✓		

TABLE I.—PROVISIONS FOR LABOR ARBITRATION ESTABLISHED
BY THE STATES.—(*Continued*)

State	Special mediation board outside of labor department	Mediator or mediation staff within labor department	Arbitration service for public utilities or general welfare	None
New Hampshire........	✓	✓		
New Jersey............	✓	✓	✓	
New Mexico...........	....	....	....	✓
New York.............	✓	✓		
North Carolina........	✓	✓		
North Dakota.........	✓			
Ohio.................	✓	✓		
Oklahoma............	✓	✓		
Oregon...............	✓	✓		
Pennsylvania.........	✓	✓	✓	
Rhode Island.........	....	....	....	✓
South Carolina........	✓	✓		
South Dakota........	✓	✓		
Tennessee............	....	....	....	✓
Texas................	....	....	....	✓
Utah.................	....	✓		
Vermont.............	✓	✓		
Virginia..............	✓	✓	✓	
Washington..........	✓	✓		
West Virginia........	....	....	....	✓
Wisconsin............	✓	✓	✓	
Wyoming.............	....	....	....	✓

TABLE II.—STATE PROVISIONS FOR CHILD LABOR

State	Minimum age for full employment	Employment certificate required	Age certificate required	Control of daytime working hours	Control of night work	Age for required full time school attendance	Age for continuation school attendance	Control of meal period	Control of hazardous employment	State enforcement agency
Alabama	✓	✓	✓	✓	✓	7-16	16-17	—	✓	State Labor Department
Arizona	✓	✓	✓	✓	✓	8-16	14-16	—	✓	Industrial Commission
Arkansas	✓	✓	✓	✓	✓	7-16	16-loc. opt.	✓	✓	State Labor Department
California	✓	✓	✓	✓	✓	8-16	16-18	✓	✓	Industrial Commission
Colorado	✓	✓	✓	✓	✓	8-16	—	✓	✓	State Labor Department
Connecticut	✓	✓	✓	✓	✓	7-16	14-16	—	✓	Labor Commission
Delaware	✓	✓	✓	✓	✓	7-16	—	✓	✓	Industrial Commission
District of Columbia	✓	✓	✓	✓	✓	7-16	—	✓	✓	Board of Education
Florida	✓	✓	✓	✓	✓	6-16	Under 16	✓	✓	Industrial Commission
Georgia	✓	✓	✓	✓	✓	7-16	—	—	✓	State Labor Department
Idaho	✓			✓	✓	8-18	—	—	✓	Department of Education
Illinois	✓	✓	✓	✓	✓	7-16	Local option	✓	✓	State Labor Department
Indiana	✓	✓	✓	✓	✓	7-16	14-16	✓	✓	State Labor Department
Iowa	✓	✓	✓	✓	✓	7-16	—	✓	✓	State Labor Department
Kansas	✓	✓	✓	✓	✓	7-16	14-16	✓	✓	State Labor Department
Kentucky	✓	✓	✓	✓	✓	7-16	—	—	✓	Department of Industrial Relations
Louisiana	✓	✓	✓	✓	✓	7-16	Boys 14-16 / Girls 14-18	✓	✓	State Labor Department
Maine	✓	✓	✓	✓	✓	7-17	14-18	✓	✓	State Labor Department
Maryland	✓	✓	✓	✓	✓	7-16	—	✓	✓	State Labor Department
Massachusetts	✓	✓	✓	✓	✓	7-16	14-16	✓	✓	State Labor Department
Michigan	✓	✓	✓	✓	✓	6-16	Unmarried minors under 17	—	✓	State Labor Department

State					Age	Age			Administration
Minnesota	√	√	√	√	8-16	—	—	√	Division of Women and Children
Mississippi	√	√	√	√	7-17	Under 16	√	√	State Board of Health
Missouri	√	√		√	7-16	Local option	—	√	State Labor Department
Montana	√	√	√	√	8-16	—	—	√	State Labor Department
Nebraska	√	√	√	√	7-18	14-16	√	√	State Labor Department
Nevada	√	√	√	√	8-16	14-16	√	√	State Labor Department
New Hampshire	√	√	√	√	—	—	√	√	State Board of Education
New Jersey	√	√	√	√	7-16	14-16	√	√	State Labor Department
New Mexico	√	√	√	√	6-17	—	√	√	Department of Public Welfare
New York	√	√	√	√	7-16	16-17	√	√	Division of Wage-Hour, Women and Child Labor, State Labor Department
North Carolina	√	√	√	√	7-16	—	√	√	State Labor Department
North Dakota	√	√	√	√	7-17	—	√	√	State Labor Department
Ohio	√	√	√	√	6-18	16-18	√	√	Department of Industrial Relations
Oklahoma	√	√		√	7-18	16-18	√	√	State Labor Department
Oregon	√	√	√	√	7-18	16-18	√	√	State Labor Department
Pennsylvania	√	√	√	√	8-17	—	√	√	State Labor Department
Rhode Island	√	√	√	√	7-16	—	√	√	Division of Women and Children
South Carolina	√	√	√	√	7-16	—	√	√	State Labor Department
South Dakota	√	√		√	7-16	—	√	√	Department of Agriculture
Tennessee	√	√	√	√	7-16	14-16	√	√	State Labor Department
Texas	√	√	to 15	√	7-16	Under 18	√	√	State Labor Department
Utah	√	√	√	√	8-18	—	√	√	Industrial Commission
Vermont	√	√	√	√	7-16	—	—	√	State Labor Department
Virginia	√	√	√	√	7-16	14-18	√	√	State Labor Department
Washington	√	√	√	√	8-16	—	√	√	Supervisor of Women and Minors
West Virginia	√	√	√	√	7-16	Local option	√	√	State Labor Department
Wisconsin	√	√	√	√	7-16	16-18	√	√	Industrial Commission
Wyoming	√	√	√	√	7-17	—	—	√	State Labor Department

√ Covered by law.   — No provisions made.

TABLE III.—UNEMPLOYMENT-INSURANCE PROVISIONS OF THE
STATES

State	Initial waiting period, weeks	Maximum payment per week	Minimum payment per week	Maximum No. weeks payable in 52-week period
Alabama.............	1	$22	$6	20
Arizona.............	1*	20	5	12
Arkansas............	1	22	7	16
California...........	1	25	10	26
Colorado............	2*	28	7	20
Connecticut.........	1*	30	8	26
Delaware............	1	25	7	26
District of Columbia..	1	20	7	20
Florida.............	1	20	5	16
Georgia.............	2	26	5	20
Idaho...............	2	25	10	26
Illinois.............	1	27	10	26
Indiana.............	1	27	5	20
Iowa...............	2	26	5	20
Kansas.............	1	28	5	20
Kentucky...........	1	28	8	26
Louisiana...........	1	25	5	20
Maine..............	1	27	9	20
Maryland...........	0*	30	6	26
Massachusetts.......	1*	25	7	26
Michigan...........	1*	27	6	20
Minnesota..........	2	30	11	26
Mississippi.........	2	30	3	16
Missouri...........	1	25	5	24
Montana...........	2	23	7	20
Nebraska...........	2	26	10	20
Nevada............	1*	30	8	26
New Hampshire......	1	30	7	26
New Jersey.........	1	30	10	26

TABLE III.—UNEMPLOYMENT-INSURANCE PROVISIONS OF THE STATES.—(*Continued*)

State	Initial waiting period, weeks	Maximum payment per week	Minimum payment per week	Maximum No. weeks payable in 52-week period
New Mexico	1	$30	$10	24
New York	1	30	10	26
North Carolina	1	30	7	26
North Dakota	1*	26	7	20
Ohio	2*	28	10	26
Oklahoma	1	28	10	22
Oregon	1	25	15	26
Pennsylvania	1	30	10	26
Rhode Island	1	25	10	26
South Carolina	1	20	5	18
South Dakota	1	25	8	20
Tennessee	1	26	5	22
Texas	1	20	7	24
Utah	1	27.50	10	26
Vermont	2	25	6	20
Virginia	1	22	6	16
Washington	1	30	10	26
West Virginia	1	30	10	24
Wisconsin	2	30	10	26
Wyoming	2*	30	10	26

* Additional payment for dependents.

NOTE: Slight changes are, of course, made from time to time, but the above table shows the order of magnitude of provisions. For latest information, consult the agencies listed in Table II.

man or his management may turn to for help and information in each state.

Table II gives the foreman a general idea as to state control of employment of minors and names the agencies which administer it. Note that the actual minimum age for child employment in each state is not shown.   Space limitations make it impossible to do so, since almost every state has established various minimum ages subject to varying conditions.   The table does, however, show whether this point is covered by state law, so that the foreman can be on

TABLE IV.—STATES WHICH HAVE "RIGHT-TO-WORK LAW"

This law supersedes the National Labor Relations Act (Taft-Hartley) which allows union security agreements, providing for the requirement that employees become and remain union members in good standing after they are permanently employed.

Arizona	Nebraska
Arkansas	Tennessee
Alabama	Texas
Florida	Virginia
Georgia	North Carolina
Iowa	South Carolina
Louisiana	North Dakota
Mississippi	South Dakota
Nevada	

guard with respect to employees in his department of doubtful employability.

Another item shown in Table II is the requirement for full-time and continuation-school attendance.   In some cases exceptions to the age range given are possible.   It may seem confusing to the reader that required age limitation for full-time and continuation-school attendance overlap in most instances.   This is due to the fact that it may be possible for a minor to switch from full-time to continuation school upon issuance of properly authorized working papers.

It is emphasized that the table serves primarily as a caution to the foreman that his state exercises certain legal controls over the employment of minors.   It will be up to the foreman to seek further information from the enforcement agency indicated, if he requires it with respect to his own department.

Table III covers unemployment insurance as administered by the respective states.

Last but not least, the foreman should be thoroughly familiar with all the provisions of the union contract if one exists in his organization. When there is none, he should make sure that he is familiar with all statements of labor policy issued by his management.

Armed with this, armed with the knowledge that his management stands in back of him in all his efforts in dealing with labor, and armed with the knowledge that ultimately the American public, its government, and its laws will not tolerate excesses of any kind, arrogance, or irresponsibility, the foreman can confidently deal with the labor problems which his management has entrusted to him. Above all, let him remember that a sound perspective gained from an awareness of what has happened in industrial relations over the past 65 years, is his best and safest daily guide.

Section Six

WORK SIMPLIFICATION AND THE FOREMAN

CHAPTER XIX

ELEVEN BASIC PRINCIPLES OF WORK SIMPLIFICATION

By Clem Zinck

"Work simplification" is an organized, common-sense attack upon the way in which work is done—usually factory operations, but the technique is applicable to the office as well—with a view to doing it better and, in fact, with the ultimate objective of doing it the *one best way*. It makes use of the techniques of time and motion study, such as discussed in Chap. V of this handbook, but it goes beyond a series of techniques, for a program of work simplification consists, in the last analysis, of instilling a *new philosophy about work* in the minds of everyone concerned, changing the direction of thinking of everyone in the company.

The "prime mover" in such a program is the foreman or supervisor. Through him the whole idea and philosophy will permeate the entire organization, and it is through his active participation and follow-through that the results of work simplification are achieved. These results consist of continuing suggestions as to how work can be done more efficiently, suggestions which are then put into effect for the ultimate benefit of all.

The fundamental and demonstrable basis of work simplification is this: *Once a person really knows how*

*and why a job is done and attacks the job with the desire
to improve the present method, an improved method will
result.*

The development of work simplification into its
present form is largely the work of Allan H. Mogensen.
Mogensen was graduated from Cornell University in
1924.   That fall he became an instructor in mechanical engineering at the University of Rochester.   As is
the common fate of young instructors, Mogensen had
the chore of conducting the routine inspection trips
which are forced upon what are usually thought to be
unwilling freshmen.   But these trips soon became live
events to Mogensen—if you listened, you could hear
the youngsters' enlightening observations on this and
that.   They asked quite embarrassing questions when
actual conditions did not jibe with classroom instructions or when their fresh viewpoints saw things that
didn't look right or logical.

At about that time the 16-mm. movie camera was
developed.   Mogensen was now doing consulting work
at Eastman Kodak.   He watched the motion-economy
experts use the movie of an activity to set time standards for wage payment.   But, far more important, he
observed that every time the workman was called in
to see the picture of how he did the job, invariably
the workman began to suggest improvements.   Work
simplification was born in Allan H. Mogensen from
the repeated observation of that universal reaction.

It has been the author's privilege to attend one of
Allan Mogensen's Work Simplification Conferences at
Lake Placid, N. Y., and there to have his own "direction of thinking" drastically changed toward the
advancement of method improvement in every work
situation.   He has, since then, conducted many programs with foremen and supervisors, helping them to

analyze their own operations—not showing them how to do their jobs but getting them to *apply purposeful thought* to their own problems in order that they themselves could be the ones to propose new and better methods.

Work simplification actually presents nothing new. Every principle used has been published in technical journals and books. Every principle has been proved in the rough and tumble of competition. Taken together, the principles have long furnished the "kit of tools" of professional-methods men. However, as already indicated, work simplification does present a new philosophy about the use of those principles. The essence of this philosophy was ably stated by James F. Lincoln, President of the The Lincoln Electric Company in his pamphlet "Intelligent Selfishness and Manufacturing." The opening sentence summarizes it: "Great as American industry is, it leaves largely untrapped its greatest resource, the productive power, initiative, and intelligence latent in every person."

Work simplification implements that philosophy by providing the means to develop and utilize the latent power, initiative, and intelligence of every employee of a company.

Obviously, if work simplification is a means of putting such a philosophy to work, it is something the foreman should understand and participate in. This is especially true inasmuch as work simplification accomplishes its results through people—and the foreman is management's direct contact with employees.

This section of the handbook will take the foreman, step by step, through the reasoning underlying work simplification. The method employed will be to present and discuss 11 basic principles, as follows:

I

The competitive position of any company in its industry is directly benefited by any action that helps produce a BETTER PRODUCT, AT A LOWER COST, DELIVERED AT THE RIGHT TIME.

Work simplification, as a generator of method-improvement ideas, has a direct, positive effect on competition. The continuous receipt of method-improvement ideas from the employees of a company makes the position of that company secure against competition.

If the reader does not readily accept the above positive statement, let him think a bit over its negative expression. Is there any surer way for a company to go out of business than to follow a policy of *never* making an improvement? Fire losses are recouped through insurance. Reorganization after bankruptcy has kept many companies in business. Redesigned products have brought renewed life to untold organizations. But what are the prospects for a company which has no definite improvement program?

What foreman would unhesitatingly stay with his company if he should find a notice on the company bulletin board, signed by the president, reading: "From now on it shall be the policy of this company never to make an improvement in any product, in any work, in any function." If, then, methods improvement is basic for survival, let alone growth, why not put it on an integrated, continuous, self-generating basis?

II

Resistance to change and resentment of criticism are recognized by work simplification as very potent

factors of human nature and the archenemy of method improvement.

Resistance to change and resentment of criticism occur in all activities of a person's life. The reader has but to check himself for a day to demonstrate how potent and how universal they are. Let him watch as he promotes even the most trivial change or new idea. Let him notice his own reactions to a suggested change or a new idea.

We have, in this respect, all mankind for company. We are all human. For example, witness Thomas Edison's statement in 1926 that in his considered judgment talking pictures would never come into general use "because the public will not support them." And that was from the man who invented the moving picture! Chauncey Depew confessed that he warned his nephew not to invest $5,000 in Ford stock because "nothing has come along to beat the horse." When, in 1907, De Forest put the radio tube into workable form, he was unable to sell his patent, and he let it lapse rather than pay $25 for its renewal.

If resistance to change and resentment of criticism are universal and powerful obstacles to improvement, what forces have counteracted and overcome them sufficiently to give us the relatively high standard of living we enjoy today? A fair question. The two major forces are *men who, through some inner urge, must improve things,* and *competition.*

There have been, are now, and always will be the big and little Edisons, Fords, Ketterings—men whose lifeworks bear out the remark of Kettering, "The whole fun of living is trying to make something better." Give the opportunity and training in work simplification to those men in every plant who want to improve things, and watch their efforts surmount resistance to change and resentment of criticism! As to competition, it has been called the great universal supervisor. It is the force that *"puts us to work or out of work."*

III

To create the sense of "belonging," of "participating," and of "accomplishing" in each and every employee is a vital responsibility of management. Work simplification stresses this human factor. Here, of course, the foreman plays a vital part.

Today we accept the sense of belonging, of participating, and of accomplishing as a matter of fact. But it was not always so. That spirit was relatively recently discovered and understood. Its story is one of the most dramatic in the field of improvement of business management. It has been vividly told by Roethlisberger and Dickson in their book "Management and the Worker."

Some years ago the management of the Western Electric Company gave permission to a group of industrial engineers, business researchers, and industrial psychologists to study the conditions of operations in the Hawthorne plant in Chicago. They were to determine management policies that would benefit the employees, the company, and the community. They drew up a tentative list of things to investigate, established procedures of approach, selected a starting place, and began in a manner befitting the caliber of the personnel engaged in the project.

They chose first to study the effect of illumination on production. A test group of employees and a suitable assembly operation were chosen; conditions were standardized. Production did increase as illumination increased. Being true engineers and scientists, they set about to prove their findings. They reversed the test and decreased the illumination until the operators were working almost in candlelight—*but production still continued to go up!*

Here was an enigma. For five years they worked away to unearth the secret. The story of that search is the story of "Management and the Worker." In the end, the official report said: "Upon analysis only one thing seemed to show a continuous relationship with improved output. This was the mental attitude of the operators."

In other words, as the girls put it, it was fun. "The girls were taking part in an interesting experiment. They were told all about it, were consulted on details that affected them, and were helping with something the plant managers thought important. The girls who became friends with one another in the test room worked out their own little informal organization; they weren't afraid of the supervisors; they relaxed and worked easily, naturally. They had a sense of belonging, of participating, and of accomplishing."[1]

However, mark this: The sense of belonging, of participating, and of accomplishing was not even on the agenda of things to be investigated when the engineers, the business researchers, the psychologists first rolled up their sleeves and tackled the problem of how to increase production to benefit employee, company, and consumer.

IV

The purpose of work simplification is, therefore, to enlist and train the productive power, initiative, and

[1] CARSKADON, T. A., "Workers and Bosses Are Human," *Public Affairs Pamphlet* 76, 1943.

intelligence of every employee in the constant effort to make progress.

The employees will catch the spirit and the desire to make improvements when the desire to improve things is an inherent part of the operation of the employees' department—*i.e., when the supervisor has the desire to improve operations.*

There are six reasons, at least, why a foreman should have a genuine desire to make improvements—and to make improvements day in and day out:

First: Do we ever make a replacement purchase in which we do not expect to receive an article with more worth built into it, be it in the form of better appearance, fewer "bugs," greater utility, or longer wearing qualities? James Truslow Adams expressed that American outlook in the lead article of the April, 1944, *Reader's Digest,* entitled "Why Are We Americans Different?" He says: "The past means little to the American. He is used to trying to make the best of the present but with his eye always on the future. True, he founds innumerable historical societies and plasters his village with memorial tablets. Yet he is willing to scrap furniture, buildings, and all else, any year, *if he thinks he has found something newer or more efficient.*"

Let us consider what that means. For that to be an actual state of affairs, someone else has had to make improvements in order that we could get more value. Therefore, does it not follow, if we are to get more value for what we *buy,* we must produce more each day of what we *make,* so that the other fellow can get his "more value"? If we do not do our share in method improvement, then we are not "paying our freight"; we are taking something we have not earned.

To keep on improving is our obligation to society.

Here are a few examples of more value, examples of how society has benefited by greater and greater productivity year after year by American workmen.

PRICES IN HOURS OF WORK—AVERAGE FACTORY
WAGE EARNER

Article	1914	1938
Felt hat.................	11.5	3.2
Work shoes..............	9.3	3.3
Bedroom suite...........	104.3	65.4
Baby carriage...........	41.0	15.7
Set of dishes..............	40.0	14.5
Light bulb...............	1.7	0.2
Automobile..............	4,514	1,098
Bicycle.................	75.5	40.2

Source: Machinery & Allied Products Institute.

The figures given above show advances made to the latest normal year before the Second World War. Comparisons to 1955 would be no less favorable since, as shown in the tables, pages 444–445, Chap. XVII, factory wages have more than kept pace with dollar inflation and since productivity per labor hour continues to show improvement.[1]

Second: The foreman's own job depends upon his company's keeping abreast of competition.

Third: A supervisor is *expected* to make methods improvements. Is there any person who has a supervisory position of any kind who does not, deep down, know that part of his job is to make improvements in

[1] Looked at internationally, this concept provides rather illuminating comparisons: It has been estimated that in 1954 the work time needed to buy a radio set was 1 day and 2 hours in the U. S. A.; 7½ days in France; 15 days in Italy; and 27 days in the U. S. S. R. (Information Please Almanac, 1954.)

the way things are done? That expectation is the
result of the foreman's being part of management.

The worth-while foreman of modern industry is conscious of that obligation to his company, as evidenced
by a survey of the plants of the Radio Corporation of
America. In that survey, the foremen rated these
five functions as the top ones of their responsibility:

Meeting production schedules
Human relations
Quality control
Cost control
Methods

The reader, in his own place of work, with its
peculiar operating conditions, may not list the five
in the same sequence, but would he not list the same
functions as the top five? Moreover, a moment's
reflection will show that methods improvement may
well be a basic element in the other four.

When a supervisor has been stimulated with a desire
to make methods improvements, the main part of the
battle has been won. Once he has that desire, he will
find ways and means to make improvements. These
are true words: "We always find ways and means to
do the things we want to do."

Fourth: When a foreman has made methods improvement a part of his thinking and actions and when his
employees see that he means business, he has created
in his department an atmosphere, a moral influence,
in which employees develop through being able to
belong, to participate, and to accomplish. This development of employees will result in methods-improvement suggestions which the foremen should accept
enthusiastically and graciously. He will have started
a snowball rolling downhill, which only his own actions

will stop. If the foreman himself makes methods improvements, he can by example and encouragement get his employees to do likewise, with ever-increasing enthusiasm and greater worth per suggestion.

Fifth: When the foreman has made methods improvement part of the thinking and actions of himself and his employees, he will gain increased help and interest from the professional-methods men of his company. No professional-methods man would dare say that he has ever put into successful operation even 25 per cent of all the ideas he *knows* will help a department. And why not? Simply because there was a lack of interest, enthusiasm, and support on the part of the department foreman in all too many cases.

What is the foreman missing under such circumstances? An official of Du Pont stated on the platform of the American Management Association that each industrial engineer in his company was expected to develop $37,500 savings per year to hold his job. A foreman in such a company would be missing part of or all that saving in his department if the professional found it easier to work with some fellow foreman than to battle through an improvement with him. The foreman can have every professional-methods man in his plant working for him—the designer, the toolmaker, the time-study man, the industrial engineer, the quality-control supervisor, the maintenance supervisor, the plant engineer—all of them if he creates and keeps fresh an atmosphere in which they can "go to town."

Sixth: The last, but by no means least, reason why the foreman should make the effort and the start, then get his employees, then the professional men to improve his department, is this. When he has himself, his employees, and the professionals on his side, top management will be only too glad to be on his side also. Top management knows how difficult it is to get even the simplest of new ideas into successful operation on the floor. Management knows the terrific loss of power and effect to a good idea as it is pushed down through several layers of resistance to change and resentment of criticism. Management will be on the foreman's side to approve employees' suggestions, the foreman's ideas, and the professional men's recommendations when it feels confident that the foreman will do his part to make them work.

And who benefits from all of this? The foreman benefits in satisfaction of a job well done, in getting recognition from his employees, his fellow foremen, and his superiors, and in getting promotions just that much faster.

V

Work simplification rests on the principle that any work that does not add value to the product, does not give or receive essential information, or does not plan or calculate is essentially WASTE.

Acceptance of that philosophy offers the broadest possible area for methods improvement. Can we demonstrate its validity?

Let us take a shoe buckle made completely in one operation in an automatic machine at the rate of x pieces per minute. It is no better or no worse than a similar shoe buckle made in separate operations, as follows: Pierce frame; cut off and form tongue; assemble tongue to frame with the necessary work of carting and storing the frames and tongues from the machines to the bench; place on bench; pick up one tongue and one frame by hand; assemble tongue to frame by hand; place assembly in die of bench power press; trip press to form tongue around bar of frame while holding the assembly by hand, and toss aside. How much *waste* is there in the separate-operations method compared to the automatic machine in getting identical end results—a serviceable shoe buckle?

Take the operation of "assemble tongue to frame" in making the shoe buckle discussed above. Visualize the work of picking up the frame with the left hand and the tongue with the right hand, placing the open heel of the tongue over the tongue bar of the frame, holding the two pieces in that assembly while placing the heel of the tongue on the closing die in the bench power press, holding the pieces securely while the press is tripped to have the punch close the heel of the tongue around the tongue bar of the frame, removing the assembly from the die with the left hand, and tossing the buckle aside. Visualize all that work so that in a split part of a second the punch and die can be operated to close the heel around the bar! What is the *value-adding work* compared to *waste work?* As one person exclaimed in a clinic as he was jarred by the impact of this outlook on waste on his conventional thinking, "Why, there is no 'do' or value-adding work in that operation." If we accept the philosophy of work simplification, there is very little "do" in the average operation.

Let us look at two incidents in everyday living as we weigh the problem of waste effort. Think of what happens in a fire station when a fire alarm rings. In a matter of seconds almost, the fire apparatus is on its way. Why? Because *purposeful thought* over a period of years developed practices with the minimum of lost motion in order to save precious time. Can it not be said that the first "drop delivery" was the pole from the sleeping floor to the ground floor in a fire house? One of the writer's clinic classes was brightened one day by having a participant in the clinic exclaim at this illustration, "But they're paid to get out quickly." Are we paid to do our job quickly or just to do it somehow, sometime?

Who has not been thrilled by the terrific impact of the cold, practical efficiency in a modern operating room as seen in a realistic movie? Not much fussing and fidgeting by the surgeon and his trained staff when seconds are precious! How little waste effort in the technique of the surgeon who stated, with pardonable pride, "I perform my appendectomy operation in 12 minutes from the time the patient is wheeled in till he is wheeled out." Yes, when the chips are down, we become efficient. We force ourselves to give purposeful thought to what we have to do and how we are doing it.

Here is a good example of what purposeful thought can do to make work easier and increase output. The product is an electrostatic condenser. The top is separate and is soldered to the can after the can is filled. The can is held in a wood holding block during the soldering operation. The detail is as follows: The block with the condenser is held in the left hand and the soldering wire in the right hand. The soldering iron is held rigid by a fixture in front of the operator, in a slanted position which enables the condenser and solder to be positioned readily against the hot iron. One side of the can is soldered. The block is given a quarter turn, and the second side soldered, and so on for the four sides. However, the rectangular block is so large that the operator has to use the right hand to help the left hand to give the block the quarter turn.

The supervisor observed the operation. Purposeful thought as to what had to be done and how to do it resulted in the use of a circular block. The operator can give the quarter turns without assistance from the right hand. Hence, the soldering operation is practically continuous, with production increased 14 per cent (see Fig. 1).

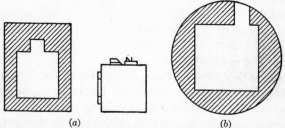

(a)　　　　　　　　*(b)*

Fig. 1.—Improvement in fixture for soldering top to condenser can. (*a*) Old fixture. The original fixture to hold the condenser was rectangular. The use of both hands was required to position the fixture to solder each of the four sides. (*b*) New fixture. The new fixture is round to fit the palm of the hand. Finger movements of left hand only are required to position the fixture to solder each of the four sides.

The change of fixture design resulted in an increase in production of 14 per cent. Rectangular fixture = 550 per 8-hour day; circular fixture = 625 per 8-hour day.

The reader should not blame the blockmaker too much. What is more "obvious" than a rectangular holding block for a rectangular condenser—*until you look ahead to see just what is to be done and how?*

VI

The recorded facts obtained by the **ANALYTICAL OBSERVATION** of a process, a man-machine combination, or an operator activity are the only effective bases for study to reduce waste and to improve methods.

The work in a process, man-machine combination, or operator activity is recorded by analytical observations on an appropriate chart. The co-ordinated use of three charts provides "word pictures" of the work done for study to improve methods and to reduce waste. Properly prepared charts are almost as effective as a movie and can be prepared by any foreman after simple, fundamental training. The three charts used in work simplification are

1. The flow-process chart
2. The man-machine chart
3. The operator chart

In the flow-process chart, we look for all the elements of waste in operation, transportation, delay or storage, and inspection, *between* value-adding operations of a process, and also record sufficient details of the operations themselves so that they can be studied for possibilities of elimination, combination, advantageous changes in sequence, and simplification.

In the man-machine chart, we analyze a *specific operation* involving a man and a machine, studying the man's work with relation to the machine to see where we can eliminate waste. The man's time is studied with respect to transportation, delay (holding), and inspection. The machine operation is studied with respect to possible reduction of idle time.

In the operator chart, we are concerned only with the *operator himself*, going into the fine points of analyzing the use made of the right and left hands.

The flow-process chart usually follows the course of a single part or quantity of material or form (in office routines) as it goes from operation to operation, although sometimes a flow-process chart is made of the movements of a man as he goes from point to point in the performance of his work. It is important in what follows to keep this in mind—it is easy to confuse the analysis by jumping from what is done to a part or material or form as it is processed, to what some operator does (which should really be the subject of a man-machine or an operator chart).

A chart is properly prepared when all the details, all the informative data of the present method have been recorded. To make that all-inclusive record, Kipling's helpers are employed:

> "I keep six honest serving-men
> (They taught me all I knew);
> Their names are What and Why and When
> And How and Where and Who."

The important part of the chart is the data, not the form. Work simplification stresses *thinking*, not copying. (A plain slip of paper on which certain fundamental facts have been recorded becomes a negotiable check as good as a check made out with the same facts on the bank's best engraved check form.) It is the actual facts recorded on a work-simplification chart for the purpose of waste reduction and methods improvement that make the chart the powerful thought generator that it is.

The flow-process chart is the one most frequently and profitably used by the foreman in any work-simplification program. Accordingly, this text goes into extensive detail on the preparation of this chart in the discussion of basic principle VII, following. However, at this point the reader may wish to refer to Fig. 2, illustrating a flow-process chart which resulted in a saving of 30 ft. of travel, 5 operations, 2 transportations, and 2 delays or storages on an

FLOW PROCESS CHART—PRESENT METHOD

QUESTION EACH STEP!

SUBJECT CHARTED _MATERIAL_

PROCESS CHARTED _ASSEMBLE TERMINAL_
RIVET TO CONDENSER

CHARTED BY _____
CHART No. _____ SHEET No. ____ OF ____

WHY IS IT BEING DONE?
WHAT IS BEING DONE?
WHERE IS IT BEING DONE?
WHEN IS IT DONE?
WHO IS DOING IT?
HOW IS IT BEING DONE?

DATE _1-10_
PLANT _No. 2_
DEPARTMENT _ELECTROSTATIC_
CONDENSER
SKETCH No. _____ OF _____

| | | O—AN OPERATION | o—A TRANSPORTATION | ▽—A DELAY OR A STORAGE | ☐—AN INSPECTION |

Element No.	DESCRIPTION—GIVE ALL DETAILS. Remember All You Will *Know* About the Process for Your Later Improvement Analysis Are the *Facts* You Record Here While *Actually* Observing the Process	An Operation	A Transportation	A Delay or A Storage	An Inspection	Distance in Feet	NOTES . . . OR FULLER EXPLANATION OF "KEY POINTS"
1	RIVETS AND WASHERS IN PARTS CABINET			▽			
2	REMOVED FROM BINS WITH HANDS BY ASSEMBLER AND PLACED IN SMALL TOTE PAN	O					
3	TOTE PAN PICKED UP BY ASSEMBLER	O					
4	RIVETS AND WASHERS CARRIED TO ASSEMBLY TABLE		o			15	
5	TOTE PAN PLACED ON TABLE	O					
6	TILL ASSEMBLED			▽			
7	WASHER AND RIVET PICKED FROM TOTE PAN, ASSEMBLED BY HAND, AND RETURNED TO TOTE PAN	●					
8	TILL LOT COMPLETED			▽			
9	TOTE PAN PICKED UP BY HAND BY ASSEMBLER	O					
10	ASSEMBLED RIVETS AND WASHERS CARRIED TO PARTS CABINET		o			15	
11	TOTE PAN PLACED IN PARTS CABINET	O					
12	TILL NEEDED FOR ASSEMBLY TO CONDENSER			▽			
13	TOTE PAN PICKED UP BY HAND BY ASSEMBLER	O					
14	ASSEMBLED RIVETS AND WASHERS CARRIED TO WORK AREA OF FOOT PRESS		o			15	
15	TOTE PAN PLACED IN PROPER POSITION IN WORK AREA	O					
16	TILL ASSEMBLED			▽			
17	RIVET AND WASHER ASSEMBLY PICKED FROM TOTE PAN BY HAND AND ASSEMBLED TO CONDENSER	●					
		9	3	5	0	45	

504

FLOW PROCESS CHART—IMPROVED METHOD

SUMMARY

METHOD	PRESENT	IMPROVED	SAVING
No. of Operations	9	4	5
No. of Transportations	3	1	2
No. of Delays or Storages	5	2	3
No. of Inspections	0	0	0
Distance Travelled	45'	15'	30'
Total Cost of Improvement			

SUBJECT CHARTED __MATERIAL__
PROCESS CHARTED __ASSEMBLE TERMINAL RIVET TO CONDENSER__
CHARTED BY __E. ROBINSON__
CHART No._____ SHEET No._____ OF_____

DATE __1-10__
PLANT __NO. 2__
DEPARTMENT __ELECTROSTATIC CONDENSER__
SKETCH No._____ OF_____

○—AN OPERATION   o—A TRANSPORTATION   ▽—A DELAY OR A STORAGE   ☐—AN INSPECTION

Element No.	DESCRIPTION—GIVE ALL DETAILS Remember All That Will Be Known About Your Proposal Are the Ideas That You Record Here as a Result of Your Analysis of the Facts of the Present Method	An Operation	A Transportation	A Delay or A Storage	An Inspection	Distance in Feet	NOTES . . . OR FULLER EXPLANATION OF "KEY POINTS"
1	RIVETS AND WASHERS IN PARTS CABINET			▽			
2	REMOVED FROM BINS WITH HANDS BY ASSEMBLER AND PLACED IN SMALL TOTE PAN	○					
3	TOTE PAN PICKED UP BY ASSEMBLER	○					
4	RIVETS AND WASHERS CARRIED TO FOOT PRESS WORK AREA		o			15	
5	TOTE PAN PLACED IN PROPER POSITION IN WORK AREA	○					
6	TILL ASSEMBLED			▽			
7	RIVET AND WASHER ASSEMBLED BY HAND, AND THEN ASSEMBLED TO CONDENSER	●					

Fig. 2.—Flow-process charts, showing present and improved methods for assembling terminal rivet to condenser. Note savings in distance, operations, and handlings, obtained at no cost. (Actual charts are 11 in. wide.)

MAN-MACHINE CHART—IMPROVED METHOD

Preceding Operation COPPER PLATE STRAP
RECEIVE PORCELAIN TUBE

Operation Charted ASSEMBLE AND
EYELET 2 STRAPS TO TUBE

Following Operation WIND

Process MANUFACTURE OF A RESISTOR

SKETCH

Date 12-22 — Chart No.____

Plant No 2   Process____
            Chart No.____

Department VOLUM CONTROL

Operator LARRY EVANS

Machine EYELET

Charted By P.W. CORNELIUS

MAN							MACHINE
LIST ALL ELEMENTS Remember *All* That Will Be *Known* About Your Proposal Are the Ideas That You Record Here as a Result of Your Analysis of the *Facts* of the Present Method					Per Cent Time Scale		LIST ALL ELEMENTS Remember *All* That Will Be *Known* About Your Proposal Are the Ideas That You Record Here as a Result of Your Analysis of the *Facts* of the Present Method

Average Cycle Time 16 SEC.

ASSEMBLE STRAP TO TUBE
POSITION ASSEMBLY ON MACHINE — IDLE

HOLD TUBE IN POSITION OVER
GAUGE BUILT IN FIXTURE
BY HAND — EYELET 1ST STRAP TO TUBE

REMOVE ASSEMBLY FROM FIXTURE
ASSEMBLE STRAP TO OTHER END
OF TUBE
POSITION ASSEMBLY ON FIXTURE — IDLE

HOLD TUBE IN POSITION OVER
GAUGE BUILT IN FIXTURE
BY HAND — EYELET 2ND STRAP TO TUBE

REMOVE ASSEMBLY FROM FIXTURE
DISPOSE OF ASSEMBLY — IDLE

PER CENT OF TOTAL MACHINE OPERATION CYCLE .... 37% 0% 0% 38% 25% Per Cent Time Scale 38% 62% .... PER CENT OF TOTAL MACHINE OPERATION CYCLE

FIG. 3.—Man-machine charts, showing present and improved methods for assembling and eyeletting two metal straps to a small porcelain tube. Gauge built into fixture reduced handling time

MAN-MACHINE CHART—PRESENT METHOD

Preceding Operation: `COPPER PLATE STRAP` `RECEIVE PORCELAIN TUBE`

Operation Charted: `ASSEMBLE AND EYELET 2 STRAPS TO TUBE`

Following Operation: `WIND`

Process: `MANUFACTURE OF A RESISTOR`

SKETCH

Date 12-15
Plant No. 2
Process: VOLUME CONTROL
Operator: LARRY EVANS
Machine: EYELET
Charted By: P. W. CORNELIUS

Average Cycle Time 20 SEC.

MAN		MACHINE
LIST ALL ELEMENTS		LIST ALL ELEMENTS
ASSEMBLE GAUGE TO TUBE " STRAP " POSITION ASSEMBLY ON MACHINE		IDLE
HOLD TUBE IN POSITION BY HAND		EYELET 1ST STRAP TO TUBE
REMOVE ASSEMBLY FROM MACHINE TRANSFER GAUGE TO OTHER END OF TUBE ASSEMBLE STRAP TO TUBE POSITION ASSEMBLY ON MACHINE		IDLE
HOLD TUBE IN POSITION BY HAND		EYELET 2ND STRAP TO TUBE
REMOVE ASSEMBLY FROM MACHINE DISPOSE OF ASSEMBLY RETAIN GAUGE IN HAND		IDLE

PER CENT OF TOTAL MACHINE OPERATION CYCLE   50 0 0 30 20   Per Cent Time Scale   30 70   PER CENT OF TOTAL MACHINE OPERATION CYCLE

4 seconds—making possible a 16-second cycle instead of the former
20-second cycle. Note that there is still 62 per cent waste of
machine time. (Actual charts are 11 in. wide.)

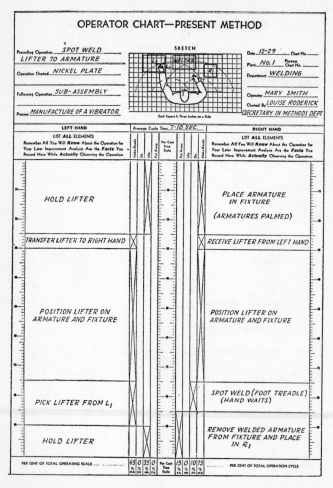

FIG. 4.—Operator chart, showing present and improved methods for spot welding lifter to armature. The position element was made positive to reduce average cycle time to 6 seconds from 8.5 seconds.

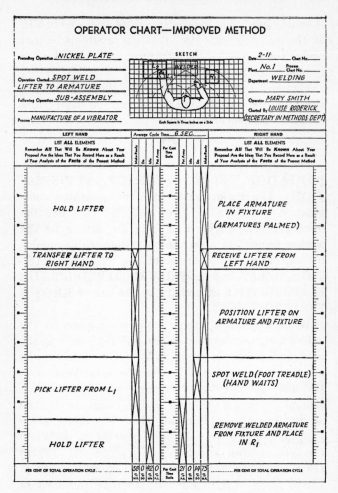

Note that the 29 per cent reduction in cycle time still leaves a cycle with 86 per cent waste. (Actual charts are 11 in. wide.)

assembly job.   The symbols used are discussed in VII.
In the author's work-simplification programs he uses
pink chart forms for the improved method and white
forms for the present method.

Figures 3 and 4 show examples of the man-machine
chart and the operator chart.   Details on these charts
are given at the close of VII.

VII

The major specific wastes in a process are TRANS-
PORTATION, DELAY or STORAGE, and INSPEC-
TION.   The major waste in a man-machine com-
bination is IDLE TIME by both the man and the
machine.   The major wastes in the activity of the
worker himself in a process, a man-machine combi-
nation, or in a hand operation are TRANSPORTA-
TION, DELAY, and the FAILURE TO REDUCE THE
ELAPSED TIME of activity by the use of KNOWN
FASTER DEVICES.

While a chart is properly prepared when all the
actual facts are recorded in chronological order as the
work being done is *actually observed*, it does help to
make the written record show the major wastes of
transportation, delay or storage, and inspection as
separate items on the chart and to designate them as
such.   A work-simplification chart is written to do
just that, using the following symbols to designate
the type of work or activity they represent.   (These
are a simplified form of the seven symbols given in
Chap. V, p. 127.)   For all practical purposes of
method-improvement study any activity can be
readily classified when the work simplification outlook of waste is believed in and when an activity is
observed for the sole purpose of locating and recording the major specific wastes.

a. An *operation* occurs when an object is intentionally changed in any of its physical or chemical characteristics, is assembled with or disassembled from another object, or is arranged or prepared for another operation, transportation, storage, or inspection. An operation also occurs when information is given or received or when planning or calculating takes place.

a

b. A *transportation* occurs when an object is moved from one place to another except when such movements are caused by the process or by the operator at the work station during an operation or an inspection.

b

c. A *delay* or *storage*. A *delay* occurs to an object when conditions except those of processing do not permit or require immediate performance of the next planned action. A *storage* occurs when an object is kept and protected against unauthorized removal.

c

d. An *inspection* occurs when an object is examined for identification, verified for quality or quantity, or measured in any of its characteristics.

d

The important thing in recording a process is to note *all details* in the items given above, to record what happens to a *single piece* as it is processed, or to record every step, every bit of work done if the "man" is being observed. To that end the basic structure of a work-simplification flow-process chart is "spelled out" in this section.

A process, for all practical purposes, consists of an "operation," a "transportation" to the next operation, and a "delay" or "storage" of varying length between operations. The work-simplification flow-process chart clearly shows this basic structure, and the "graph" of the symbols used to describe the work done shows how closely the process has been developed toward the elimination of all transportation and delay between operations.

A *value-adding operation*, or a major preparatory or disposal operation, is performed within a clearly defined work area. For example, the operation of drilling a hole on a drill press is a value-adding "operation," and the work area for the container of work to be drilled, the operator, the drill press, and the container of work drilled is distinctly allocated. A pay-roll clerk, "figuring the extension" of a time card, has a separate work area of a desk for his comptometer, papers, and floor space for his chair. The work performed by the "man" within the work area of an operation is considered not to contain any transportation for chart recording.

Facts recorded of an "operation" for a flow-process chart are a description, in general terms, of the effect of the operator's activity within the work area of the operation. The description includes picking up the piece from a container holding the pieces to be worked upon by the operation, and placing the piece after it has been worked on in a container for complete pieces.

There is a "delay" in the flow of the object before every operation when the object is processed in lots of two or more. That is, there is a delay of "await turn," as the object waits its turn to be picked from the container to be worked upon during the "operation." Similarly, there is a delay of "till lot completed," as the object waits in the container of finished pieces while the balance of the pieces pass "one-by-one" through the operation.

The basic structure of an operation in a process is shown on a chart as in Fig. 5. (In the charts, the value-adding operations are shaded.)

A *transportation* is, of course, always recognized in a process. However, unless the pieces are moved individually by a conveyor, there must be the minor operations of "pickup" before the transportation and "place" after the transportation.

Should there be any hesitancy to accept "pickup" and "place" as minor operations of sufficient importance to be considered as separate steps or elements of a process, look at the problem of "pickup" and "place" in actual processes. The "pickup" work required to get a 10,000 ton Liberty ship launched is a major operation. The "pickup" and "place"

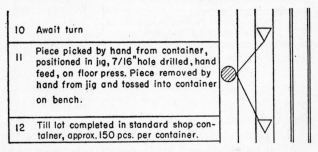

10	Await turn
11	Piece picked by hand from container, positioned in jig, 7/16" hole drilled, hand feed, on floor press. Piece removed by hand from jig and tossed into container on bench.
12	Till lot completed in standard shop container, approx. 150 pcs. per container.

FIG. 5.—Segment of a flow-process chart illustrating the basic structure of an operation.

operations in a medium-size machine shop require overhead cranes, jib cranes, hoists, slings, and chains and are distinct factors in processing. The "pickup" and "place" operations in a small-parts plant are equally important because of their continual occurrence. Truckers, stockmen, die setters, and line service men are "picking up" and "putting down" all day long.

The work-simplification chart, therefore, shows the "pickup" and "place" as minor operations before and after a transportation to show where extra help from the operator, or from specially assigned men, is needed to make the transportation and to put away after transportation.

The basic structure of a transportation in a process is shown on a chart as in Fig. 6.

A *delay* is, likewise, always recognized in a process. Unless a piece is on a conveyor and the conveyor stops, a piece or a container of pieces must have been

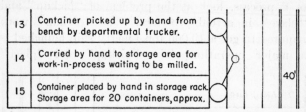

13	Container picked up by hand from bench by departmental trucker.
14	Carried by hand to storage area for work-in-process waiting to be milled.
15	Container placed by hand in storage rack. Storage area for 20 containers, approx.

40'

FIG. 6.—Segment of a flow-process chart illustrating basic structure of a transportation.

"placed" in the position of its delay for the delay to occur, and there must be a "pickup" to remove the piece or container from delay.

The reasons given above for the importance of "pickup" and "place" for transportation apply with equal force to the basic feature of delay in a process.

15	Container placed by hand in storage rack. Storage area for 20 containers, approx.
16	While waiting for lot to be run on #6 Cincinnati Miller.
17	Container picked up by hand by Milling machine operator.

FIG. 7.—Segment of a flow-process chart illustrating basic structure of a delay.

The basic structure of a delay in a process is shown on a chart as in Fig. 7.

An *inspection* is the same as an operation with respect to the basic structure of a chart. When the pieces are inspected "one-by-one" there is the delay of "await turn" before the "one-by-one" inspection, and the delay "till lot completed" after the inspection of the piece "observed."

The basic structure of an inspection is shown on a chart as in Fig. 8.

The basic structure of a work-simplification chart as illustrated and explained above will cover nearly all the situations encountered in following an object, man or material, or form in a process.

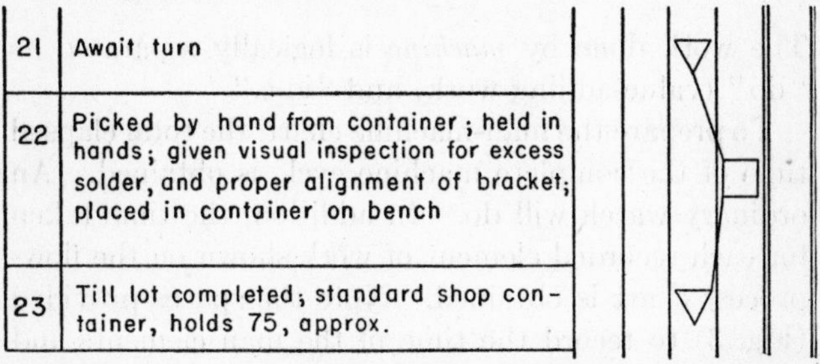

21	Await turn	
22	Picked by hand from container; held in hands; given visual inspection for excess solder, and proper alignment of bracket; placed in container on bench	
23	Till lot completed; standard shop container, holds 75, approx.	

FIG. 8.—Segment of a flow-process chart, illustrating basic structure of an inspection.

The most common "special" situation that will be met is *combined elements;* that is when some combination of an operation (inspection) or a transportation or a delay or storage occur simultaneously. Examples are an operation performed while the part is being moved by a conveyer, which is shown thus ⊙; an overhead conveyer chain acting as the storage rack for the work-in-process between operations, which is shown thus: ▽

The informative data for the man-machine chart are obtained and shown as for the flow-process chart. The basic structure is the same for the same elements of work—an operation, a transportation, a delay, and a storage. These informative data are recorded on the back of the man-machine chart to have all data on one piece of paper.

For the man-machine chart the elements of the total work of the *man* are considered to be of four types:

Make Ready..... All elements of work done to prepare the product for the value-adding work

"Do"........... The value-adding elements of work

Put Away........ All elements of work done to dispose of the product after the value-adding work has been done

Inspect.......... The elements of work to inspect

The work done by *machine* is logically separated as "do" (value-adding work) and "idle."

To prepare the man-machine chart, the total elapsed time of the complete machine cycle is obtained. An ordinary watch will do. In addition, the time taken for each recorded element of work shown on the flow-process chart is obtained. Note the spaces provided (Fig. 3) to record the time of the man elements and the machine elements. On the chart, the total time for both the man and the machine is expressed as 100 per cent.

The chronological "blocks" of each type of work are then totaled to find what per cent each block of the same type of work is of the total machine-cycle operation. Note the vertical columns giving the per cent scale for the man and the per cent scale for the machine for each block of Make Ready, Do, Inspect, Idle, and Put Away for the *man* and do and idle for the *machine*.

Finally, the descriptions of the blocks of elements are written in their respective places and the chart totaled at the bottom, giving the total per cent of the machine cycle for each type of work.

The operator chart (Fig. 4) is prepared in the same manner as the man-machine chart in terms of the work done by the left hand, and the right hand separately. Each hand, of course, has operation, transportation, and delay (idle) elements of work. A holding hand is considered an idle hand.

The man-machine chart form and the operator chart form and the technique for their preparation have but one objective—to force the observer, *while on the spot,* to look for, find, and *appreciate* the extent of the waste and opportunities for improvements that exist in that operation.

It is to bring out the extent of the waste and opportunities for improvement that the chart is prepared as a per cent chart rather than an elapsed-time chart. We are more interested in doing something about a 10-second waste in an operation when we appreciate it as 35 per cent of the total cycle rather than just 10 seconds. Further, the per cent type of chart continuously forces attention on the waste in a machine operation or operator activity, no matter how much improvement is made. For example:

Average (machine) operation cycle. . 10 minutes
Waste................................ 9 minutes
"Do"................................. 1 minute
Per cent waste...................... 90 per cent

If the cycle is cut in half and all the improvements made by reducing the waste, the performance becomes

Average (machine) operation cycle. . 5 minutes
Waste................................ 4 minutes
"Do"................................. 1 minute
Per cent waste...................... 80 per cent

Eighty per cent waste is a situation that cannot be passed off even though the cycle has been cut from 10 to 5 minutes.

The work-simplification philosophy is not interested merely in preparing accurate charts of present condi-

FLOW PROCESS CHART—PRESENT METHOD

QUESTION EACH STEP!

SUBJECT CHARTED _DIESETTER_

PROCESS CHARTED _SET UP FOOT PRESS TO STAKE STAFF OF VOLUME CONTROL_

CHARTED BY _JOE VANET_

CHART No._____ SHEET No._____ OF_____

WHY IS IT BEING DONE?
WHAT IS BEING DONE?
WHERE IS IT BEING DONE?
WHEN IS IT DONE?
WHO IS DOING IT?
HOW IS IT BEING DONE?

DATE _1-11_
PLANT _No. 2_
DEPARTMENT _VOLUM CONTROL_
SKETCH No. _1_ OF _1_

	O—AN OPERATION	o—A TRANSPORTATION	▽—A DELAY OR A STORAGE	□—AN INSPECTION

Element No.	DESCRIPTION—GIVE ALL DETAILS Remember All You Will Know About the Process for Your Later Improvement Analysis Are the Facts You Record Here While Actually Observing the Process	An Operation	A Transportation	A Delay or A Storage	An Inspection	Distance in Feet	NOTES ... OR FULLER EXPLANATION OF "KEY POINTS"
1	RISES FROM CHAIR, WALKS TO PARTS STORAGE		○			10	
2	PICKS UP PARTS AND PLACE THEM IN TOTE PAN	○					
3	PICKS UP TOTE PAN BY HAND	○					
4	CARRIES PARTS TO WORK AREA OF FOOT PRESS		○			10	
5	PLACES TOTE PAN IN POSITION IN WORK AREA	○					
6	WALKS TO DIE CABINET FOR STAKING DIE		○			18	
7	LOCATES AND PICKS UP DIE	○					
8	CARRIES DIE TO FOOT PRESS		○			18	
9	PLACES DIE ON BENCH AT SIDE OF PRESS	○					
10	WALKS TO NEXT PRODUCTION LINE FOR WRENCH		○			60'	
11	PICKS UP WRENCH	○					
12	CARRIES WRENCH BACK TO FOOT PRESS		○			60	
13	PLACES WRENCH ON BENCH	○					
14	WALKS BACK TO DIE CABINET FOR WASHERS		○			18	
15	PICKS OUT WASHERS FROM BOX	○					
16	CARRIES WASHERS TO FOOT PRESS		○			18	
17	PLACES WASHERS ON BENCH	○					
18	SETS UP DIE TO STAKE STAFFS	○					
19	STAKES TRIAL STAFF	○					
20	WALKS TO BLUE PRINT FILE FOR PRINT COVERING JOB		○			36	
21	LOCATES AND PICKS OUT PRINT	○					

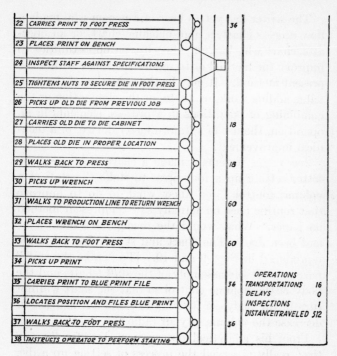

22	CARRIES PRINT TO FOOT PRESS		36
23	PLACES PRINT ON BENCH		
24	INSPECT STAFF AGAINST SPECIFICATIONS		
25	TIGHTENS NUTS TO SECURE DIE IN FOOT PRESS		
26	PICKS UP OLD DIE FROM PREVIOUS JOB		
27	CARRIES OLD DIE TO DIE CABINET		18
28	PLACES OLD DIE IN PROPER LOCATION		
29	WALKS BACK TO PRESS		18
30	PICKS UP WRENCH		
31	WALKS TO PRODUCTION LINE TO RETURN WRENCH		60
32	PLACES WRENCH ON BENCH		
33	WALKS BACK TO FOOT PRESS		60
34	PICKS UP PRINT		
35	CARRIES PRINT TO BLUE PRINT FILE		36
36	LOCATES POSITION AND FILES BLUE PRINT		
37	WALKS BACK TO FOOT PRESS		36
38	INSTRUCTS OPERATOR TO PERFORM STAKING		

OPERATIONS
TRANSPORTATIONS 16
DELAYS 0
INSPECTIONS 1
DISTANCE/TRAVELED 512

Fig. 9.—Flow-process chart for analyzing a setup operation for a foot press. This "word picture," together with the diagram (Fig. 10), brought to light obvious opportunities for improvement.

tions. It *is* interested in getting a supervisor to look for, find, and appreciate waste and opportunities for improvements—*and then doing something about it.*

VIII

Work simplification derives its power from the fact that once any activity is subjected to analytical observation and once the WHY, WHAT, WHERE, WHEN, WHO, and HOW of an activity are known, an improvement can be made.

The writer has yet to hear of a person who made a flow-process chart, a man-machine chart, or an operator chart who has not himself seen opportunities to improve the method or to reduce the waste within the present method. It may be the reduction of the non-value adding work, or waste, or the elimination or the combining of operations in a process, elements in an operation, the use of a known faster device, or a technical improvement.

Joe V____, foreman, made a chart of his best die setter setting up a foot press to stake the staff of a volume control. Joe knew what to do to improve that routine once he actually saw the present method on paper. What would the reader have done if he had been Joe? The chart and sketch Joe made are reproduced in Figs. 9 and 10. [To "stake the staff" means to set the assembly of the staff (shaft) and the body of the volume control so that the shaft will not turn in the body—if it did, you could not increase or decrease the volume of your radio.]

From his analytical observation, Joe, *for the first time*, really observed the process of setting up a die. As he said when he turned in the chart, "I got tired just watching him walk around." (Yet the die setter had been doing the same useless walking for years!) That is, the foreman saw the die setter go to the die cabinet three times when once could have been enough; he saw him walk 60 ft. to pick up a wrench and 60 ft. to return it; saw him fail to pick up the blueprint when he went to the die cabinet.

Joe, having really observed how the job was done, immediately saw ways to reduce the waste of walking. They were

    a. To provide each die setter with a complete toolbox

b. To have each die setter return the old die when going for a new die and pick up the print on the way

c. To begin to teach and train each die setter always to be conscious of the fact that all walking is a waste

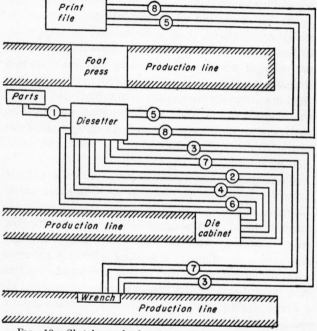

Fig. 10.—Sketch made by foreman to illustrate operation analyzed in Fig. 9. The lines with their circles indicate the sequence of the die setter's walking—first to the parts supply, second, to the die cabinet for the new die, etc.

With the above proved psychological background, work simplification directs the generated methods-improvement thinking to obtain the maximum results through the *questioning attitude*. Kipling's "six honest serving men," *why, what, where, when, who,* and *how*, are used again but with different instructions. They are used to ferret out the waste efforts, to seek opportunities to *eliminate*, to find places to *combine* operations, to locate possibilities to *change sequence*, and, finally, to apply *known faster devices* to reduce the elapsed time of element activity. These all add up to *simplify*.

Maybe relocating a supply cabinet will reduce walking. Perhaps upon investigation an accurately drilled hole may be satisfactory, thus eliminating the necessity of reaming after drilling. It may happen that operations can be better routed to reduce backtracking from one operation to another. Sometimes the quantity now being produced may warrant the cutting of a stencil rather than hand typing, or a quick-acting clamp rather than a simple wing nut on a drill jig.

This improvement technique gives critical attention to the fundamentals of *economy of personal effort*, which expresses the thought without using the much maligned, misunderstood, and misapplied term, "motion economy." The importance of "fixed location" to rhythm and skill is developed. Has the reader ever thought what would happen to the playing skill and technique of a present-day Paderewski if it had to be applied to a piano having four additional keys introduced into the *standardized* keyboard on which that skill and technique were developed? The result would be a more discordant sound, if possible, than the first attempt of a ten-year-old child on a difficult piece. Move the keys on a standard typewriter around a bit and you will see the most skilled typist reduced to the impotency of the "hunt-and-peck" system.

Since so many of the opportunities for improvements by the foreman will be in assembly operations, it will be well to list at this point six rules followed by methods men in improving such operations. The rules are based on a check list of six items given by Dr. Gilbreth in "Principles of Motion Economy." They are listed here with appropriate comments by the present author to tie in their application with the general principles of *rhythm* and *fixed location*.

1. *Tools, material, and controls should be located around the workplace and as close to the front of the worker as possible.*

Tools, materials, and controls should be within the normal working area. (Note sketch at top of Fig. 4; see also Chap. V, pp. 124–125.) It must be pointed out, however, that in applying the principle of rhythm along with this rule, the normal working area is not a full semicircle, but an ellipse. It is fatiguing to reach into the outer and lower part of the semicircle. The location of the parts must be such that rhythm of movement can be developed. The parts must be put in a fixed position within the rhythm area to allow skill development. This principle, of course, reduces the distances of transportation, a major waste.

2. *Tools and materials should be pre-positioned wherever possible.*

The fundamental requirement of skill is a fixed location for the physical factors of the activity; hence, when the worker is through with a tool, it should be placed where he will know it is the next time he needs it. Materials should be placed in specific bins, *fastened down*. Toolholders should be designed to allow rapid insertion and release and to permit the tool to be grasped in the position in which it will be held during its use.

3. *Drop deliveries should be used wherever possible.*

The quickest way to get rid of anything is to drop it—and a fixed place in which to drop it is a pre-

requisite for the development of skill. If possible, the piece should be dropped from the position where it was completed, to save the time of carrying it to the drop-delivery opening. Moreover, in most assembly operations this will allow a better rhythm pattern.

4. *Gravity feed bins and containers should be used to deliver the material as close to the point of assembly as possible.*

Materials to be used in hand assemblies should be delivered to *one definite location* by means of gravity feed. Application of this rule will eliminate the time needed to search for and select the part. In addition, the travel will be at a minimum. Moreover, and most important, because the part will *always* be there, a higher degree of skill will be developed. Skill is based on developed knowledge of the relative distances between the physical factors of the operation.

5. *Motion of arms should be in opposite and symmetrical directions, instead of in the same direction, and should be made simultaneously.*

When it is possible for the two hands to move at the same time in opposite directions by arranging similar work on each side of the workplace, the operator performs the work more quickly and with less mental and physical effort. The symmetrical movements of the arms tend to maintain body balance. The hands and arms perform naturally motions that are opposite and symmetrical.

6. *The use of a simple fixture, bracket, or holding device will often free the hand so that it may proceed with other constructive work.*

The human hand is a poor holding device. Yet how many industrial and office operations are performed with one hand used as a clamp, vise, fixture, or other holding device for a large part of the cycle!

This is seen clearly when an operator chart is drawn of the operation.

Rhythm will always be poor and the work unduly fatiguing when one hand must be kept still (holding). A soldier can march for hours but will often collapse from fatigue when required to stand at attention for a relatively short time . . . which illustrates the fatigue of nonrhythmic or "controlled" movements (or even lack of movement).

IX

The extent of the improvement will depend mainly upon how well the activity has been observed. Every activity is different. Each must be approached with an open mind to locate the opportunities for improvement in that particular activity.

The heart of method improvement is this: Just what will improve a particular activity? And who knows better than the foreman and the operator the basic problem in each operation? With simple, fundamental training, the foreman can spot the opportunities for improvement. Often the correction can be made with the department's own facilities. If not, the designer, engineer, chemist, or other staff man can be directed to the opportunity at once.

A case in point: A secretary in a methods department chose to study the electrobrazing of an armature to a lifter as her work assignment on operator activity. When she had prepared her operator chart and had really observed what could be done to improve that particular operation, she came up with the answer, "Improve the positioning element." She would never in the wide world have located the trouble with that operation had she followed the orthodox method of looking to see if the parts were in normal working areas, if a drop delivery could be used, if the tools could be pre-positioned, and so on down through the list of the standard principles of motion economy (see Fig. 4).

The work-simplification chart clearly shows the extent of improvement already made toward elimination of transportation, delay or storage, and inspec-

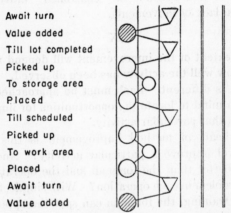

Await turn
Value added
Till lot completed
Picked up
To storage area
Placed
Till scheduled
Picked up
To work area
Placed
Await turn
Value added

FIG. 11.—Typical charting of manufacturing a lot of material in a factory.

tion. That feature of a chart is now shown and explained.

The usual form of manufacturing a lot of material in a factory or processing a bunch of forms in an office is as follows: The material is in a storage area, from which it is taken to the work area of the operation, the individual pieces are worked on, and the completed lot moved to the storage area for the work-in-process ahead of the next operation, etc.

The chart of the above method is illustrated in Fig. 11.

If the above seems like "too much," remember that the nonvalue adding work (waste) of inspecting, or weighing for pay-roll purposes, is not shown, nor are the common make-ready operations such as "degreasing," "place in special containers," "string on wires for plating," nor the routine that occurs frequently in a process of sending the parts to a parts stores, which requires a requisition to get the parts back into the production flow, etc.

An improvement of the process can be made by having the container of work taken directly from the

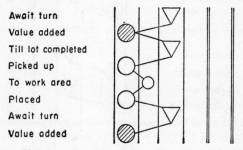

| Await turn |
| Value added |
| Till lot completed |
| Picked up |
| To work area |
| Placed |
| Await turn |
| Value added |

Fig. 12.—First improvement over operation charted in Fig. 11.

work area of the value-adding operation to the work area of the succeeding value-adding operation. This requires closer production control. The chart now becomes as shown in Fig. 12.

An improvement in the layout of the department can place the two operations adjacent, but the second operator must stop work to service herself (or be supplied) with the parts from the first operation, such as obtaining the container of parts from the floor. However, the work of securing the parts is performed within the work area, so that transportation has been eliminated. The chart now reads as in Fig. 13.

An improvement can be made so that the parts from the first operation are placed directly in the work area of the succeeding operation. (The "pickup one-by-one" and "place aside one-by-one" is part of the recognized work within the value-adding operation.) The chart now appears as in Fig. 14.

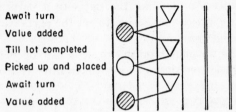

Await turn

Value added

Till lot completed

Picked up and placed

Await turn

Value added

FIG. 13.—Further improvement by eliminating transportation.

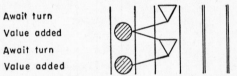

Await turn

Value added

Await turn

Value added

FIG. 14.—Further improvement by elimination of pickup and place.

Value added

Value added

FIG. 15.—Final elimination of all major wastes.

Finally, the process can be made so that there is no "float" whatever between the operation; the piece moves directly from the jig or fixture of one value-adding operation to the jig or fixture of the next value-adding operation. The chart now becomes as in Fig. 15.

Thus, the graph of the flow-process chart symbols shows clearly the degree to which the major wastes of a process have been eliminated or the extent of the improvement possibilities.

X

EXPERIENCE from other activities will usually help to improve a method.

Let us consider that shoe buckle again. The equipment in many companies is suitable to making shoe buckles in multiple operations. Suppose a company were to start the manufacture of shoe buckles. How many months of effort and dollars would the writer's years of personal experience in the manufacture of shoe buckles save that company in getting into production and meeting competitive prices? Likewise, within any organization, the collective experience of the personnel could give many leads on many operations. Also, within each supervisor's own experience, there is much he could take to his present activities.

Furthermore, there are the technical publications with the stories of how other people have solved some of their problems. That experience made readily accessible may give many hints in the solution of a particular problem confronting the reader now.

XI

INGENUITY has great possibilities. Often the results of a "new twist" are startling. Work-simplification techniques give full scope to ingenuity and see to its proper application.

We all have seen in our respective companies' activities the result of some ingenious thinking. For example, the writer thinks of a snap made from a coil of wire in one operation or of a can opener cut off, formed, pierced, and stamped in one operation.

All suggestions for improving methods and reducing waste have to be integrated into the existing process, man-machine combination, or operator activity, whether they come from experience, ingenuity, or are generated by analytical observation. When the integration is done by work-simplification techniques, the maximum results from eliminating, combining, changing sequence, and simplifying are obtained.

As stated at the beginning, the principles of work simplification are the most modern and the sharpest tools in the kit of the professional-methods man. However, the successful application of work simplification in hundreds of diversified companies by thousands of supervisors has proved beyond doubt that the principles can be learned and used effectively by supervisors and rank-and-file workers.

There is one vital prerequisite—*the complete, enthusiastic support and continuous follow-up of a progressive top management.* Like *esprit de corps,* work simplification "does not ooze from the bottom; it trickles from the top down." Work simplification introduced, developed, and continuously backed up by a progressive top management will:

1. Create a co-operative, sympathetic, and helpful attitude of the supervisors and workers to the introduction of new methods by professional methods men.

2. Train and develop the supervisors and key workers to make improvements themselves that grow broader in scope as their newly developed skill gives recognized expression to their latent productive power, intelligence, and initiative, and the sense of belonging, or participating, and of accomplishing becomes the most tangible thing in their department.

3. Allow the professional methods men to concentrate more and more on the broader aspects of the company's activities.

4. Co-ordinate, integrate, and apply the improvement thinking of the entire personnel, from the chief executive down, toward a *better product*, at a *lower cost*, and *delivered at the right time*.

5. Provide the most satisfactory base upon which to set up an effective, plant-wide labor-cost-reduction program.

To sum up, work simplification *as a technique* is something that the foreman can readily learn and apply in his own daily routine duties—which include methods-improvement suggestions.

Work simplification *as an idea* is something that any foreman will readily grasp once he has demonstrated it to himself by an application to a specific activity. He will firmly believe thereafter that something can be done to improve any situation if the facts are obtained and purposeful thought given to finding a better way.

Work simplification *as a philosophy* is something the foreman will readily appreciate once he has demonstrated to himself the response that will be given to an enthusiastic and gracious approach to his employees regarding improvement suggestions.

Work simplification *as a spirit*—an *esprit de corps*—which will make a company a leader in its industry will come about just that much sooner if the foreman does his part to further top management's constant efforts to improve operations. True, those efforts will not all start in, be effected by, or end in the activities of the foreman's own department, but if he can be counted on to be ready and willing at all times to lend a helping hand, he will be amazed at the number of improvements which he will be able to originate or have a major share in developing.

Section Seven

SELF-QUIZ FOR EXECUTIVE DEVELOPMENT

CHAPTER XX

EXECUTIVE DEVELOPMENT
FOR SUPERVISORS

The objective of this manual, as stated in the very beginning, has been to help the foreman develop his job beyond the point at which he assumed it—*to help him grow*. Since a company's production team is no better than its foremen, the advantages to the company of having the foreman make the best possible use of the material presented are obvious. And equally obvious are the advantages to the foreman in terms of self-advancement.

The idea behind this section is to help the reader review the concepts and techniques given in the various chapters. There is a well-known learning principle that material absorbed by reading "sticks with you" if, as you study the text (or immediately following reading a section of the text) you write down the basic ideas presented, in your own words.

As a guide for this sort of reflection and study, the reader is presented with a carefully thought-out set of questions covering the whole manual—453 in all. The principle to be followed is for the reader to write down the material after he has gone over it—not as a memory quiz, but rather as a means, with the text at hand as a reference, to fix the points in his mind.

The answers to the questions are all found in the text—but the reader is not immediately given keyed page numbers. The learning value lies in having him ponder the questions, and if he is not sure of an answer, to check back in the chapter concerned, to see just how the matter is treated.

As a final reference, the following chapter in this section provides a page-number guide to all of the questions. This guide should, however, be used only as a last resort.

Chapter I

A BREAKDOWN OF THE FOREMAN'S JOB

1. What is one of the most important factors that determine whether a foreman's job remains a fixed thing, or grows?
2. Give the American Society of Mechanical Engineers definition of "management."
3. With respect to the ASME definition, what should be emphasized about the foreman's job, as distinguished from his former work as a rank-and-file employee?
4. On what will a man who has been promoted to foreman stand or fall, as a rule?
5. Why is leadership considered such an important attribute of a foreman?
6. Give five important parts of the foreman's know-how, over and above the human-relations aspects of his job.
7. Give four important aspects of the foreman's direct personnel responsibilities.
8. Give four important types of the foreman's co-operative personnel responsibilities.
9. Give four important types of background information valuable to the "growing" foreman.

Chapter II

THE FOREMAN AS A LEADER

1. Is leadership something you are born with, or else you must do without—or is it possible to develop leadership?
2. Give some examples of actions and attitudes of employees whose morale is high.

3. Tell what leadership is, and give some examples of characteristics which mark a leader of men.

4. Name five major immediate duties and responsibilities which call for leadership on the part of the foreman.

5. What is one of the first requirements of effective leadership?

6. List 12 important things expected of a foreman by the men and women of his department.

7. Name four kinds of actions which are especially apt to make employees feel that there is no fair play in their company or their department.

8. Give three simple but important principles with respect to fair wages.

9. What are three characteristics of persons to whom others seem to turn naturally when they want to talk things over?

10. What are six important points to keep in mind in getting the facts about a grievance?

11. Give nine additional things which the foreman should do to "lean over backwards" in giving an employee a satisfactory adjustment of a grievance.

12. Give 10 fundamentals of effective supervision.

13. Give 10 fundamentals of the effective foreman's relations with top management.

Chapter III

QUALITY CONTROL AND WASTE REDUCTION

Part One

1. What are the three main "tools" with which the foreman can work to attain *A* quality consistently?

2. What five important characteristics of mass production have intensified the foreman's problem of quality control?

3. In what way can the existence of inspection organizations tend to lessen the worker's sense of responsibility for quality?

4. What are five important factors of working conditions,

within the control of the foreman, which have a bearing on quality?

5. What are two important foremanship functions with respect to the manpower factor in quality control?

6. What are three things the supervisor should know or do with respect to training of new employees, to be sure that they will get proper quality pointers?

7. Give the four fundamentals of training emphasized by the Training Within Industry Division of the War Manpower Commission.

8. What are some of the things older employees do that cause poor-quality workmanship?

9. Over a thousand foremen listed 18 reasons for poor workmanship that the foreman will do well to keep in mind. Can you name 10 important ones that are apt to apply to most plants?

10. What is the big danger of passing less than top-standard production during a rush period?

11. What are some things that can be done to combat lack of interest on the part of workers?

12. What is a good technique to keep in mind if you have to criticize a worker for poor quality?

13. In the case study on quality control described by Westinghouse, how big was the percentage of defective workmanship directly chargeable to the failure of the worker to produce as good a product as could be done with the materials, equipment, or processes made available to him?

14. What were the fundamental purposes and appeals of the Westinghouse program to reduce scrap?

15. What kind of publicity devices to employees can be used to keep alive a program of scrap reduction?

Part Two

1. Why cannot customer complaints in consumer-goods industries be relied upon to get a true picture of poor quality?

2. How close to actual operations should testing stations be? (Give reasons.)

3. In what area of operations is it generally best to start control activities?

4. What relationship, in so far as giving orders is concerned, should quality- or waste-control technicians have with operators on the job?

5. What levels will normally be set up in the control department to parallel the manufacturing organization levels?

6. List the important types of information which should be included in product specifications, relating to general requirements.

7. List the same for detailed requirements.

8. List the same for testing procedure.

9. List the same for sampling.

10. Who should approve product specifications?

11. Discuss the desirability or lack of desirability of 100 per cent inspection of incoming materials, or of requiring the supplier to do 100 per cent inspection.

12. What is meant by the following terms: "per cent defective"; "lot-tolerance per cent defective"; "average outgoing quality limit"?

13. What is the paramount feature of modern sampling plans?

14. What is the ratio of sample size to lot size, as compared with increasing lot sizes?

15. Why is "constant-ratio sample size" unsound?

16. Give an example of single sampling.

17. Give an example of double sampling.

18. What do control charts accomplish? What are the salient features of a quality-control chart?

19. What size samples are generally used in a quality-control chart?

20. How many subgroups can normally be depended upon for establishing the central tendency and control limits for averages and ranges?

21. If it is found that upper and lower specification limits are far within upper and lower control limits, and tight specification limits are necessary, what courses of action may be indicated?

22. Is the application of control charts limited to process work?

23. What are the advantages of placing control charts right at the machines where operators can see them?

24. Under what circumstances is the "*p* chart" used?

25. What is meant by the fraction defective of a subgroup of products?

Chapter IV

PLANNING AND SCHEDULING

1. Define the planning and scheduling function.

2. What are the three basic aims of a systematic procedure of controlling production?

3. What are some of the direct responsibilities of the foreman with respect to planning and scheduling?

4. What are two very important co-operative responsibilities the foreman has with respect to scheduling production?

5. Into what four functions can the principal planning and scheduling activities be subdivided?

6. What does the routing of operations for the manufacture of a product consist of?

7. Give some differences in the routing problems as between continuous-manufacturing plants, and diversified or job-order manufacturing.

8. Define "production schedule."

9. Name three sources from which preliminary information needed in the construction of a production schedule is usually obtained.

10. What factors must usually be taken into account in constructing a production schedule?

11. What are the two principal types of production schedules? (Give a brief definition of each.)

12. What departments or persons are usually responsible for making up the two types of schedules?

13. What two difficulties with respect to foremen often occur where there is a highly centralized system of control?

14. What procedure can a company use to help make scheduling a co-operative function?

15. For what six things does dispatching provide official authorization and information?

16. What is the factor of greatest concern in determining the necessary degree of centralization of dispatching?

17. What department usually has the responsibility for follow-up on materials?   What can foremen do about it?

18. Regarding work-in-process, in what types of operations are follow-up by product and follow-up by process best applied?

19. How can foremen and supervisors co-operate in follow-up of work-in-process?

20. What three common visual aids can the foreman use in planning and scheduling?

21. What is usually the best type of progress chart to use?

Chapter V

TIME STUDY AND METHODS IMPROVEMENT

Part One

1. Give at least nine important reasons why the foreman should obtain a working knowledge of time and motion study.

2. What four general responsibilities belong to foremen as a class, to help industry step up production?

3. What are the four parts into which time spent should be divided, to make simplified and constructive observations possible?

4. Distinguish between "indirect" time and "lost" time.

5. What does "handling" include?

6. What are some common examples of causes of waiting time beyond the operator's control, which would be found in most plants?

7. To how low a percentage figure has lost time been driven, in departments where there is outstandingly good supervision?

8. Give some common examples of indirect time to look for in analyzing a department or operation.

9. Why is it necessary to make a relatively large number of observations, in making a detailed analysis, in order to arrive at a proper estimate of indirect and lost time?

10. Why is it important to study reaching? Tell briefly what the time-study man means by "circular workplace."

11. What can often be done with respect to the use of the hands?

12. How can "aside" time often be eliminated?

13. Draw seven symbols, commonly used by time-study men in analyzing operations, and state what they mean.

14. Why is a study of jigs important in speeding operations?

15. Give a common example of reducing time by combining operations.

16. What are some common opportunities for improvement with respect to cutting tools?

17. What are time-study elements?

18. Distinguish between "constants" and "variables."

19. What does a time-study engineer mean by "rating"? If 60 is the base, what would be the rating in minutes per hour if the man studied is rated at 10 per cent better than normal?

20. What does the time-study engineer include in "relaxation"?

21. What are the two general procedures by which operation-standard times are determined?

22. Must a foreman be more "on his toes" in an incentive department than in a daywork department. If so, why?

Part Two

1. What are the three principles common to all PTS systems?

2. What are the five best-known PTS systems?

3. What is a TMU?

4. What are two basic advantages of PTS systems in methods-analysis work?

5. What are three basic advantages of PTS systems in setting time standards?

6. Cite some advantages of PTS systems in training and in settling disputes over incentives.
7. What three points should be included in an integrated program of PTS instruction?
8. Cite some human-relations advantages of a PTS system.

Part Three

1. What is an important underlying principle of the Standard Minute system?
2. What are some advantages of using minutes instead of percentages of an hour in expressing production?
3. If the normal incentive time for an operation has been determined, what would you multiply it by in order to determine the standard time in such a way as to permit the worker to reach 25 per cent bonus without undue strain?
4. Why is the Standard Minute plan called a 100 per cent premium plan?
5. What is the purpose of the operator's grading factor in the derivation of a Standard Minute?
6. What are personal allowances given for?
7. What are fatigue allowances given for?
8. What is meant by the factor of unavoidable delays?
9. How much is usually allowed for a total of personal, fatigue, and unavoidable delays?
10. What is accomplished by posting the Daily Production Report?

Chapter VI

COST CONTROL BY FOREMEN

1. In a typical industrial establishment, what per cent of operating costs (excluding raw materials) are foremen as a rule responsible for?
2. List seven of the more common cost items that are wholly within a foreman's departmental responsibility.
3. Under a good cost system, to what sort of costs should a foreman's responsibility be restricted?
4. Name three important advantages that should accrue to

a foreman by familiarizing himself with the main features of a modern cost system.

5. State briefly the three steps that must be taken when a company sets up a cost system in which the foreman can co-operate on controls.

6. What are some of the most frequently occurring off-standard-overhead costs that can be pictured advantageously in cost graphs?

7. Is there a constant relationship between standard hours of direct labor and the cost of a given account?

8. What are two important principles that are basic for the adequate control of costs by the foreman?

9. What does the flexible budget provide the foreman?

10. Who usually sets the cost allowances?

11. What are some of the common sources of information used in setting the cost standards?

12. What is meant by "variances" in cost control?

13. Name nine principles that are followed when management sets up cost reports for foremen.

14. What is meant by "shingling" reports?

15. What four important steps do advanced managements follow in training foremen in cost-control and budgetary procedures?

Chapter VII

THE FOREMAN'S TRAINING RESPONSIBILITIES

1. Approximately what percentage of industrial training today is done right on the job?

2. Name eight types of information which the foreman must get across in his training work.

3. Who needs training by the foreman?

4. What did World War II demonstrate as to the amount that can be cut from training time by the use of proper instructing methods?

5. Distinguish between the terms "training" and "instruction."

6. What eight qualifications should a foreman have to be a good instructor?

7. What basic slogan should a foreman keep in mind when he acts as an instructor?

8. State some dangers a foreman runs when he indiscriminately delegates the training function to an experienced worker.

9. What are some important advantages when the foreman assumes responsibility for training?

10. Give some of the important things a foreman must do before he gives instruction.

11. Why is it important to break a job down into instruction units?

12. How many points, as a rule, are all that can be "put over" effectively in one instruction unit?

13. What are the four basic steps in instruction?

14. Give three important things for the foreman to do in preparation of the learner.

15. What combination of methods should be used in presentation of instruction matter?

16. What is the purpose of the performance tryout?

17. Why is it so important to the learner to be "put on his own" just as soon as the right time has come?

18. What are two important things a foreman should do in developing a departmental training plan?

19. What is meant by the term "upgrading"?

20. What are some important morale benefits to the worker obtained by an upgrading plan?

21. What considerations are important in selecting a man to be the foreman's understudy?

22. What are some important things a foreman should do in training his understudy?

Chapter VIII

WHAT TO DO ABOUT SAFETY

1. Cite some figures showing the losses of productive manpower and materials due to accidents.

2. Cite some figures showing the benefits that have come from accident-prevention work.

3. What are some accident-producing conditions that come with a period of stepped-up production?

4. What special kinds of wearing apparel should be considered for women in industry, to enhance safety?

5. What does workmen's compensation provide for?

6. Where do the funds for compensation insurance come from?

7. How can an employer achieve reduction in his workmen's compensation insurance charges?

8. What are some advantages of safe operation, in addition to the legal and humane considerations?

9. Roughly, what percentage of industrial accidents are avoidable?

10. What two types of causes are predominant in industrial accidents?

11. Where should the primary emphasis be put in industrial safety work?

12. List eight common "primary causes" of industrial accidents as classified by the National Safety Council.

13. Give some practical safety pointers in handling objects.

14. What are some common, avoidable hazards that lead to "falls of persons"?

15. What human weakness often causes accidents with machinery?

16. Give some practical safety pointers to prevent accidents with machinery.

17. What effective controls help cut down accidents in connection with the use of industrial vehicles?

18. What are some common reasons for accidents resulting from the use of hand tools?

19. What are some practical safety pointers to prevent accidents from falling objects?

20. Give some pointers about clothing and some other precautions to cut down accidents from dangerous and harmful substances.

21. Give some practical safety pointers to prevent accidents from workers stepping on or striking objects.

22. Upon what does the success of any safety program depend primarily?

23. Name five important phases of the foreman's safety responsibilities.

24. What are some of the safety measures a foreman should take with respect to the selection of an employee?

25. What are some of the safety measures a foreman should take with respect to training employees?

26. What definite rule should the foreman enforce with respect to injuries sustained by employees?

27. Define the American Standards Association term, "frequency rate," used in connection with injuries.

28. Define the ASA term, "severity rate."

29. Why is it necessary, whenever the formulas for frequency and severity rate are used, to compile the factors used on an accumulated basis up to at least 12 months?

30. What are some of the things that can be done by safety committees?

31. What are some of the training aids that are used effectively in safety education?

Chapter IX

INDUSTRIAL FATIGUE

1. Give the definition of fatigue, including the special remarks about "activity" and "rest."

2. What is the common, *erroneous* view with respect to industrial fatigue?

3. Give five important facts with respect to fatigue.

4. What is industrial fatigue from moderate and light occupations usually due to?

5. What makes it possible for the human body to carry out its various activities?

6. What is meant by "static effort"?

7. Is the body ever really at rest? (Give some examples to explain the answer.)

8. What is the average rate of energy expenditure by a man doing vigorous manual work, continued for 8 hours, compared with a man resting?

9. In light and moderate industrial occupations, what is the energy-expenditure rate compared with resting?

10. What is the principal reason for "fatigue" from light and moderate industrial occupations?

11. What is usually the best way to obtain relief from fatigue caused by continued strain?

12. What are the two factors of which fatigue is always the product?

13. What are some of the usual factors which make a person susceptible to fatigue?

14. Why is movement of air desirable?

15. Why should salt sometimes be administered to workers?

16. What are some common psychological and sociological strains which cause fatigue?

17. Can rest periods be set by a definite formula related to the work done?

18. Give some indications of the fact that psychological factors are very important in connection with rest periods.

Chapter X

SPECIAL PROBLEMS IN SUPERVISING WOMEN

1. Give some points to remember with respect to skill and physical endurance of women workers.

2. What three errors of judgment commonly hamper a foreman in dealing with women workers?

3. Name three common industrial-group problems that arise where large numbers of women are employed.

4. What are currently some important reasons why women workers are, as a rule, more efficient under male supervision than under women as foremen?

5. What sort of approach should the foreman take to the problem of mass female employment in industry?

6. Should the induction period of new women workers be longer than that of new men workers?

7. What are some of the special points that should be included in an induction program for women workers?

8. Does a healthy woman recover rapidly from fatigue?

9. What is getting to be the common practice with respect to rest periods for women in factories?
10. What is a common failing among women with respect to diet?
11. What is an "Oslo meal"?
12. What are the three most common classes of safety problems encountered with women workers?
13. What is one good way to make a safety program acceptable to women workers?
14. Give some pointers with respect to safe clothing for women workers.
15. What do statistics show with respect to susceptibility to accidents of *trained* women workers?
16. List some well-marked stress periods which occur in most persons' lives, and which a foreman should especially keep in mind with respect to women workers.
17. State briefly eight points in summary, which the foreman should keep in mind with respect to women workers.

Chapter XI

MODERN WAGE-PAYMENT PLANS

1. What is the key to good wage payment?
2. What is the first requirement of a satisfactory wage plan?
3. Why did the old piece-rate system fall into general disrepute?
4. What is the only remedy for the evils inherent in the old piece-rate systems?
5. What is the underlying idea of premium and bonus plans?
6. State briefly what the Bedaux plan is.
7. What have some companies done to protect workers against sharply fluctuating prices of the things they have to buy?
8. What is the ultimate test of the fairness of a wage in a free labor market?

9. In advanced practice, what should precede the setting of a time allowance on a job?

10. What type of payment plan has proven very satisfactory for standardized repetitive jobs involving no special problems of quality discrimination?

11. Describe briefly the 100 per cent premium plan.

12. Where is the 100 per cent premium plan normally employed?

13. What is meant by point plans, and for what types of jobs have they been found advantageous?

14. What are some disadvantages that have been found in the use of bonus plans for foremen?

15. What is the best scheme of payment for jobs where it is not practicable to set any standard for performance?

16. What is meant by "measured day rate"?

17. What is the distinction between premium plans and "true" profit-sharing plans?

18. What does experience indicate as the chief benefit of profit-sharing plans?

19. What are some types of operations, or groups, where group piece rate or bonus plans have proven advantageous?

20. What are three characteristics of a good wage plan?

21. Give three examples of nonfinancial incentives.

Chapter XII

JOB EVALUATION

1. What is job evaluation?

2. What does a program of job evaluation involve?

3. Does job evaluation involve *man* evaluation?

4. About when, where, and by whom was systematic job evaluation first applied?

5. What are some advantages of a job-evaluation program to employees?

6. What are some advantages of a job-evaluation program to management?

7. Under what three headings may the foreman's definite responsibilities in connection with a job-evaluation program be grouped?

8. Give some of the foreman's direct responsibilities in a job-evaluation installation.
9. How may a foreman often be asked to serve during the job-evaluation program with which a foreman may be faced?
10. What are some educational problems in connection with a job-evaluation program with which a foreman may be faced?
11. List the four major types of job evaluation.
12. State briefly the essentials of the ranking system. Should it normally be recommended?
13. State briefly the essentials of the grading or classification system. What is an important disadvantage?
14. What are the job factors usually used in the point system?
15. Discuss briefly how the job factors are used in the point system.
16. State briefly the essentials of the factor-comparison system.
17. List the 13 basic steps to be followed in developing the type of job-evaluation program treated in Chap. XII (combination of point system and factor comparison).
18. What kind of jobs should be used for the key jobs, and how should they be chosen?
19. What type of information should be included in the original descriptive data on jobs?
20. Why is a Rank List prepared?
21. What are the three steps in reasoning followed in translating point values into money?
22. Why are all jobs grouped into relatively few labor grades?
23. How is the wage scale brought into conformity with the community pattern?

Chapter XIII

MERIT RATING OF EMPLOYEES

1. What does "merit rating" (sometimes called "performance rating") produce?

2. What are four essential features of the merit-rating technique?

3. Why are the top managements of so many companies interested in merit rating?

4. What are some advantages of a merit-rating system to foremen?

5. What, as a rule, makes merit rating important to employees?

6. For what three things is the foreman directly responsible in a merit-rating program?

7. Why is it so important for a foreman, in co-operating with a department administering a merit-rating system, to report the performance of each employee *exactly as he sees it* (rather than "giving him a break")?

8. Define "ranking."

9. Define "grading" or "classifying."

10. Define "rating."

11. In what type of employee rating is a "graphic profile" produced?

12. Where has the "check-list" method of rating been widely used?

13. Describe briefly the "grading form" which many personnel men advocate because of its simplicity.

14. Describe briefly the "paired-comparison" method of rating.

15. Is there general uniformity in the selection of qualities or traits that are rated in rating systems in use today?

16. What are some of the common traits that appear on many rating forms?

17. List eight steps that the foreman should follow in carrying out his responsibilities in a rating system.

18. What procedure is probably least open to error in developing a standard for comparison of individuals?

19. What is meant by the "halo effect" in rating?

20. Do ratings indicate general trends and probabilities, or quite precise degrees of certainty?

Chapter XIV

THE TOOLS OF INDUSTRIAL PSYCHOLOGY

1. What are five activities of the foreman in which a knowledge of applied psychology can be helpful?
2. Of what has much of the work of scientific psychology consisted?
3. Define "ability."
4. Define "aptitude."
5. Are aptitudes measured directly, or inferred from measure of ability?
6. Give the meaning of the following "correlations": +1; −1; 0.
7. Define "criterion."
8. What is meant by "critical score" in a test?
9. What is "dexterity"?
10. What is meant by "halo effect"?
11. What is the term used to indicate the response which comes next after sensation?
12. Is it true that if a person has perfect vision, he will necessarily have perfect "perception"?
13. What is the "physiological limit" of a person?
14. What is meant by "skill"?
15. What is a test?
16. What were the famous Alpha and Beta tests of the First World War?
17. Does high general hand dexterity guarantee the possession of any of the other specialized dexterities?
18. What are "ability profiles"?
19. Describe briefly a test which has been used successfully in measuring hand-and-foot co-ordination.
20. Name some specific benefits of scientific selection and training.
21. When are rating scales frequently used—and are they as good as approved tests?
22. What is a psychiatrist?
23. Why is it good to be on one's guard against the belief

that the best applicant for a job is the one who has performed the same or a similar job in some other organization?

Chapter XV

THE BACKGROUND OF SCIENTIFIC MANAGEMENT

1. When did the public first read about "scientific management" in the headlines?
2. What startling testimony did Harrington Emerson give at the Eastern Rate Case Hearings?
3. Who is known as the "father of scientific management"?
4. At what company did Taylor do his early work?
5. What general practice with respect to piece rates during Taylor's younger days kept employers from really preventing "soldiering" on the job?
6. What great principle did Taylor arrive at as a result of his early experiments to determine a "fair day's work"?
7. Name some of the scientific management techniques that were developed in the early years of this century.
8. Who were the mathematicians and the economist-engineer who helped Taylor in refining his system?
9. Who was the man who made the first micromotion studies?
10. What were the title and date of Taylor's first paper on his principles?
11. What were the title and date of Taylor's great book on scientific management?
12. What four great underlying principles did Taylor propound in his book?
13. What is the American History Committee's definition of scientific management prepared for the 1938 International Management Congress?
14. Is scientific management the same as "mass production"?   (Give a brief example in your answer.)
15. What is meant, in industry, by "rationalization"?
16. Why was organized labor opposed to scientific management at the beginning, and what is its position, by and large, today?

17. What is "operations research"?
18. What is "linear programming"?
19. What is "automation"?
20. Name some of the important management societies.

Chapter XVI

FORMS OF INDUSTRIAL ORGANIZATION

1. What do the processes of organization combine?
2. Name three common types of organization.
3. What are the basic purposes of all three types of organization, or combinations of them?
4. State briefly what "line organization" is.
5. State briefly what is meant by "line-staff organization."
6. What is meant by "functional organization"?
7. Basically, what three fundamental functions are involved in all organized work?
8. In a typical large-scale manufacturing organization, what are some of the departments that function both as a line and a staff unit?
9. Give an example of an important department that can function as a *line*, a *staff*, and a *functional* unit.
10. What does a typical Finance Department control?
11. Distinguish between *policy* and *performance* in the structural setup of a company.
12. List as many as you can of the 37 policies usually found in an industrial company.
13. What should be the relationship between authority and responsibility?
14. List the "ten commandments of good organization."
15. Give 13 good policy rules.
16. Give three good performance rules.

Chapter XVII

WHAT THE FOREMAN SHOULD KNOW ABOUT ECONOMICS

1. What is "economics"?
2. How does a knowledge of economics help the foreman?
3. Define "Capitalism."
4. Define "Socialism."

5. Define "Communism."

6. Define the common system called, variously, "Fascism," "Nazism," "Francoism," etc.

7. What are the four principal phases into which the system of free enterprise may be broken down?

8. What are the four principal activities in the production of economic goods?

9. What are generally considered to be the four main factors of production?

10. What American is considered one of the first to bring the division of labor down to a science?

11. Under our modern system of production, what four forms does the division of labor generally take?

12. Give some outstanding advantages of the division of labor.

13. Under our system, where does capital ultimately come from?

14. State briefly, what is meant by the "law of diminishing returns."

15. What are the simplest and best-known types of business enterprise?

16. What are three advantages of the proprietorship form of business organization?

17. What are three disadvantages of the proprietorship?

18. In a partnership, are all the partners liable for the action of any one of them?

19. How may "corporation" be defined?

20. Why was it necessary to devise the corporation form of business organization?

21. What is one especially important feature of the corporation?

22. What are seven definite advantages of large enterprises?

23. What are five definite advantages to small-scale production?

24. What benefits can intelligent speculation contribute to business in general?

25. Describe, by a brief example, how "hedging" can protect a businessman against risk.

26. What are the names of two of the most widely used "cost-of-living indexes" (Consumers' Price Indexes)?
27. How are the cost-of-living indexes made up?
28. When are over-all wage increases justified economically?
29. How are "real" hourly earnings computed?

Chapter XVIII

GOVERNMENT, LABOR, AND THE FOREMAN

1. Except for certain measures dealing exclusively with railroad personnel, what was the first Federal law actually dealing directly with labor—and the date of its passage?
2. What were the two major reasons why the United States was far behind all other predominantly industrial nations in labor legislation?
3. What act was the primary legal force in restricting organized labor up to 1914?
4. What largely tended to neutralize the Clayton Act up to 1932?
5. What set of conditions was the primary force in shifting the attitude of the Federal government toward organized labor in the early 1930's?
6. Give the six limited sets of circumstances to which the Norris-LaGuardia Act of 1932 restricted issuance of injunctions against labor by Federal courts.
7. What is generally known as a "yellow-dog contract"?
8. When was the Wagner Act (National Labor Relations Act) passed—and was it pro-labor or pro-management?
9. Give some important features of the Walsh-Healey Act (Public Contracts Act) of 1936.
10. Even if the Walsh-Healey Act does not govern situations not part of a contract with the Federal government, why is it of such great significance?
11. What are some significant features of the Wage and Hour Law (Fair Labor Standards Act) of 1938?
12. Does the Wage and Hour Law define interstate commerce broadly or narrowly?

13. Under what four basic situations is the foreman *not* subject to the Wage and Hour Law?

14. Cite some figures to show the trend in union membership over the years from 1932 to 1954.

15. What law (give date of passage) passed in the early 1940's was the first indication of a new trend in labor legislation? Give some features of the law.

16. When was the Taft-Hartley Act passed?

17. What extremely significant feature with respect to foremen does the Taft-Hartley Act contain?

18. Does the Taft-Hartley Act prevent a foreman or supervisor from joining a union or any other organization?

19. How does the Taft-Hartley Act define "supervisor"?

20. What were some of the abuses by organized labor which led to the Taft-Hartley Act?

21. What are some of the important unfair practices by organized labor which the Taft-Hartley Act forbids?

22. What is the "closed shop"?

23. What qualifications with respect to freedom of speech on the part of employers does the Taft-Hartley Act set up?

24. Has the attitude of state governments, in the main, followed that of the Federal government with respect to labor legislation?

25. Discuss briefly the nature and objectives of the so-called "right-to-work" laws.

26. What outstanding fact with respect to the status of the foreman emerges out of a historical survey of labor legislation and labor experience?

27. What are the three major reasons for the rejection by American labor of the European version of class thinking and class strife?

28. What are two broad responsibilities of the foreman with respect to relations with organized labor?

29. What signposts should the foreman look for to decide whether or not union bargaining is being carried on in good faith.

Chapter XIX

ELEVEN BASIC PRINCIPLES OF WORK SIMPLIFICATION

1. Give the definition of "work simplification."
2. What does work simplification consist of, *beyond* a series of techniques?
3. What is the fundamental and demonstrable basis of work simplification?
4. Who is largely responsible for the development of work simplification into its present form?
5. Does work simplification present something new, or is it based on established principles?
6. What is the first basic principle of work simplification?
7. What does work simplification have to say with respect to *resistance to change* (second basic principle)?
8. What two major forces have always counteracted resistance to change?
9. What *human factor* does work simplification stress (third basic principle)?
10. What is the *purpose* of work simplification (fourth basic principle)?
11. State briefly six reasons why a foreman should have a genuine desire to make improvements.
12. What does work simplification have to say about *waste* (fifth basic principle)?
13. Is there very little, or a great deal of "do" in the average operation?
14. What are the only effective bases for study to reduce waste and improve methods (sixth basic principle)?
15. What are the three basic types of charts used in work simplification?
16. What do we look for with a flow-process chart?
17. What is analyzed with a man-machine chart?
18. What is the operator chart concerned with?
19. What pointer must be kept in mind to prevent confusion in constructing the flow-process chart?
20. Give the famous Kipling jingle quoted by methods men.

21. Which one of the work-simplification charts is the one most frequently and profitably used by the foreman in any work-simplification program?

22. List the major wastes in a process; in a man-machine combination; and in the worker himself (seventh basic principle).

23. Draw and identify the simplified methods-improvement symbols used in work simplification.

24. Define "operation."

25. Define "transportation."

26. Define "delay" or "storage."

27. Define "inspection."

28. What is the important thing to remember in recording a process?

29. What, for all practical purposes, does a process consist of?

30. What is a "value-adding operation"?

31. What types of facts are recorded of an operation in a flow-process chart?

32. Unless pieces are moved individually by a conveyor, what two minor operations occur respectively before and after a transportation?

33. Give two examples of "combined elements" representing special situations sometimes encountered in constructing a flow-process chart.

34. For the man-machine chart, of what three types are the elements of the total work of the *man?*

35. In a man-machine chart, how is the work done by the machine logically separated?

36. In constructing an operator chart, what is a holding hand considered to be?

37. What is the one objective of the man-machine chart form and the operator chart form?

38. Why are the man-machine chart and the operator chart expressed in percentage form, rather than merely in terms of elapsed time?

39. From what does work simplification derive its power (eighth basic principle)?

40. What four types of opportunities, looked for by the *questioning attitude*, add up to *simplify?*
41. What are six basic rules followed by methods men in improving assembly operations?
42. Upon what will the extent of an improvement mainly depend (ninth basic principle)?
43. Can experience from another activity be applied to one under study (tenth basic principle)?
44. How does ingenuity enter into improvements (eleventh basic principle)?
45. What is the vital prerequisite to a successful work-simplification program?
46. What five positive benefits will a work-simplification program, introduced, developed, and continuously backed up by a progressive top management, provide?

CHAPTER XXI

KEYS TO EXECUTIVE DEVELOPMENT QUESTIONS

(Numbers in bold type refer to questions; associated numbers in light type refer to pages.)

INDEX

A

Abilities, profiles of, 364
Ability, definition of, 358
Accident Facts, 237
Accident-prevention work, 217
Accident proneness in women, 267
Accident records, 232
Accidents, causes and types of, 223–231
  and clothing, 227
  and dangerous and harmful substances, 238
  and falling objects, 229
  and falls of persons, 226
  and fatigue, 252
  frequency rate of, 235
  and hand tools, 228
  and handling objects, 224
  and injury rates, 234
  investigation of, 233
  and machinery, 226
  man-hours lost in 1953, 217
  and personal protective equipment, 238
  reports for 1953, 216
  severity rate of, 235
  and stepping on or striking objects, 230
  and vehicles, 227
  (*See also* Safety)
Adams, James Truslow, 495
Administration, general, organization of, 408
American Management Association, 394

American Marketing Society, 395
American Society of Mechanical Engineers, 393
American Standards Association and industrial injury rates, 234
Aptitude, definition of, 358
Aptitudes, measurement of, 363
Arbitration agencies, 475–477
"Aside" time, 126
Authority, lines of, 412
Automation, 392
Average Outgoing Quality Limit (AOQL), 72

B

Barth, Carl G., 384
Basic Motion Timestudy (BMT), 145
Bedaux point plan of wage payment, 281
Behavior, abnormal, 354
Bonus plans of wage payment, 279
Brandeis, Louis D., 378
Budgets, flexible, 185–187

C

Capital, definition of, 423
Child labor, state provisions for, 478
Classification system of job evaluation, 303
Clayton Act, 450–453